DIGITAL COMPUTERS
IN THE
BEHAVIORAL LABORATORY

THE CENTURY PSYCHOLOGY SERIES

Kenneth MacCorquodale
Gardner Lindzey
Kenneth E. Clark

Editors

DIGITAL COMPUTERS
IN THE
BEHAVIORAL LABORATORY

Edited by

BERNARD WEISS

University of Rochester
School of Medicine and Dentistry

New York

APPLETON-CENTURY-CROFTS

Educational Division

MEREDITH CORPORATION

CONTENTS

PREFACE

Although the laboratory computer has become a fixture in a number of behavior laboratories during the past few years, it is still true that surprisingly few investigators have made use of its potential. Part of the reason, especially most recently, is financial, but several other reasons seem to me to be almost equally responsible. One is surely a lack of familiarity with the range of situations to which the laboratory computer has been applied. A good part of this lack is due to the paucity of published work on computer applications to behavior. A second reason is the feeling, on the part of many investigators, that involvement with computer technology means plunging into a novel research arena without guidelines. They have been led to believe that making full use of computer technology means expending an inordinate amount of time and energy on a pursuit with no immediate tangible reward.

I hope that this book helps allay these two sources of concern. It brings together, in one source, a wide range of applications presented in much more depth than is seen in a typical journal article. But these are not simply technical details; they are details about how projects began, how planning was undertaken, what problems arose, and how they were solved. In many respects, I aimed for the kind of book that I would have been happy to have when I began my own ventures into computer technology.

It seems to me that three types of readers can profit from this volume. One is the investigator who already has access to computers but who is always alert to new possibilities. A second is the investigator newly arrived on the scene, or about to, whose work could take many shortcuts if he were apprised of what already has been done. A third is the experimenter who has not yet made a decision about an investment in computers or who simply wants to expand his understanding of the kinds of contributions that computer technology is now making.

I have been fortunate in securing chapters from a number of pioneering, experienced investigators, loyal to the aims I have described. They have performed a most useful service for their fellow scientists in preparing their chapters. I have been struck, moreover, by one other facet of this book that will become apparent to many readers. Computer technology has forced us, coming from many diverse fields, to speak a common language and to face common problems. In the course of doing so, it is difficult to avoid the conclusion that much of what we thought were differences in outlook turn out to be differences in jargon. The inscrutable machines that sit in our laboratories, blinking lights, force us to state our experimental objectives more clearly and precisely than even the most bilious editor.

Bernard Weiss

DIGITAL COMPUTERS
IN THE
BEHAVIORAL LABORATORY

CHAPTER ONE

ON-LINE SEQUENTIAL CONTROL OF EXPERIMENTS BY AN AUTOMATED CONTINGENCY TRANSLATOR

J. R. MILLENSON [1]
Oxford University

[1] Department of Experimental Psychology, South Parks Road, Oxford, England. Development of the system described here was supported in part by grants from the National Research Council (Canada) and the Science Research Council (UK).

INTRODUCTION

As psychological science advances, its procedures increase in complexity. At the same time, greater and greater experimental precision is demanded. Time intervals must be accurately controlled and measured, probabilities of events must be set and varied, stimuli and responses must be quantified and recorded to ever increasing degrees of detail. The demands of procedural complexity and measurement precision eventually tax the administrative abilities of even the most agile unaided human experimenter, and resort must finally be made to some kind of automation.

At an early state, automation takes the form of a variety of special purpose hard-wired devices. Gradually, as common features emerge across experiments, equipment modularity may be achieved. New experiments may be devised by connecting up a small set of basic hardware elements in a new way. At a still more advanced stage, demands are made for parametric changes and procedural modifications *in situ*, and for implementing adaptive techniques requiring access to considerable amounts of information about the past history of the system being studied. A point is reached when the special instrumentation approximates the general purpose decision making and information processing abilities of a digital computer.

At precisely that point the need arises for a conceptual framework to exploit the new technology. Computers are unlike conventional control apparatus in many ways. Their basic hardware operations and the way they perform them are usually unfamiliar to the experimental psychologist. To be useful, their storage capacities, calculational abilities, and decision making properties must be functionally combined into a *program* of coded instructions in the language of the particular machine. To employ a computer as a device to run experiments, the psychologist is in danger of being forced to become a machine language computer programmer. Aside from the understandable reluctance on the part of most psychologists to take this step, extensive programming of behavioral procedures in machine language would be undesirable even by a professional programmer. The machine language of computers is generally recognized to be a poor vehicle for representing and creatively manipulating high-level concepts of any sort (Newell and Simon, 1963). It is cumbersome, unwieldly, not especially easy to learn and use, and its mnemonic structure relates to computer operations and not to operations in the problem field. The representation of procedures directly in machine language is a lengthy, tedious, and time-consuming task. Even a modest problem in experimental control could easily take several man-months to be programmed in machine language. As the history of computer science shows, a given substantive field exploits the computer maximally when a language oriented towards and natural to the problems of that field is formulated (Sammet, 1969).

PROBLEM-ORIENTED LANGUAGE FOR PSYCHOLOGY

Although there exist many problem-oriented languages for tasks as diverse as algebraic formula manipulation, text handling, directing machine tools, and sorting business files, none of these are natural to the domain of experimental psychology. All these languages build up (*compile*) from primitive machine instructions higher level instructional compounds or routines that can be named appropriately to the problem areas and thereafter invoked directly by the user. Thus, FORTRAN and ALGOL, for instance, provide powerful and extensive conceptual building blocks for expressing problems in numerical analysis. On the other hand, their concepts are far less useful for expressing the sequential flow of events in a behavioral experiment. What is needed are building blocks appropriate for constructing the procedures of experimental psychology. To this end, some workers have augmented existing problem-oriented languages by grafting control facilities to them (*e.g.*, Hendry and Lennon's [1967] FORTRAN with control extensions) and others have made major modifications (McLean's [1968] ALGOL-like PSYCHOL) but these *ad hoc* solutions lie some distance from a natural language for experimental psychology.

The development of a true problem-oriented language for expressing behavioral procedures hinges on a formal conceptual framework for representing and relating those procedures. The myriad varieties of behavioral apparatus extant, and the many terminologies to be found in procedure sections of the literature, seems to preclude any unified representational system. Nevertheless, as Mechner (1959) observed in proposing a notation system for behavioral procedures, one characteristic shared by every behavioral experiment is that stimuli are presented to a subject according to a set of pre-arranged rules or *contingencies*. These contingency rules may be as simple as the presentation of a nonsense syllable whenever a subject says "ready", or as complex as a set of non-linear functions governing the randomly perturbed movement of a target being tracked under delayed feedback conditions. Sometimes, experiments entail a large number of contingency rules and potential conditions, each one of which may itself be simple, yet the complete description of the resulting logical network may be quite complex indeed. Many of the reinforcement schedules for operant behavior exhibit this latter kind of complexity.

This chapter describes a problem-oriented programming language for expressing these various contingencies and conditions of behavioral experiments, and thus for turning a digital computer into a device for producing the logical network of such experiments. The language has therefore been named an *A*utomated *C*ontingency *T*ranslator (ACT). The chapter sections fall naturally into one of two headings: those concerned with abstract description of this language and its conceptual basis, and those detailing a specific implementation of ACT on a small laboratory computer dedicated to time-sharing the control of a group of human and animal experiments.

EXPERIMENTAL CONTINGENCIES REPRESENTED AS STATE DIAGRAMS

As a point of departure, consider the notion that in every behavioral experiment stimuli are presented to a subject according to a set of prearranged rules. Equivalently, a behavioral experiment may be thought of as a system for generating a sequence of stimuli according to prearranged rules. In a series of seminal papers, Snapper and his associates (Snapper, Kadden, Knapp, and Kushner, 1967; Snapper, Knapp, and Kushner, 1969; Snapper and Knapp, 1969) have pointed out that such a sequential system may be formally represented as a finite-state automaton (Gill, 1962). As such, any behavioral experiment may be represented as a sequential system with a finite number of interrelated potential states. An experiment begins in an arbitrary initial state and progresses by moving in time from one state to another in the system depending on measured properties of the subject's behavior. These moves or *transitions* from one state to another define the actual path of the experiment in any particular session. The notion that behavioral procedures are finite automata plays a key role in the development of several general purpose programming languages in this field (Snapper and Kadden, Chapter 2; Millenson, 1967, 1968; Grason-Stadler, 1968), for its adoption effectively reduces the various problems in language design to the single simpler problem of representing in computer core two classes of data, the states and transitions of experiments.

At any moment in time, an experiment is in a given state. The current state of a behavioral experiment is specified by (i) the stimuli then being presented to the subject, and (ii) the rules or conditions then in effect governing transitions to other states of the experiment. Typically, an experiment consists of many such states and many such transitions interconnected in a logical network. Verbal descriptions of these networks tend to be both verbose and idiosyncratic, and frequently ambiguous. Pictorial diagrams prove an altogether more unambiguous representation vehicle and they have the further desirable property of permitting the user to grasp the overall structure of a complex network at a glance. In the diagrams utilized in this chapter, states are drawn as nested rectangles and transitions as vectored lines. The leftmost state is conventionally the initial state, and the sequential flow tends to move from left to right across the page. Independent (unconnected) state systems or *sets* or *planes* are arrayed vertically one above the other.

Consider the simple fragment below showing two recycling states, abbreviated S1 and S2, each containing a single transition. (The dotted vector points

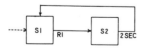

Figure 1. Two-state diagram.

to the initial state.) If S2 was associated with food presentation and R1 designated a lever press, this diagram accurately represents the contingencies of a continuous reinforcement schedule (CRF) with a 2-sec reinforcement duration. Alternatively, if S1 and S2 happened to denote a tachistoscopic shutter closed and open respectively, and R1 a voice key, the diagram designates a procedure for making a 2-sec visual presentation contingent upon speech above a certain intensity level. In a simple state diagram as Figure 1, one and only one state can be in effect (*active*) at any one time. Either S1 or S2 is active, but never both together.

The two-choice reaction diagram of Figure 2 illustrates a finite state diagram applied to an experiment of moderate complexity, and will serve to illustrate the following discussion concerned with the main properties of such diagrams. The experiment is an instance of an adaptive sequential psychophysical testing procedure (Kappauf, 1969) represented as two mutually exclusive state sets. An upper set of seven states determines the experimental sequence of stimuli, and a lower set of nine states determines the logic of the stimulus intensity changes and evaluates the quit criterion. The diagram shows a procedure in which one of

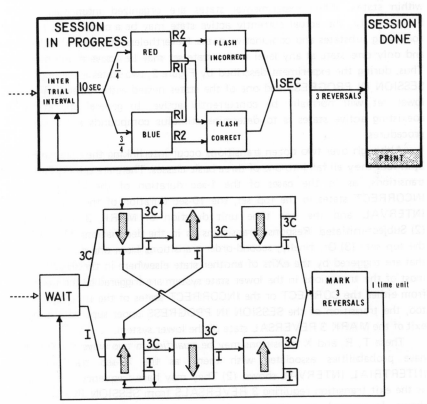

Figure 2. Two-choice reaction experiment with three reversal quit criterion. The symbols ↓ and ↑ stand respectively for lower and raise stimulus intensity.

two stimuli (red or blue) is presented after an intertrial interval of 10 sec. The proportion of red to blue stimuli is defined as 25/75. After a response, "CORRECT" or "INCORRECT" indications are flashed to the subject, and the procedure recycles.

The lower group of states is concerned with raising (↑) or lowering (↓) the stimulus intensity. A single incorrect response (I) raises the intensity, three successive correct responses (3C) lower it. This group of states also marks when three reversals (I-3C-I-3C, or 3C-I-3C-I) have occurred by moving to a unique state (MARK 3 REVERSALS) that serves to halt the experiment by moving the upper system to a final persisting state (SESSION DONE) in which a message is printed to the experimenter.

From Figure 2 we may induce most of the general properties of state diagrams of this type applied to behavioral experiments. One such property, a negative one, bars direct interconnections between the states of one set, and the states of another set. None of the states of the lower set is connected to any of the states of the upper set and *vice versa*. Another property, as the upper set of Figure 2 shows, is the hierarchical organization that permits states to nested within states. When experimental states are organized independently and hierarchically, the actual currently active state may be a compound of several coexisting substates and conjunctive states. Nevertheless, the rule holds that one and only one state at any level in any state set may be active at any moment. Thus, during the experiment described by Figure 2, two states in the upper (the SESSION IN PROGRESS and one of the states nested within it) and one in the lower set will normally be concurrently active. In general, the effect of coexisting active states is to determine stimulus compounds and concurrent procedures.

Although over two dozen transitions occur interlinking the states in Figure 2, in fact they all fall into one of three basic classes. There are one (1) *T*emporal transitions, as in the cases of the 1-sec duration of the CORRECT and INCORRECT states in the top set, the 10-sec duration of the INTERTRIAL INTERVAL and the one time unit duration of MARK 3 REVERSALS. (2) Subject-initiated *R*esponse transitions as in the designations R1 and R2 in the top set. (3) Or, finally, second-order transitions from one state to another that are triggered by the e*X*its of another state elsewhere in the diagram. Thus, most of the transitions in the lower state system are triggered by the transitions from either the CORRECT or the INCORRECT states of the upper system. So too, the transition of the SESSION IN PROGRESS upper superstate is via the exit of the MARK 3 REVERSAL state of the lower system.

These T, R, and X transitions may be *qualified* in two ways: (1) They may have probabilities associated with them, as the 10-sec transition from INTERTRIAL INTERVAL shows. (2) They may have frequency requirements, as the exit transition requiring 3 REVERSALS from SESSION IN PROGRESS shows. In general, any state may have an unlimited number of transitions associated with it, but the rule holds that the first transition condition to be satisfied causes an exit and terminates processing of any other transitions of that state. Should that state ever be reentered, the qualifiers of all its transitions assume their original values.

ACT NOMENCLATURE[2]

The current state of the computer art does not yet permit state diagrams such as Figures 1 and 2 to be read directly by a computer. It is now conventional to input computer programs by cards, teletypewriters, or paper tape, and thus an intermediary English nomenclature and syntax has been developed to transmit the information contained in these state diagrams to the central processor unit (CPU). It is that nomenclature that is usually referred to as the ACT language.

State diagrams provide a natural and powerful conceptual framework for constructing a problem-oriented language for controlling behavioral experiments. For the language designer, however, adoption of that framework is only a first, albeit critical, step in producing a programming language with features that are likely to be desired by a heterogeneous population of experimental psychologists. The final product must be as easy to read and write (transparent) as possible, and moreover it should be as general, powerful, parsimonious, flexible, and easy to debug as possible. Unfortunately, these attributes are not all mutually exclusive and some of them (*e.g.*, power and parsimony, flexibility and transparency) even imply a degree of incompatibility, so the best that can be achieved is some kind of compromise. The generality of the finite automata representation of contingency networks is very great indeed, but when behavioral experiments involve continuous functions as well, they are not so parsimoniously described by finite-state notation. Moreover, when automating an experiment, the actual procedure is only one of several aspects to be computerized. Data must be recorded and summarized; status messages must be delivered to the user; midstream halts and restarts must be accommodated; and so forth. To attempt to accommodate a variety of experimental problems, ACT is designed to be augmented by some kind of algebraic language such as FORTRAN or ALGOL, and the section on CALC shows one way that this can be accomplished in practice.

Space prohibits a tutorial presentation of the ACT language here. What follows is intended merely to convey the flavor of this language for representing experimental logic. A more complete presentation may be found elsewhere (Lehigh Valley, 1969).

The vocabulary of ACT consists of the English pseudo-words[3] WHEN, WHILE, GIVE, IF, AFTER, FOLLOWING, GO (equivalently GOTO, or THEN),

---

[2] Formal syntactical definitions of ACT expressions are given in Appendix A.

[3] They are *pseudo*-words because the ways in which they can be combined to make ACT statements are extremely restrictive in comparison to the ways that they can be combined to make English sentences in ordinary language.

PROBABILITY, COUNT, TOTALTIME, DURATION, and the time units UNITS, SEC, MIN, and HR. The words IN, BACK, and WITH are noise words that may be used at certain places to increase readability. States themselves are designated by the symbols S, U, or V, followed either by one or two integers (1,2,3...) or integer variables (I, J, ...N). Responses are identified by the letter R followed by an integer or an integer variable. A few special symbols such as the teletype tab character (in the reference language the ! symbol) and the blank space, the dollar sign, the comma, parentheses, and square brackets are reserved for nesting and delimiting expressions or program blocks respectively. The oblique stroke (/) at the beginning of a line signifies a comment to follow. After the word PROBABILITY, this character flags the denominator of a probability fraction.

In the English nomenclature of ACT, these words and symbols are combined by a set of rules (see Appendix A) into three classes of statements (see Figure 3). (1) State declarations, corresponding to the rectangles of state diagrams, (2) Transition statements, corresponding to the vectored lines of state diagrams, and (3) Data recording directives. Algebraic statements for performing mathematical computations on the variables of the state network, moving and storing data, and other on-line housekeeping chores, are usually interlarded with the ACT statements, but strictly speaking they are not part of the ACT language itself.

State Declarations

WHEN S1

GIVE U12.5

WHILE V(J)

Transitions

IF 20 R2 GO TO S44

AFTER 5 SEC GO WITH PROBABILITY 1/2 TO S(K).14

FOLLOWING K V60 GO TO S5.63

Data Recording Directives

IN S3, R1 COUNT

IN U(K).2, S2 COUNT

S44 TOTALTIME

V(J) DURATION

Figure 3. Examples of the three classes of legal ACT statements.

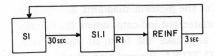

Figure 4. State diagram for fixed-interval 30-sec reinforcement schedule.

From the three examples of state declarations in Figure 3 it may be induced that a state declaration consists of the words WHEN, WHILE, or GIVE, followed by the state identifier symbols S, U, or V, followed by an integer or a variable integer, and optionally a point followed by a second integer. The integer or variable to the left of the point is a stimulus identifier and the integer to the right of the point (if any) is a simple label to distinguish different states with the same stimulus identifiers. Thus, the point and the integers have the following meaning: S12 designates a state with stimulus value = 12 (one method for determining exactly what stimulus that number signifies is described on p. 16) and is equivalent to the more complete S12.0. S12.5 is simply another state also with stimulus = 12. To see the need for such a convention, consider the 30 - sec fixed-interval reinforcement schedule diagram of Figure 4. After 30-sec, the state S1 (in which response R1 has no effect) moves to a state S1.1 (without a stimulus change), a state in which a response R1 now has the significant effect of producing reinforcement.

The nesting of states (as in the upper state set of Figure 2) is accomplished by the tabulation character that indents the nested states to the right of its superstate on the printed page. Thus,

> WHEN S1
> ! WHILE U12.5
> ! ! GIVE V(J)

maps the state fragment corresponding to Figure 5.

The three examples of transitions of Figure 3 illustrate how the three basic classes, R, T, or X transitions of the state diagrams are mapped to ACT statements. Subject-initiated events are flagged by the word IF and the response is identified by the symbol R, followed by an integer or an integer variable. The

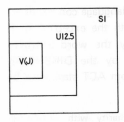

Figure 5. Three-state nest.

words GO TO are equivalent to the lines of the pictorial diagrams, and the name of the state at the end of the transition statement indicates where the line must be vectored. Response transitions may also take the form of input teletype strings, as in the example IF R"YES" GO TO S4, the meaning of which is self evident, and IF R"--B" GO TO S4, which means go to State 4 if a three-letter input string ending with B is received from the appropriate teletype.

Temporal transitions are flagged by the word AFTER and make use of the time units UNITS, SEC, MIN, and HR.

State exit transitions are flagged by the word FOLLOWING and indicate that so many exits of a state (*e.g.*, K V60 in Figure 3) in one state set lead to another state in the present set (*e.g.*, S5.63 in Figure 3).

An example of a probabilistic qualifier splitting the words GO... TO is shown in the temporal transition of Figure 3. Frequency qualifiers are the *20* of 20 RS, the *5* of 5 SEC, and the *K* of K V60.

ACT is principally a language for sequential control, and as such contains no sophisticated features for manipulating experimental data. Nevertheless, it does permit access to the raw data of an experiment in the form of the four data recording directives of Figure 3. These direct an ACT system to COUNT response or state exits; and to record TOTALTIMES and transient DURATIONS or states. A transient duration is the duration of a state from its most recent entry, and in practice takes the form of reaction times, latencies, interresponse times, and other temporal measures. By appropriate references to these directives (see Applications), experimental data may be manipulated, summarized, and output to teletypes, paper tape punches, magnetic tape and cathode ray tube displays.

CALC[4]

The ACT system is intended to be used in conjunction with a procedure-oriented algebraic language. ACT itself is silent as to exactly what facilities this algebraic augmentation should have, and they will generally depend both on the sophistication of the object machine, and the type of experiments to be conducted at the installation. A language known as CALC (ACT *C*ompatible *AL*gebraic *C*ompiler), which borrows its features from both FORTRAN and ALGOL but which is simpler than either, is typical of the kind of facility likely to be required by experimental psychologists. The basic language commands are shown in Figure 6. Variables are single letters and with the exception of H through O are assumed to be real, unless flagged by the word STRING. One-dimensional subscripted arrays must be declared by the DIMENSION statement. CALC commands are flagged distinctively from ACT statements by their enclosure within square brackets.

[4] This section presumes at least some rudimentary familiarity with ALGOL or FORTRAN.

LET $\langle variable \rangle$ = $\langle expression \rangle$

GOTO $\langle statement\ label \rangle$

CALL $\langle statement\ label \rangle$

RETURN

FOR $\langle variable \rangle$ = $\begin{cases} \langle start\ value \rangle\ \langle(step\ size)\rangle\langle terminal\ value\rangle \\ \langle expression1 \rangle\ ,\langle expression2 \rangle\ ,\ ... \end{cases}$ DO $\langle statement \rangle$ END

IF $\langle expression \rangle$ $\langle relation \rangle$ $\langle expression \rangle$ $\langle statement \rangle$

LABEL $\langle integer \rangle$: $\langle statement \rangle$

DIMENSION $\langle variable \rangle$ $\langle integer \rangle$

STRING $\langle variable \rangle$

COMMENT $\langle statement \rangle$

PRINT $\langle\langle ACT\ record\ line \rangle\rangle\ \Big|\ \langle\langle\text{''}text\ string\text{''}\rangle\Big|\langle variable \rangle\rangle$

WRITETAPE

Figure 6. Summary of CALC commands. $\langle\ \rangle$ enclose entities. Braces or vertical bars signify alternatives.

The relational operators are =, $<$, and $>$. Arithmetic operators are $-$, $+$, $=$, $/$, * (for multiply), $\uparrow$ (exponentiation), and $\leftarrow$ (for assignment). The names SQRT, LOG, SIN, COS, ABS (absolute value), and TAN are reserved functions. Statement terminators are the semicolon or the carriage return character.

The LET and GOTO are the assignment and control transfer statements respectively. The CALL is a jump to subroutine, and the return is accomplished by the RETURN. The IF...THEN allows a single relational operator between expressions, and control passes to the next statement if true, or skips it if false. The FOR...DO...END statement is used to produce reiteration control as in the statement FOR I=1(1)10 DO Y[I] : = X[I]↑2 * P[I] ;END; which

forms $Y_i = \sum\limits_{i=1}^{10} P_i\ X_i^2$, for i = 1 to 10.

Statement labels take the form of the word LABEL followed by an integer and the colon character. Comment statements are preceded by the COMMENT.

The PRINT is used to output data messages on teletype. Any of the 26 characters of the alphabet, the numerals from 0 to 9, and the symbols % and ## meaning carriage return and line feed, may be concatenated between " " to form a textstring that is transmitted directly to the teletype. ACT Data Recording Directives are referenced by their recording line number in parentheses. In addition, the word PUNCH, DISPLAY, WRITETAPE, CURSON, BLANK, READTAPE are reserved for other input/output functions appropriate to other peripheral equipment.

```
/TWO CHOICE REACTION EXPERIMENT, ADAPTIVE STIMULUS INTENSITIES
/K CONTROLS THE VALUE OF A NEUTRAL DENSITY WEDGE SET TO 500 INITIALLY
/
PROCEDURE
[LET K←500]
GIVE S(K)                                           /SESSION IN PROGRESS
   GIVE S0                                           /INTERTRIAL INTERVAL
      AFTER 10 SEC GO WITH PROBABILITY 1/4 TO S1
      AFTER 10 SEC GO WITH PROBABILITY 3/4 TO S10
   WHEN S1                                           /RED STIMULUS
      IF R2 GO TO S2
      IF R1 GO TO S4
   WHEN S10                                          /BLUE STIMULUS
      IF R1 GO TO S4
      IF R2 GO TO S2
   WHEN S2                                           /FLASH "CORRECT"
      AFTER 1 SEC GO BACK TO S0
   WHEN S4                                           /FLASH "INCORRECT"
      AFTER 1 SEC GO BACK TO S0
   FOLLOWING 4 U20 GO TO S0.1
WHEN S0.1  [PRINT "NUMBER OF TRIALS= " (1)           /SESSION DONE
               "SESSION TIME= " (2)]
   $                                                 /DUMMY TRANSITION
/
/U STATE SET EVALUATES QUIT CRITERION ONLY
GIVE U0                                              /WAIT
   FOLLOWING 3 S2 GO TO U0.1
   FOLLOWING 1 S4 GO TO U0.11
WHEN U0.1  [LET K←K-5]                               /LOWER INTENSITY
   FOLLOWING 3 S2 GO BACK TO U0.1
   FOLLOWING 1 S4 GO TO U0.2
WHEN U0.2  [LET K←K+5]                               /RAISE INTENSITY
   FOLLOWING 3 S2 GO TO U0.3
   FOLLOWING 1 S4 GO TO U0.11
WHEN U0.3  [LET K←K-5]                               /LOWER INTENSITY
   FOLLOWING 3 S2 GO BACK TO U0.1
   FOLLOWING 1 S4 GO TO U20
WHEN U0.11  [LET K←K+5]                              /RAISE INTENSITY
   FOLLOWING 3 S2 GO TO U0.12
   FOLLOWING 1 S4 GO TO U0.11
WHEN U0.12  [LET K←K -5]                             /LOWER INTENSITY
   FOLLOWING 3 S2 GO BACK TO U0.1
   FOLLOWING 1 S4 GO TO U0.13
WHEN U0.13  [LET K←K+5]                              /RAISE INTENSITY
   FOLLOWING 3 S2 GO TO U20
   FOLLOWING 1 S4 GO TO U0.11
WHEN U20                                             /MARK 3 REVERSALS
   AFTER 1 UNIT GO TO U0
   $$
/
RECORD
   1:IN S(K),S0 COUNT
   2:S(K) TOTALTIME
   3:$$                                              /PROGRAM TERMINATOR
```

Figure 7. Sample ACT program corresponding to the diagram of Figure 2. The tab character (!) is omitted but implied by indentation.

A SAMPLE ACT PROGRAM

The three previous sections establish the basic facilities of an experimental control language. A typical complete ACT program consists of a procedure section containing state declarations and transitions, a record section containing data recording directives, and interlarded CALC statements. The two choice reaction experimental network of Figure 2 is shown as an ACT program in Figure 7. The English labels of the states have there been replaced by arbitrary symbolic identifiers. The reader may judge by inspection to what extent the format meets the various criteria discussed in Section 3 for a problem-oriented language in this field.

PDP-8/S ACT IMPLEMENTATION IN A BEHAVIORAL LABORATORY

ACT itself is a moderately machine-independent vehicle for experimental control. Compilers have been written for the PDP-8 family, the PDP-9, and compilers are projected for the ICL903 and Data General *Nova*. The following sections describe the major features of the 8k PDP-8/S system in the Department of Experimental Psychology, Oxford University. It should be emphasized that the Oxford system represents only one of many possible realizations of ACT. Nevertheless, the hardware and software problems encountered in the implementation are representative of a broad class of general problems that must be solved in automating behavioral experiments.

RESPONSE INPUT AND STIMULUS OUTPUT HARDWARE

At Oxford, an 8k PDP-8/S has been ACTified to govern the behavioral contingencies of a group of diverse human and animal experiments. The experimental milieu is depicted in Figure 8 and may be described as an on-line real time-shared control system. Four experimental *stations* are shown in Figure 8 grouped about a single rack-mounted central processor. An input teletype transmits ACT programs in the form shown in Figure 7 to the central processor, and an output teleprinter and punch are used to preserve desired raw data.

The experimental stations of Figure 8 are said to be *on-line* because they are electrically connected directly to the central processor. The system is said to operate in *real time* because the response time of the system to significant events incoming from the experiments is accomplished with lags not exceeding a few dozen milliseconds. Finally, the experiments are said to be *time-shared* because in every small unit of time, each experiment is allocated a share for its updating. To all intents and purposes, therefore, all four experiments are thus controlled automatically, immediately, and simultaneously by the central processor.

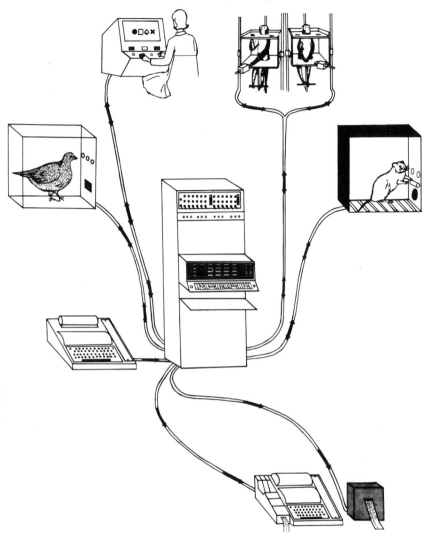

Figure 8. An automated behavior laboratory. The physical distance from the central processor to the experimental stations varies from about 20 feet to 50 yards.

Consonant with the general character of behavioral experiments, the principal job of the control system is to present and withdraw stimuli to the experimental stations depending on the occurrence of either significant subject-initiated events from the station, the sheer passage of time, or the result of calculations based on measured aspects of the past history of the experiment. In the four experimental stations shown in Figure 8, the stimuli take the form of discrete or *binary* events such as lights, displays, shocks, and food presentation. All these stimuli are said to be binary because they have only two possible values: a given light is either on or off, a display is either present or absent, food and shocks are either being delivered, or are not being delivered. Analogously, the subject-initiated events in Figure 8 are also binary. The pigeon either pecks a key or it does not, the human observer either does or does not turn a knob, and the monkeys and rat either press their levers or they do not. Of course, stimulus and response events need not be simply binary. The intensity of light on the pigeon's keys may be a continuous variable; the human observer may adjust a knob over a continuous range; the blood pressure of the monkeys and the skin resistance of the rat's feet may be measured as continuous, or *analogue*, quantities. Nevertheless, for the purposes of digital computer processing, such analogue variables must eventually be coded as a configuration of binary events. Translating both discrete and analogue input/output (I/O) events into electrical events that the computer can process is the function of the stimulus and response I/O station interface.

A helpful analogy in understanding the I/O interface between experiments and computers is to think of the possible input and output events to and from given experimental stations as the actions of extremely rapid-acting toggle switches. Although at first it may seem surprising, we shall see presently that with a slight extension this analogy holds equally well for analogue I/O signals. In this scheme, the key pecks, knob turns, and lever presses from the subjects of Figure 8, can be viewed as actuating input toggle switches, whose states the computer can sense. The lights, displays, and food and shock presentations result from the computer itself actuating a different set of output toggle switches.

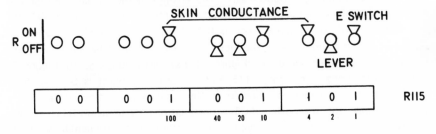

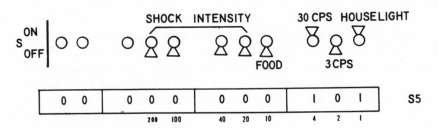

Figure 9. Eleven-bit stimulus and response interface hardware for a typical automated experiment.

An actual experimental station thus consists of two banks of such toggle switches, one for the subject-initiated input events, and one for the computer-initiated output events. The concept of a *bank* of switches is appropriate, because it corresponds closely to the chunks, called *words*, by which computers can often take in and put out binary information. In our analogy, the inputting and outputting of computer words consists of reading or setting, respectively, a complete bank of toggle switches at one fell swoop.

The I/O bank of Figure 9 is typical of such an interface connected to an experiment such as the rat-testing compartment of Figure 8. The relevant response events are the binary lever press and the analogue skin conductance. The experimenter (E) controls one toggle switch. The stimulus events shown are a houselight, 3 and 30 click per second noise stimuli, food delivery, and the intensity of grid shock. In Figure 9 we see these events represented by the settings of 11 response switches and 11 stimulus switches. Below each bank is the representation of the 11-bit computer word corresponding to the momentary state of the bank above it. Not all possible bits are in use in either bank. In Figure 9, the on position of a switch corresponds to bit zero in the computer. The analogue variables, skin conductance and shock intensity, are represented by several switches that are to be interpreted as a functional group.

At the moment of Figure 9, the E-switch is on, the rat is not depressing its lever, and the measured skin conductance of the subject corresponds to the binary value 10011. The stimuli on are only the houselight and the 30-cps clicker. Shock intensity is 0000 = zero. The settings of the switches in Figure 9 correspond to binary numbers. Thus, the state of the response word is 1,001,101 and the state of the stimulus word is 101. To facilitate the identification of response and stimulus words, the octal number system, (the small numbers under the computer words in Figure 9) has been adopted. In Figure 9, the response word is currently 115 and the stimulus word is 5. It is these numbers that are in fact coordinated to the response and stimulus identifiers of ACT; hence, the appropriate ACT concatenations for them are R115 and S5.

This particular method of mapping behavioral and environmental events to computer events economizes computer space simply because it requires a minimum of translation from the ACT identifier to the hardware state. It is also a fairly natural scheme, in that the meaning of any given ACT identifier in a program is immediately apparent at the interface. On the other hand, the method does require the user to be familiar with the octal number system. A principal restriction imposed by this hardware is the range of I/O events. Because the PDP-8 family are 12-bit machines, and in the 8/S ACT compiler the most significant bit is reserved for housekeeping purposes, states and responses must be designated as octal numbers in the range 0 − 3777. Although this might seem to imply that only up to 11 independent responses and stimuli respectively could be handled, in fact, by straightforward gating circuitry the number can be increased to a maximum of 2^{11}, a value well beyond the requirements of most current experimental work.

Now, of course, the I/O events of an ACT station do not in fact make and break actual toggle switches. Rather, they set and clear solid state switches (flip flops) at speeds exceeding 50 kHz. In the present system, the response inputs take the form of circuit closures or alternatively the output of an analogue to digital converter. Stimulus outputs are 24-volt levels or the output of digital to analogue converters. For the user's convenience, toggle switches at the console rack parallel the response inputs, and all response and stimulus bits are monitored there by small lamps. The actual method of converting internal computer words to stimuli, and reading buffered response words into the CPU are straightforward and as they are described in detail elsewhere (Ciofalo, Tedford, Goldberg and Dodge, 1968) they are not discussed further here.

SYSTEM HARDWARE CONFIGURATION

In addition to the stimulus and response hardware, several other special components play an important role in the present ACT implementation. The first of these is a clock that serves to synchronize the procedural automation. The period of this clock determines the maximum time allocated for updating the experimental stations. This clock also provides the basic timing for translating the temporal transition statements of ACT; and where the resolution is sufficient, it may serve to time-tag incoming data. In the present implementation, this synchronous clock runs at values from 20 to 60 Hz (50 to 16.7 msec resolution) depending on the number and complexity of the experiments running concurrently. The machine being used (8/S) is relatively slow (32 μsec ADD time) and with other members of the PDP-8 family the clock could run 10 times faster with a corresponding increase in resolution.

The probabilistic qualification of ACT transition statements requires random number generation. Software routines exist for generating random numbers, but they are slow and cost core space. A hardware random number generator that uses the leakage across a reversed biased noisy diode as the random source proves handier. (Further details and circuit diagrams can be found in Millenson and Sullivan, 1969.) The hardware generator occupies no core locations and can be referenced in two memory cycles at repetition speeds in excess of 3 Hz.

Because the frequency of the synchronous clock in an 8/S running ACT is two slow for accurate measurements of events such as reaction times and electrophysiological events, a supplementary 1-msec clock is provided at each station. Through patch connections at the console this station clock can be reset and initiated by any desired stimulus bits of the station, and stopped by any desired response bits. Its value is referenced by CALC statements as the variable C.

The complete schematic configuration showing three stations, the probability generator, and the synchronizing clock is shown in Figure 10. The

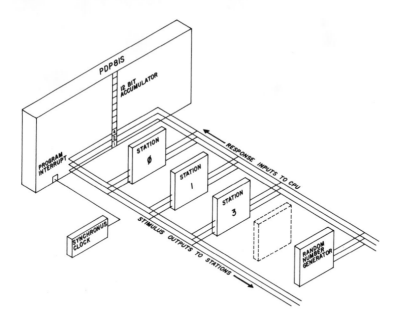

Figure 10. Schematic diagram of PDP-8/S ACT I/O interface.

stations have direct electrical connections to the main arithmetic register (accumulator) of the CPU and are addressed by an appropriate I/O command repertoire. For purposes of addressing, the probability generator appears as a one-way (in only) station. The individual station clocks are omitted in Figure 10, and to simplify the figure only three bits in and three bits out are shown.

STATION SERVICING

To prepare and run an actual ACT program, the user is encouraged first to draw a state diagram of the desired experimental contingencies. He then prepares a corresponding list of ACT and CALC instructions such as Figure 7, and inputs these by teletype to the computer operating under the control of the ACT software package consisting of a supervisory monitor, a compiler for translating programs, and an operating system for executing the compiled programs. CALC and ACT instructions are decoded line by line by the compiler, and translated into appropriate machine instructions and a data structure representing the contingency network of the experiment. During this program input phase, the user is said to be in conversational mode with the ACT compiler. At this time, the compiler reports to the user by a set of 45 diagnostics any syntactical and

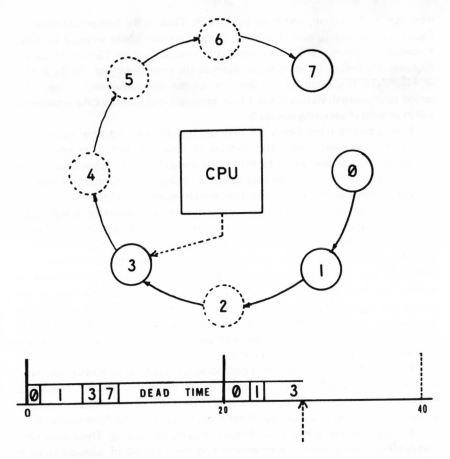

Figure 11. Round-robin service of eight ACT stations. Inactive stations are shown as dotted circles.

semantic program errors that he may make. When the program terminator ($$) is encountered, the compiled data structure is handed over to the operating system, which then proceeds to execute it. Execution consists of presenting the desired stimuli at the appropriate times, recording input data, and carrying out the indicated calculations upon them. The op system also arranges to return numerical printouts and other messages to the user via teleprinter.

The op system concurrently services up to eight independent stations by the round-robin time sharing scheme shown schematically in Figure 11. The experimental stations are arrayed about the CPU. Stations 0, 1, 3, and 7 are active, that is, have current ACT programs to run. The remaining four stations are not in use at this time. In Figure 11, two successive ticks of the synchronizing ACT clock running at 50 Hz (with a period therefore of 20 msec) have occurred. The figure is intended to illustrate that service times may vary from station to station, and from tick to tick. Thus, in the first period shown in Figure 11, station 0 took 1 msec to service, station 1 was serviced in about 4 msec, and stations 3 and 7 took about 1.5 msec each. Some 13 msec of "dead" time was left before servicing began again at the next clock tick. At the instant of Figure 11 (indicated by the positions of the dashed arrows), 8 msec of a period have elapsed, station 0 and 1 have been serviced, and the CPU is presently still in process of servicing station 3.

It is apparent from Figure 11 that stations are serviced once every clock tick, and in a fixed order. The method of servicing used is to permit the synchronous clock sole access to the program interrupt line. When a clock tick occurs, anything the computer may have been doing is interrupted, and monitor transfers control to the ACT op system, which begins to poll the active stations to see if any significant events are present at their R word interface. A significant event is considered either a change from the last clock tick in any discrete (on/off) R bit, or a non-zero level in any configuration of bits used for decoding analogue signals. If there have been one or more significant events since the last clock tick these are evaluated according to the instructions of the ACT program resident for that station and any data recording and state transitions required are carried out. Even if there are no significant R input events, the time value of this current tick may be significant for a current state of this station, and that is checked. Control then passes to the next station in the ring, and the process is repeated until the final station is processed.

The rate of significant events in psychological experiments is often very slow relative to the speed of computer processing. In the typical period between two clock ticks there is very little to do and so most of the period is dead time as far as servicing stations is concerned. Dead time, however, is far from wasted time, for it is used to perform bursts of lower priority computing. These dead time computations are known as *background* and they consist of such activities as outputting data to teletypes, compiling new incoming ACT programs, handling the conversational routines that modify existing running programs, and performing lengthy calculations the results of which can be delayed for a few seconds. In principle, some background time could be allocated to programs having nothing to do whatsoever with the ACT system, but the small core size and absence of any auxiliary backup memory at our installation has so far precluded this sophistication.

ACT STORAGE STRUCTURE

The heart of the computer program that translates a series of ACT and CALC instructions into an executable data structure in core is known as the ACT compiler. It is the function of the compiler to read in each ACT statement and turn it into a corresponding core storage structure that can then be executed by the ACT operating system.

ACT regards an experiment as a succession of internal states, each one generating an external state (a stimulus) and holding within its data structure information about possible transitions to other states within the network. The general storage structure by which this is achieved is a multi-linked list structure (Knuth, 1968) in which core memory is organized non-sequentially in linked *blocks*. These blocks are segmented into various functional *fields* for holding information about transitions and stimuli, and for storing incoming experimental data. The field is a functional unit and depending on its role it may itself occupy a block of core, a single location, or even a part of a register.

A fully compiled program for controlling a given experiment, performing the necessary computations, and retrieving the desired data will consist of (i) a set of experimental states, (ii) a set of transitions, and (iii) generally several fixed blocks of compiled CALC code. The storage structures by which ACT represents the states and transitions resemble some of the multi-linked list structures used to represent strings of text and their interrelationships (D'Imperio, 1969). In particular, ACT structures show affinities with those of CORAL (Raphael, Bobrow, Fein, and Young, 1968) and the Reaction Handler (Newman, 1967), languages used for on-line modeling of graphic display data. ACT's function, of course, is principally to move from one part of a complex logical network to another, depending on its ability to match a current input signal or current time value with a stored list of significant inputs and times. As such, it is far less concerned with manipulating interrelationships between its data elements than are the symbol manipulation languages with which it shares structural similarities. Moreover, an ACT structure does not grow, shrink, or proliferate during execution, except by the explicit directions from an interactive user.

A generalized experimental state appears in Figure 12. The state is seen to be represented in core as a block of pointers and an identifier field (shaded). The latter contains the binary representation of the flipflops to be actuated in the experimental environment during this state, bits to determine whether the CALC field should be executed in foreground or background, and state identification bits. The various pointers are of several sorts. For purposes of compiler housekeeping and executive garbage collection (*i.e.,,* returning structures no

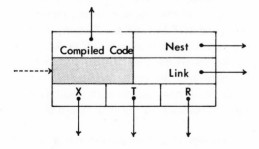

Figure 12. Core storage structure of an ACT state.

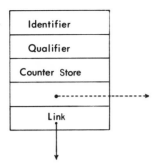

Figure 13. Core storage structure of an ACT transition.

longer in use to available space) the states of a given experiment are linked together in a linear one-way list. Thus, the link field of Figure 12 points to the next state in the list. This is a purely administrative link used at compile time for organizing the data structure, and at run time for modifying the data structure (including garbage collection) but not to specify transitions. The hierarchial nature of ACT states is accomplished by the nest pointer which points to the state, if any, nested one level below this state. The CALC pointer locates a block of compiled machine code corresponding to the algebraic statements of CALC that are to be carried out or queued as background upon initiation of the state. The X, T, and R fields point to lists of the three possible kinds of events, state eXits, Time, and subject initiated Responses that can terminate this state and initiate a new state.

A representative transition block is shown in Figure 13. One field identifies the transition event so that matches can be made to actual clock times (T), input signals (R), or internally calculated exits (X). A second field contains the qualifying information about the identifier such as its required frequency or its probability of initiating an actual transition. If the current event (clock, internal, or external condition) matches the identifier, *and* meets the qualifying conditions, the dashed arrow points to the new state that is to replace the present state as the active state for this experiment. The counter store provides a permanent repository for cumulating observed instances of the given identified event during the given state, and it is this field that the data record statements COUNT in the case of X and R blocks, and TOTALTIME for T blocks. Finally, since there may be any number of significant events of types X, or R for any given state, one-way links are provided to enable them all to be found and tested. Only one Time transition is permitted per state, and its link field is replaced by a second data storage field that is reset to zero each time its parent state is entered. This second data field corresponds to the data record directive DURATION.

Figure 14 represents the core storage structure corresponding to the procedural portion (the S state set) of the two-choice reaction experiment of Figures 2 and 7. The seven potential states of that experiment are shown

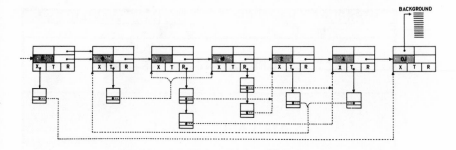

Figure 14. Internal representation of the S state set of the choice reaction experiment of Figures 2 and 7.

interconnected by eight transition elements. Administrative list links appear in Figure 14 as solid lines, transition branches are shown as dotted lines. The qualifier and counter fields of the transition blocks have been coalesced for ease in readability.

The structure shown in Figure 14 is executed as follows. On any signal from the ACT synchronizing clock (a sampling instant), a subset of the defined states are *active*, and their indicated transition symbols *relevant*. Reading from left to right, the experiment begins with State K. The next state to the right in this figure, State 0, is shown nested in State K. Hence, at the commencement of this program, States K and 0 are both active. That is, the stimulus information contained in the shaded fields of both States K and 0 is being communicated to the experimental environment from the moment of the first synchronizing clock signal (t_0) sensed by this program. On subsequent synchronizing sampling times (t_0 to t_n) matches are attempted for the one X symbol (4U20) of State K and the one T symbol (10 SEC) of State 0. Whenever a match is actually made, a transition will occur. That is, a new state will become active, thus bringing in new experimental stimuli and the transition symbols associated with the new active state(s) will become the relevant transitions to be scanned at each subsequent sampling instant. Any active state having background calculations tied to it (*e.g.*, rightmost State 0.1) would have these queued up to be executed in bursts during dead time. As it happens, none of the states of Figure 14 point to any foreground CALC compiled code, but had any done so, this code would have been executed immediately upon transition to that state.

It is apparent that with the inclusion of occasional bursts of foreground and background computation, the present implementation of ACT defines a table-driven synchronous automaton. The ACT compiler builds a storage structure that consists not of instructions to be executed, but of tables of data that an operating system interprets and decodes into the procedure of the experiment. The representation of experiments as multi-linked list-structures, although more costly of both core space and time than a completely compiled representation, provides a maximally flexible framework for on-line conversa-

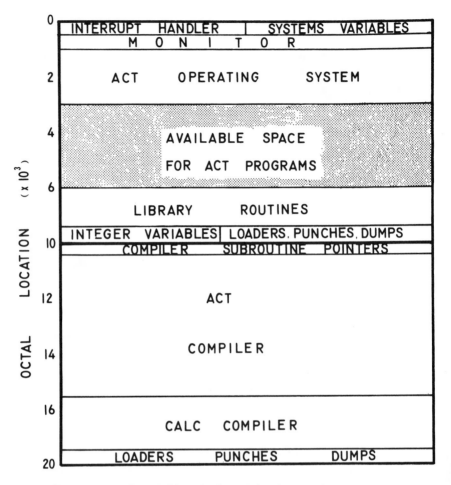

Figure 15. Core map of 8K PDP-8/S ACT. The scale is only approximate.

tional modification of ongoing procedures. In sequence control, as in all on-line computer controlled experiments, but in contrast to most industrial process control applications (Savas, 1965), procedures must be flexible and easily modified at the momentary whim of the investigator. ACT, in common with many on-line systems, permits parameters to be changed from the keyboard. (For instance, the variable K in the example may be set or modified during run time by the user by the commands given on p. 25.) But the list structure format of ACT allows the actual structures of a current complex experimental procedure to be modified from keyboard as well. Transitions can be deleted or added, branches may be moved, and states may be created via the conversational command repertoire of p. 25 during program run time.

From the point of view of a group of users time sharing the same small computer, a table-driven list structure affords maximum memory protection among users. Since the responsibility for assigning blocks, pointers, and garbage collection lies completely in the hands of a monitor that supervises both the compiler and executive, it is impossible for one user to inadvertently overwrite another, or for an assembled program to "blow up".

CORE ALLOCATION

Previous sections have discussed the storage structure of compiled programs, the way they are executed, and many of the facilities of the control system incorporating ACT and CALC compilers. An 8k PDP-8/S is large enough to contain both the compilers and the operating system, and still have about 2k left for available program space. In practice, this proves adequate space for about four concurrently running programs of moderate complexity. With the op system and compilers simultaneously resident in core, a small monitor serves to pass control from one to the other, establish priorities, queue up background programs, and to check that all active stations are processed within the period of the synchronous clock. A core map of the various programs is shown in Figure 5. In addition to the ACT and CALC software, a few short systems programs such as loaders, punches, and dumps are resident. Space is also reserved for library routines to perform decimal printing, multiply and divide functions, and floating point conversion. It should be noted that whereas the present ACT compiler incorporates all of the reference features of ACT except string responses, the CALC compiler at present accepts only about 20% of the CALC reference commands.

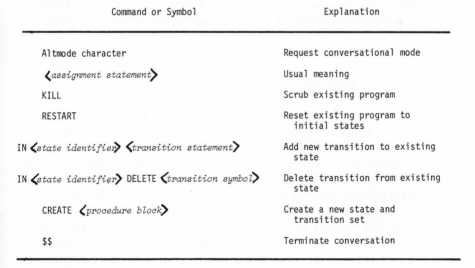

Command or Symbol	Explanation
Altmode character	Request conversational mode
⟨*assignment statement*⟩	Usual meaning
KILL	Scrub existing program
RESTART	Reset existing program to initial states
IN ⟨*state identifier*⟩ ⟨*transition statement*⟩	Add new transition to existing state
IN ⟨*state identifier*⟩ DELETE ⟨*transition symbol*⟩	Delete transition from existing state
CREATE ⟨*procedure block*⟩	Create a new state and transition set
$$	Terminate conversation

Figure 16. Run-time conversational command repetoire.

CONVERSATIONAL COMMAND REPERTOIRE

After a program has been compiled and is running, a user may wish to modify his experiment without stopping to write an entirely new program. Depending on the path the experiment is taking, the user may feel that the values of time intervals, probabilities, or response criteria may need changing. Certain unanticipated data may need to be collected or used in calculations. The experimenter may even wish to touch up the actual procedure as the experiment is progressing.

To permit direct user interaction with his running program, the group of conversational commands tabulated in Figure 16 has been defined that may be input from the keyboard whenever a station holds an active program. Judiciously used, they provide a quantum power jump in experimental automation.

APPLICATIONS

The Oxford ACT system has been used to date to control a variety of human and animal experiments entailing discrete stimulus and response events, and also as an aid in teaching students concepts of behavioral contingencies and stimulation. Several instances of these applications are described below, and one in detail, to illustrate the practical power to a problem-oriented language in the behavioral laboratory. These examples given are only a small sample of the types of experiments that ACT is capable of computerizing. In general, programs are expressed as state diagrams, but the translation to ACT statements is accomplished in a straightforward manner by the rules given in the section on ACT nomenclature.

ANIMAL PSYCHOPHYSICS

ACT is currently being used by Elizabeth Jacobs to automate a series of visual psychophysical experiments with doves. Figure 17 shows a schematic plan of the apparatus, with the devices controlled by the computer marked by English labels. The projector stands above the plane of the apparatus itself. Its beam, after passing through the splitting system shown roughly here, passes via two electromechanical shutters onto tilting mirrors. When the shutters are oepned, images from the projector slide can be reflected down into the apparatus and focussed on tangential vertical screens. These images provide discriminative stimuli for the bird, which stands in a confining but transparent box at the center of the arena with access to three vertically arrayed keys at beak level, and a food hopper below.

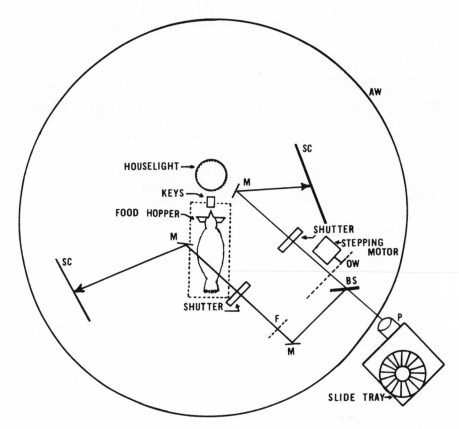

Figure 17. Testing arena used for avian psychophysical studies. Radius c. 60 cm. Not drawn to scale. Devices controlled by computer are given English labels. P = projector, AW = arena wall, SC = screen, BS = beam splitter, F = neutral density filter to correct standard beam, OW = optical wedge (rotating filter) controlled by stepping motor, M = tilted plane mirrors.

Birds are trained to discriminate features of the visual environment such as the presence or absence of flashes, their numerosity, angular separation, hue, or form characteristics. Performance on these tasks is used to measure visual fields, visual acuity, monocular bias, and interocular relationships.

The basic schedule consists of a series of discrete trials. On each trial, the observing keylight is first lit. When the bird pecks it (R1), one shutter is opened for a short time, exposing one or two stimuli (or classes of stimuli) according to which slide is in the projector gate. At the same time, the two reponse keys are dimly illuminated, and the bird must peck one (R2) or the other (R4). Correct responses are reinforced with 3-sec access to grain, on a proportion of trials; incorrect responses result in a timeout in darkness (about 10 sec., varying between subjects) with the same probability. After reinforcement ends, or after unreinforced pecks, the events of the trial are recorded (by the program or by electromagnetic counters), the stimulus for the next trial is selected by moving the projector magazine, and the next trial begins.

Stimulus Coding. The number of devices to be controlled in this apparatus (houselights, three keylights, food magazine, shutters, projector slide-tray, optical wedge motor and several electromagnetic counters) exceeds the maximum of 11 stimulus bits available. Consequently, five bits of the stimulus bank (bits 1, 2, 4, 10, and 20) have been gated via conventional transitor logic, so that any combination of these S bits specifies a unique output line. There are thus 2^5 gated + 6 independent = 38 possible stimulus lines available. In the accompanying state diagrams, S1 to S37 are gated states, and S40 to S2000 are independent.

It is essential to note that gating S bits, although creating more output lines, removes the important additive property of ACT stimuli. For example, if, in a test apparatus, S1 = houselights, and S2 = keylight, it is no longer possible by specifying S3 to produce simultaneously houselights + keylight, since S3 now codes a totally different stimulus device than either S1 or S2. More crucially, nesting states, and executing concurrent state planes is almost impossible if only gated stimuli are available. To run programs of any complexity, some S bits must be left independent.

Programming. In the following discussion of program techniques, special emphasis is placed on aspects of ACT that have become prominent when programming more sophisticated procedures. They include the use of multiple state planes, variable probabilities and variable states, and problems with adaptive threshold procedures.

Figure 18 shows a typical adaptive testing program in state diagram form. The meaning of stimulus and response labels is given in the caption. The "black box" stands for one of a number of possible procedures to select the stimulus for the next trial. One of these is given in Figure 19, and is discussed later. Figure 18 illustrates a testing program in which either stimulus A (network beginning with S1.1) or stimulus B (network beginning with S1.2) is presented. The correct response to A is R2, and to B, R4.

The procedure will be seen to consist of four main branches representing from top downwards, A standard trials, A test trials, B test trials, and B standard trials. The standard branches are straightforward; they provide partial reinforcement and timeouts for correct and incorrect responses, respectively.

From the state at the beginning of the trial, S1.1 or S1.2, an observing response takes the program with probability M (set either to 1 or 7/8) to a standard or a test stimulus (S40.1 or S40.3). Note that the standard and test versions of the stimulus are exposed through different shutters (S10, or S11) that is, they use different light paths, so that the rotating neutral density filter that controls the intensity of the test stimuli may not be in the path of the standard stimuli. The standard beam's constant intensity is set by a fixed filter

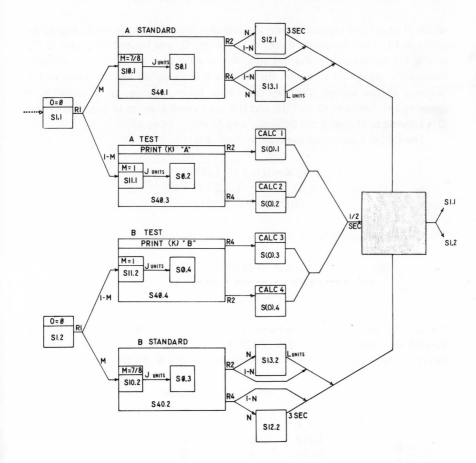

Figure 18. Procedural network for adaptive threshold determinations. The "black box" is explained in the text and expanded in Figure 19. S1 = observing key lit, S40 = used for monitoring only, S10 = A shutter open, S11 = B shutter open, S12 = feeder, S13 = houselights off, S14 = decrease stimulus intensity, S15 = increase stimulus intensity, R1 = peck observing key, R2 = correct A response, R4 = correct B response.

(see Figure 17). The mirrors onto which the beams fall when the shutters are open are tilted so that the two beams fall on the same or different spots in the visual field, according to the demands of the particular experiment.

On test trials, no reinforcement is given for any response, as these constitute infrequent trials to probe the threshold of the discriminative response patterns being maintained by the standard trials.

Adaptive test stimulus intensity, designed to estimate the 50% point on the psychometric function is achieved by the variable O (oh) which appears in four variable states, S(O).1 to S(O).4. The value of O is zeroed at the beginning of each trial. There are CALC sequences corresponding to each S(O) which after correct reponses lower the stimulus intensity by setting O, and hence S(O), to 14. After incorrect response sequences O, and hence S(O), is set to 15, raising the stimulus intensity one step. At the same time that O is being adjusted to step the wedge up or down, the variable K is being adjusted to monitor the position of the wedge. To keep the wedge from stepping out of range, K is contained to limits of O and 36, and it is only when K is not at these limits that O is allowed to change from its initial zero to either 14 or 15.

The CALC 1 block associated with S(O).1 is

> [IF K = 0 GO TO LABEL 1;
> LET K = K - 1; LET O = 14;
> LABEL1: PRINT "A"]

The CALC 2 sequence is

> [IF K = 36 GO TO LABEL2;
> LET K = K + 1; LET O = 15;
> LABEL2: PRINT "B"]

The CALC3 sequence is the same as CALC 1 except that "B" is printed, and the CALC4 sequence is the same as CALC2 except that "A" is printed. A sample record of the performance printout during the session might be:

K	stimulus	response
0000	A	B
0001	B	A
0002	B	B
0001	A	B
0002	B	A
0003	A	A

The value of K and the stimulus letter is printed during S40.3 or S40.4. The response letter is printed during one of the S(O)s.

Figure 18 shows on careful inspection that two test trials cannot occur in succession. This is because the variable M governing the probability of a standard trial is set to 1 at the onset of a test trial, and restored to 7/8 at the onset of a standard trial.

The experimenter can fix various parameters by run-time conversation as follows: (J) = stimulus duration, (L) = timeout duration, and (N) = probability of reinforcement for correct responses.

Projector Control, Illustrating Use of U-plane and Variable States. A universal problem in automated psychophysics is that of generating a stimulus sequence that is unpredictable by the subject, but known to the machine. Here, the problem is compounded by the following facts. (1) The stimuli, A, and B, are not generated by the computer program, but depend upon which slide is in the projector gate. The contingencies set up by the computer must correspond to the current slide. (2) The projector (unlike most programming equipment) must be in the same room as the animal, and the noise of the slide-tray movement between trials may be perceptible. High levels of masking noise are undesirable, hence, whatever the order of slides in the tray, the occurrence or non-occurrence of tray noise must not provide a cue to the subject about events in the next trial. Since the tray cannot remain permanently still, it must either move randomly with respect to stimulus change, or move (forwards or backwards) on each trial. The former situation is highly complex in terms of programming, so we come to the latter. There are two possible solutions.

(i) The desired random sequence of slides is placed in the magazine, and the projector moves forward on each trial. The computer has some information about the sequence, for instance, a coded list that it consults on each trial, or some physical, probably photoelectric, cue from the current slide itself.

(ii) The slide sequence in the projector is systematic; on each trial the computer selects a stimulus by a suitable random process, and is able to procure the correct slide by a simple, auditorily indiscriminable motion of the projector. Though (i) is more common, a method of type (ii) is here utilized that allows true random sequences to be generated by the computer. These differ on each session, and obviate the need to change the order of slides in the tray. Replicas of slide A and B are placed in alternating *pairs* round the tray. The sequence can be represented by ...A1 A2 B1 B2 A1 A2 ... etc. The table below shows the results of single steps forward or backward at every point in the repeating sequence.

Current slide	Move forward	Move backward
A1	A	B
A2	B	A
B1	B	A
B2	A	B

Thus, from any point in the sequence, the computer may move to either A or B (as selected by any random or quasi-random sequence) by making the appropriate single step of the slide tray.

The state diagram of Figure 19 can be substituted for the "black box" in Figure 18, and includes a U-plane "memory network". This program generates a truly random sequence in which A and B are always equiprobable.

The system illustrates the use of variable states and state exits as follows. S(H) and S(I) are set to S16 and S17, respectively, depending on the stage of the sequence. S16 causes the slide tray to move forwards, S17 moves it backwards. In each case, S(H) is the movement necessary to produce stimulus A on the next trial, while S(I) produces stimulus B.

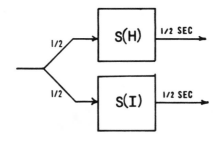

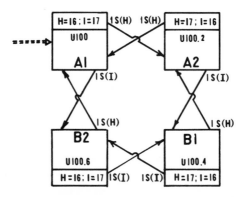

Figure 19. Expansion of the "black box" of Figure 18: slide control and memory network for generating random slides of two stimulus classes. S16 = step slide tray forward, S17 = step slide tray backward.

The U-plane network "remembers" where in the sequence the slide tray is, and sets the values of H and I accordingly. It has four states, one for each point in the sequence. The state diagram has been labeled to show which pair of states corresponds to each stage in the slide sequence.

The slide tray is initially placed at A1, and when the program is started, the U-plane sets the values of H and I to 16 and 17 respectively. It then waits till the next movement of the tray. If this is S(H) leading to A2, the U-plane moves to the A2 state, changing H and I to new values in U100.2 and U100.3. If S(I) occurs, it moves to the B2 state, where H and I keep the same values. In this way the U-plane, which is not driving any events in the apparatus as such, maintains control over events in the S-plane.

ADJUSTING COD IN CONCURRENT REINFORCEMENT SCHEDULE

P. deVilliers and the writer are collaborating on a series of studies of conditioned emotional response effects on a variety of behavioral baselines. In one experiment, a rat works on a two-lever concurrent variable-interval milk

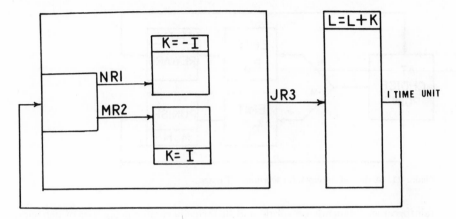

Figure 20. Network for incrementing or decrementing changeover delay (L), depending on the first occurrence of either N R1, or M R2, respectively, in every block of J responses.

reinforcement schedule. The two levers are associated with different reinforcement durations. At variable time intervals a fixed duration "danger" stimulus is presented, during which time brief electric grid shocks occur randomly in time.

The PDP-8/S in ACT mode controls the reinforcement contingencies, and adjusts reinforcement durations, change-over-delays (COD), and shock probabilities according to behavioral properties. The program also stops and starts ink recorders, and prints out comparative response data in danger and safe periods. Typically, the experiment is managed concurrently with the psychophysical experiments described in the previous section.

In one training procedure, prior to shock, the COD is continuously adjusted to force the concurrent performance to stabilize with relative response rates on the two levers matching the associated relative reinforcement durations. The state diagram fragment in Figure 20 illustrates one method for achieving this effect. Since the interest in this figure lies in the calculations and network logic, no stimulus identifiers are shown. In a given block of J successive responses, if N or more of them have been type R1, then the COD (L) will be lowered by the value of K. But if M or more of them were type R2, then the COD will be raised by K. Block size (J), matching proportion (N/M), and increment size (I) are all variable so that the experimenter can set or modify them via conversational commands at run time.

The use of R3 in Figure 20 illustrates the disjunctive interpretation of R values adopted in the Oxford ACT implementation. R3 in the diagram means: if J R1 *or* R2, or any mixture of both, execute the transition.

The example of this section is only one of a host of contingencies that we are using and have used in the general area of reinforcement schedules. Experience has shown that most of the classical schedules can be written in ACT by the novice in a matter of minutes. More complex schedules, in which

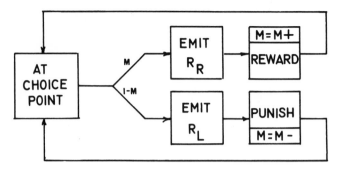

Figure 21. A stat rat network for learning a T maze.

reinforcement depends on subtle and historically remote properties of behavior, require more skill, but the saving in time over programming such procedures in machine instructions is commensurate.

BEHAVIORAL SIMULATION

The simulation of a complex system by constructing a network of the hypothetically relevant variables constitutes a working model of the system. Because the construction of such a model forces the theorist to make explicit the nature of all his theoretical elements, simulation can often be a salutary step towards increased theoretical specification and precision. From the pedagogical point of view, we have found that simple simulation exercises in the field of conditioning and learning frequently aid the beginning student in formalizing the variables that must be specified in any complete account of such behavioral processes.

Even the simple T maze network of Figure 21, written by an undergraduate student's first contact with a computer, illustrates some fundamental aspects of behavior and environmental feedback. The diagram defines a stat Rat that starts with equal probabilities of going right (R_R) or left (R_L) and eventually goes consistently to the reinforced side. By requesting various calculations for incrementing the probability of the correct response in the reinforcement state, the student was able to see the occurrence of a variety of learning curves. The effects on the learning curve of various punishment possibilities were also observed. Once the simple network was available, questions arose about how to represent more complex effects such as sequence effects, satiation, occasional incorrect responses after the maze had been "learned", one-trial learning, extinction, and spontaneous recovery.

A model of a more complex maze was built that incorporated two interacting ACT stations. One station represented the processes necessary for a stat Rat to behave, and the other represented the contingencies of the maze environment. Thus, the rat station emitted brief stimulus pulses corresponding to responses, while the environmental station emitted stimuli corresponding to the rat's different position in the maze. The environmental station took in the rat's responses and changed its positions, while the rat station took in the position information and modified its behavior by law-of-effect principles. The more complex example proved instructive in demonstrating the conditional nature of environmental contingencies, and raised new problems of how to represent such behavioral effects as latent learning, secondary reinforcement, blind alley elimination, and the goal gradient.

Not all the problems were solved at the termination of the project, but the experience of being able to translate textbook concepts into a working model proved especially reinforcing. ACT, unaugmented, expedited the student's initial contact with a computer and proved a stepping stone to more advanced programming techniques.

CONCLUSIONS

The intent of the preceding sections has been to show the nature and power of a problem-oriented programming language for experimental psychology. The basis of the language described here is the fundamental notion that the procedural core of behavioral experiments constitutes a finite-state machine in which stimuli play a prominent part in the constitution of states, and temporal and behavioral events play a prominent part in the specifications of state transitions.

The automated contingency translator that has evolved from that basis appears to possess the generality to represent the logical structure of the great body of past and present psychological procedures, wherever these can in principal be automated. On the other hand, to produce practical experiments, this translator must be augmented by various data recording facilities, and an algebraic compiler for manipulating data and variables.

The proof of a language is in its speaking, and pending its use by a variety of independent users with different experimental requirements, the life span and future development of ACT are highly speculative. Certainly the weak algebraic facilities provided by CALC will require strengthening as behavioral procedures increase in sophistication. ACT itself is open on how this could be accomplished, but given available memory, presumably a complete marriage with ALGOL or FORTRAN might be arranged.

There are now nearly a dozen problem-oriented languages in this field, some of which are based on finite state representation, some on control extensions to existing procedure-oriented languages, and some built up by subroutining procedures most common in the laboratory using the language. Only experience will show the virtues and deficiencies in these various tongues and pass the final judgment on their generality. Comparisons are difficult in a field where differences in computer hardware and existing machine configurations complicate any idealized relative assessment of languages. In any case, the past history of computer languages would suggest that proliferation is inevitable because the uses to which computers are put vary so widely.

To date, the main use of ACT has been to lend flexibility to established procedures. As familiarity is gained with the concepts of the language, our dependence on procedures spawned by the first generation of automation will lessen and we may expect an ever-increasing common stock of new procedures that assume the high-level computation abilities of the new tool.

The language of ACT itself, while easy to learn, read, and write, has a disturbing loquacity. Networks such as those of Figure 18 require many words to define, and if networks are repeated within procedures (as they are there) one may expect some sort of macro facility eventually to emerge. In macro, once defined, a complete network may be called by a single name, and networks of networks can then be quickly and easily cascaded. How this macro facility will proceed, and whether it will build from units like the present elements of ACT, is anybody's guess. But it does seem certain that while ACT definitely seems a problem-oriented language in 1972, a quantum increase in programming power is likely to render it "low level". Already it has the feel and look of an assembly language for an imaginary computer containing an associative memory made up of states. Of course, if in fact ACT or other languages do succeed in representing fundamental elements of psychological procedures, then what is in computer terms an assembly language, is in other terms the assemblage of theoretical elements for synthesizing, describing, and ordering our diverse procedures. Theorists have long talked of simple and parsimonious frameworks for subsuming the independent variables of psychology, but the scheme has so far eluded us. In the progressive refinement of problem-oriented programming languages for psychology emerges one practical model to which the behavior theorist may have to pay increasingly closer attention.

APPENDIX A

SYNTAX OF ACT

The syntax of ACT is defined in this appendix using a metalanguage that combines features of both Backus-Naur form and the COBOL report. The table below illustrates the metalinguistic symbols and their meaning. In the definitions that follow, symbols or strings of symbols outside of angle brackets represent themselves. The juxtaposition of symbols and expressions means concatenation. If there are alternate definitions the alternatives are separated by a vertical bar. Whenever it is necessary to use additional lines to continue a definition, the continuation is indented.

Symbol	Meaning
:=	Equivalence
< >	Surround metalinguistic variables
|	Or
{ }	Choice
[ ]	Optional

$<$comment flag$>$:= /
$<$tabulation symbol$>$:= ! | *non-printing tabulation character*
$<$indentation$>$:= $<$tabulation symbol$>$ | $<$indentation$>$$<$tabulation symbol$>$
$<$decimal digit$>$:= 0 | 1 |2 | 3 | 4 | 5 | 6 | 7 | 8 | 9
$<$decimal integer$>$:= $<$decimal digit$>$ | $<$decimal digit$>$ | $<$decimal integer$>$
$<$octal digit$>$:= 0 | 1 | 2 | 3 | 4 | 5 | 6 | 7
$<$octal integer$>$:= $<$octal digit$>$ | $<$octal digit$>$$<$octal integer$>$
$<$integer variable$>$:= (H) | (I) | (J) | (K) | (L) | (M) | (N) | (O)

$<$assignment statement$>$:= $<$integer variable$>$ $<$decimal integer$>$

$<$state symbol$>$:= S | U | V

$<$state identifier$>$:= $<$state symbol$>$ $\left\{ \begin{array}{l} <\text{integer variable}> \\ <\text{octal integer}> \end{array} \right\}$ • [octal integer]

$<$response symbol$>$:= R

$<$response identifier$>$:= $<$response symbol$>$ $\left\{ \begin{array}{l} <\text{integer variable}> \\ <\text{octal integer}> \end{array} \right\}$

$<$time units$>$:= UNITS | SEC | MIN | HR

$<$time specification$>$:= $<$integer variable$>$ UNITS | $<$decimal integer$>$ $\left\{ \begin{array}{l} \text{UNITS} \\ \text{SEC} \\ \text{MIN} \\ \text{HR} \end{array} \right\}$

$<$probability expression$>$:= $\left\{ \begin{array}{l} \text{PROBABILITY} \\ \text{P} \end{array} \right\}$ $=$ $\left\{ <\text{integer variable}> \\ <\text{decimal integer}> / <\text{decimal integer}> \right\}$

$<$state declaration$>$:= [indentation] $\left\{ \begin{array}{l} \text{WHEN} \\ \text{WHILE} \\ \text{GIVE} \end{array} \right\}$ $<$state identifier$>$

$<$state nest$>$:= $<$state declaration$>$$<$indentation$>$$<$state declaration$>$ |
        $<$state nest$>$$<$indentation$>$$<$state declaration$>$

$<$response transition statement$>$:= $<$indentation$>$ IF $<$response identifier$>$

$\left\{ \begin{array}{l} \text{THEN} \\ \text{GO} \\ \text{GO TO} \\ \text{->} \end{array} \right\}$ [$<$probability expression$>$] $<$state identifier$>$

$<$time transition statement$>$:= $<$indentation$>$ AFTER $<$time specification$>$

$\left\{ \begin{array}{l} \text{THEN} \\ \text{GO} \\ \text{GO TO} \\ \text{->} \end{array} \right\}$ [$<$probability expression$>$] $<$state identifier$>$

$<$state exit transition statement$>$:= $<$indentation$>$ FOLLOWING $\left\{ \begin{array}{l} <\text{integer variable}> \\ <\text{decimal integer}> \end{array} \right\}$

$<$state identifier$>$ $\left\{ \begin{array}{l} \text{THEN} \\ \text{GO} \\ \text{GO TO} \\ \text{->} \end{array} \right\}$ [probability expression]

$<$state identifier$>$

$<$null transition$>$:= $<$indentation$>$ $

$<$program segment terminator$>$:= $<$null transition$>$ $

$<$transition symbol$>$:= $<$response identifier$>$ | $<$state identifier$>$ | $<$time specification$>$ | $

$<$transition statement$>$:= $<$response transition statement$>$ | $<$time transition statement$>$ | $<$state exit transition statement$>$ | $<$null transition$>$

$<$transition set$>$:= $<$transition statement$>$ | $<$transition set$>$ $<$transition statement$>$

$<$record statement$>$:= IN $<$state identifier$>$ $\left\{ \begin{array}{l} <\text{response identifier}> \\ <\text{state identifier}> \end{array} \right\}$ COUNT |

$<$state identifier$>$ $\left\{ \begin{array}{l} \text{TOTAL TIME} \\ \text{DURATION} \end{array} \right\}$

$<$ACT statement$>$:= $<$assignment statement$>$ | $<$state declaration$>$ | $<$transition statement$>$ | $<$record statement$>$

$<$procedure block$>$:= [$<$assignment statement$>$] $<$state declaration$>$ $<$transition set$>$

$<$procedure segment$>$:= $<$procedure block$>$ | $<$procedure segment$>$ $<$procedure block$>$

$<$procedure section$>$:= $<$procedure segment$>$ $<$program segment terminator$>$

$<$record segment$>$:= $<$record statement$>$ | $<$record segment$>$ $<$record statement$>$

$<$record section$>$:= $<$record segment$>$ $<$program segment terminator$>$

$<$ACT program$>$:= $<$procedure section$>$ $<$record section$>$

REFERENCES

Ciofalo, V. B., Tedford, R. H., Goldberg, M. E., and Dodge, D. L. The use of a digital computer for control of behavioral research on animals. *Behavioral Science*, 1968, 13, 252–256.

D'Imperio, M. E. Data structures and their representation in storage. In *Annual review of automatic programming*, M. I. Halpern and C. J. Shaw (Eds.), 1969, 5, 1–75.

Gill, A. *Introduction to the theory of finite state machines.* New York: McGraw Hill, 1962.

Hendry, D. P. and Lennon, W. *On-line programming II in Symposium, Automation of behavioral experiments.* American Psychological Association, Washington, D. C., September, 1967.

Kappauf, W. E. Use of an on-line computer for psychophysical testing with the up-and-down method. *American Psychologist*, 1969, 24, 207–211.

Knuth, D. E. *The art of computer programming.* Vol. I: Fundamental algorithms. Reading, Massachusetts: Addison-Wesley, 1968.

Lehigh-Valley. *The ACT primer: computer language and hardware interface for controlling psychological experiments.* Fogelsville, Pennsylvania: Lehigh Valley Electronics, 1969.

McLean, R. S. *PSYCHOL: A formal language for the control of psychological experiments.* Unpublished PhD thesis, Carnegie-Mellon University, 1968.

Millenson, J. R. An automated contingency translator ACT I, A computer system for process control of psychological experimentation. *Psychonomic Bulletin*, 1967, 1, 17.

Millenson, J. R. A programming language for on-line control of psychological experimentation. *Digital Equipment Computer Users Society Proceedings*, Spring, 1968, Pp. 137–144.

Millenson, J. R. and Sullivan, G. D. A hardware random number generator for use with computer control of probabilistic contingencies. *Behavior Research Methods and Instrumentation*, 1969, 1, 194–196.

Newell, A. and Simon, H. A. Computers in psychology. In D. Luce, R. Bush, and E. Galanter (Eds.) *Handbook of mathematical psychology,* Vol. I, 1963, Pp. 363–428.

Newman, W. N. *A system for interactive graphical programming.* Computer technology group Report 67/7. Imperial College London, 1967.

Raphael, B., Bobrow, D. G., Fein, L., and Young, J. W. A brief survey of computer languages for symbolic and algebraic manipulation. In *Symbol manipulation languages and techniques.* D. G. Bobrow (Ed.) Amsterdam: North Holland, 1968, Pp. 1–54.

Sammet, Jean E. *Programming languages: history and fundamentals.* Englewood Cliffs, N. J.: Prentice Hall, 1969.

Savas, E. S. *Computer control of industrial processes.* New York: McGraw Hill, 1965.

Snapper, A. G., Kadden, R. M., Knapp, J. Z., and Kushner, H. K. *A notation system and computer program for behavioral experiments.* Digital Equipment Computer Users Society, Biomedical Proceedings, New York, June 1967.

Snapper, A. G. and Knapp, J. Z. *A multi-purpose logic module for behavioral experiments.* Proceedings Digital Equipment Computer Users Society, Spring, 1969.

Snapper, A. G., Knapp, J. Z., and Kushner, H. K. Mathematical descriptions of schedules of reinforcement. In W. N. Schoenfeld and J. Farmer (Eds.) *Theories of reinforcement schedules.* New York: Appleton-Century-Crofts, 1969.

CHAPTER TWO

TIME-SHARING IN A SMALL COMPUTER BASED ON A BEHAVIORAL NOTATION SYSTEM[1]

ARTHUR G. SNAPPER

Western Michigan University, and

RONALD M. KADDEN

Franklin Delano Roosevelt VA Hospital, Montrose, N. Y.

[1] Supported in part by Grant MH-13049 from the National Institute of Mental Health, USPHS to William N. Schoenfeld, Queens College, New York, and in part by the Veterans Administration. The authors wish to thank Vivian B. Snapper for her helpful comments and suggestions, and Julius Z. Knapp and Harold K. Kushner for their part in the development of the notational language. The system described here was current in 1968-1969 at the time the paper was written. Since then, a more efficient version has been developed, based on the suggestions contained in the "Systems Alternatives and Improvements" section. It has been submitted to, and is available from Digital Equipment Computer Users Society, No. 8-465, Maynard, Massachusetts, 01754. The notational language and general considerations concerning system features remain unchanged.

41

INTRODUCTION

In 1964, while designing a research installation for the study of behavioral and cardiovascular effects of aversive stimuli, we selected a small general-purpose digital computer (PDP-8) for programming experiments and recording data. Our initial justification for a computer, rather than traditional transistorized or relay logic systems, was based on the need to obtain greater precision in programming experiments, greater power in data acquisition, and greater reliability of operation for the same price per experimental station.

After several years of experience with a computer-controlled laboratory, in which up to 10 simultaneous experiments can be conducted, we feel that our original justification was, in fact, realistic. Furthermore, we have discovered advantages not anticipated, (e.g., increased efficiency in setting up new experiments and greater convenience in day-to-day operation of the laboratory).

On the other hand, a number of unanticipated difficulties have arisen that were corrected only by trial-and-error. Thus, the evolution of our present system has required a considerable amount of time and is still liable to improvements. Some of the problems we encountered can be eliminated by using newer laboratory computers and associated peripheral equipment; rapidly decreasing prices make more powerful systems economical investments. However, many of the considerations that guided us in designing the present system may be of general interest to those considering computer control.

GENERAL CONSIDERATIONS

Several features of the computing system depend upon the research interests of the investigator. In some laboratories, in which operant procedures are used to maintain behavior as a baseline for the effects of pharmacological or physiological variables, the same schedule of reinforcement may be administered indefinitely in a number of experimental stations with only small parametric variations of procedure ever being required. This type of laboratory needs an initial programming effort in which the major emphasis is on operator convenience and reliability with much attention to the format of data recording.

At the other end of the spectrum, the computer can, in some well-equipped laboratories, be used to control only one experiment at a time. With this type of approach, reinforcement schedules of great complexity may be studied and data acquisition and analysis may be very elaborate, requiring extensive and time-consuming computer programming before each new experiment is undertaken.

Our laboratory falls somewhere in the middle of this spectrum. We use the computer to control a number of simultaneous experiments and we frequently program extensive changes in procedure to answer new experimental questions arising from ongoing research. The experimental contingencies range in complexity from classical conditioning, with simple temporal pairings of two stimuli, to complex operant adjusting schedules of reinforcement involving a variety of stimulus and temporal discriminations. Some experimental sessions may be quite short and others occupy most of each day. The amount of data acquisition, too, varies with some procedures requiring only a few simple response rate determinations; other studies are analyzed in terms of conditional interresponse-time distributions or sequential measures.

TIME-SHARING

A single computer can control several independent simultaneous experiments through a technique called time-sharing. This procedure depends upon the fact that the computer is needed to record data, make decisions, and generate stimuli for each experiment only when a response occurs (or a time interval elapses). With the speed of modern computers, each response can be completely treated in a millisecond, while the data rate from one experimental station rarely exceeds one response per 100 msec. During the interval between responses from one station, the computer is free to handle data from other parallel experiments. In this way, each experiment has access to the full power of the computer when necessary, and more than one study may be controlled at a time. For those applications where the structure of the computer and the laboratory requirements permit the use of time-sharing, the result is the most efficient allocation of resources.

There are two different methods commonly used to achieve time-sharing with the PDP-8, and each has its own advantages and disadvantages. Each method utilizes a feature of the computer called the program interrupt, which causes the computer to react to incoming data, and each method requires a digital logic interface to store response data until the computer can handle it. The computer receives information from the interface for each possible response input, and pulses from a free-running source (or clock) for timing the contingencies and stimuli of the experiment.

With the first method, the storage devices for all responses are scanned in succession in a pre-specified sequence. A pulse from the free-running clock triggers the scan by operating the interrupt circuit, and the computer then examines the first storage device for response data. (The same clock pulse also is used for timing experimental contingencies.) If a response has occurred since the last scan, the response is entered and the program for that experiment is initiated. On completion of the treatment of the response (or immediately, if there is no response stored), the next input device is examined. After all of the inputs are scanned the computer awaits the next clock pulse. Thus, response data are entered into the computer only when a pulse occurs from the free-running timing source. A major advantage of this method is the simplicity of the computer program and external logic needed to implement it. The major drawback is that the clock inputs must be spaced by an interval long enough to handle the worst possible case, *i.e.*, all possible response inputs occurring within one scan. In this case, the scan interval must be equal to the time needed to process all of these inputs, even though the simultaneous occurrence of all of them is rare. If the clock is set at a higher rate, some clock pulses will be lost when too many inputs occur within a single scan. Furthermore, the delay between a response and stimuli contingent upon it is a function of the number of different response inputs, even when the rate of some of these responses may be quite low.

The second method of time-sharing requires a slightly more complex computer program and associated hardware logic. It is implemented by causing every response or clock input to operate the program interrupt. If the computer is free (*i.e.*, not treating an earlier response) when an input occurs, it is immediately handled. If, on the other hand, prior data have been entered, the new response will be acted upon immediately after the previous one has been completed. In most cases, then, the response will receive immediate attention and need not await a clock input to be entered. Moreover, the clock is treated like any other input and its rate may be much higher than in the alternative system, thus affording more precision in the timing of contingencies and stimuli.

We chose the latter method to obtain the higher clock input rates. Details of hardware and software used to implement it are found in later sections of this chapter.

PROGRAMMING THE COMPUTER

Although computers can be programmed to carry out a large number of complex calculations, these are accomplished by surprisingly small numbers of basic arithmetic and logical operations. The PDP-8 has only seven instruction sets for this purpose. These instructions are coded as 12-bit binary numbers that cause the computer to perform desired operations. Even for a simple experiment a sequence consisting of a large number of the basic computer operations must be generated. Fortunately, the computer can be used to simplify its own programming by means of other computer programs that translate either mnemonic statements (Assemblers) or higher-order symbolic instructions (Compilers) into the appropriate binary code required to instruct the computer. The PDP-8 is provided with an Assembler program for converting a simple set of mnemonics into the appropriate binary coded (machine language) instructions. This process consists of three stages: first the mnemonics are typed on a teletype producing a printed copy and a punched tape called the symbolic tape. Second, the symbolic program tape is read into the computer under control of the Assembler which, after three separate readings of the symbolic tape, produces a new tape in binary coded format. This tape contains the desired computer instructions, and it is then read into the computer (replacing the Assembler) to operate the desired computer program. If a mistake has occurred at any stage or is detected on program operation, this whole sequence must be repeated.

Therefore, writing correct programs in an Assembly language usually requires a considerable length of time.

The major objection to using the machine language of the Assembler in our application is the amount of programming and assembling time needed to prepare a new experiment. Since the computer is primarily occupied in its role of controlling experiments, getting enough computer time to program new studies and to check out new programs can be quite difficult. Furthermore, designing computer language programs can be hazardous with a time-sharing system because the computer is running several experiments in parallel. Reprogramming for one experimental station, even if only to change parametric values, requires a great deal of skill and care to avoid interference with other ongoing studies.

As an alternative to programming in Assembly language, the use of FORTRAN for controlling experiments deserves consideration. A FORTRAN compiler has been written for the PDP-8. However, due to the small size of its memory (4K), only short FORTRAN programs can be written and these require a relatively long time to be executed. These limitations of program length and time prevent the use of FORTRAN for time-shared experimental control in systems as small as ours. Also, because it was originally designed as a mathematical notation, some aspects of schedules of reinforcement are cumbersome to notate using FORTRAN terminology.

To solve these problems, we have developed a new computer language designed to simplify computer programming of behavioral experiments. The strategy of this approach resembles that underlying the original development of FORTRAN, which was constructed to translate algebraic symbols into binary coded computer instructions. Similarly, we decided to develop a symbolic notation of behavioral procedure in terms of stimuli and responses. Ours is a symbolic language that describes all features of experimental control and recording, and the computer can be used to translate the notation into machine language. The user of this system need not understand the underlying computer steps, but only need learn how to notate his procedures to be able to run them and collect data from them. In this way, the full capabilities of the computer are used to simplify day-to-day operation of the system and to permit more rapid program development than is possible by any other technique.

THE NOTATIONAL SYSTEM

To serve as a useful and general computer language, a notational system must meet several requirements. Most important of these is that the language be complete, *i.e.*, it must be capable of describing all features of experiments assigned to computer control. Second, it should be flexible enough to describe a wide variety of experimental procedures so that the original design of the language and associated computing system does not limit future experimental investigation. Third, to be practical as a computer language for systems as small as the PDP-8, the notational description must be based on a minimal set of rules and precise definitions.

The theory of finite automata as applied in the design of digital computers (Mealy, 1955; Moore, 1956) provides a graphic notation of sequential states that meets these requirements. State graphs describe any finite sequential system both completely and precisely, and since behavioral procedures (especially schedules of reinforcement) are sequential in nature, only a few identifications of behavioral variables with units of the system need be made for it to serve our purposes. Additional advantages accrue from this system because it has been painstakingly developed and modified by logicians for several years. For example, the state system, when applied to the design of switching circuits, eliminates timing problems that were often introduced by older design methods (*e.g.*, Boolean notation). Another advantage of the system is that since it describes any sequential procedure, it can serve in many different areas of science, and may thus improve inter-disciplinary communication. These features seem to us to make the theory of finite automata a more general notational language than that suggested by Mechner (1959). On the other hand, with suitable modifications, Mechner's notational system could serve as a reasonable alternative to the present approach.

A brief description of the notational language follows to illustrate its ability to describe reinforcement schedules. Furthermore, this discussion develops the essential characteristics of the language that must be provided for a computer system based on it. For a more complete discussion of the state graph notation of schedules of reinforcement, see Snapper, Knapp, and Kushner, (1970).

BASIC DEFINITIONS

The units of the notational system are called states. Each state represents a portion of a behavioral procedure and may have a stimulus output associated with it, *i.e.*, the stimulus is presented when the state becomes current and it may terminate on state change. States are shown as in Figure 1 by enumerated circles, and any stimulus outputs coexistent with a state are listed to the right of a slash following the state number (*e.g.*, stimulus 1 or houselight in S2). Any stimulus can be presented or terminated on state change, as the reinforcement stimulus is

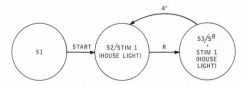

Figure 1. State graph of regular reinforcement.

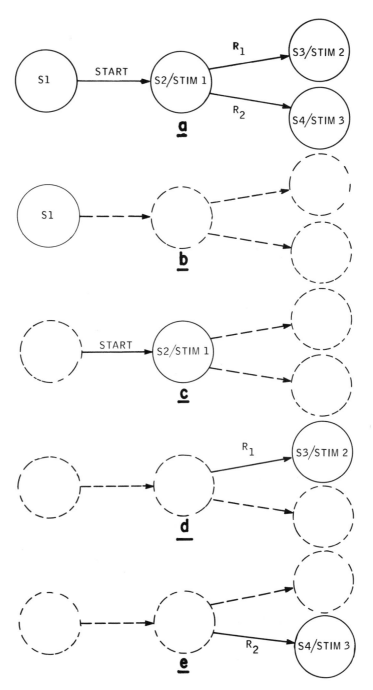

Figure 2. State graphs of a hypothetical procedure. Panel *a* shows the potential states. Panels *b* through *e* illustrate that only one state may be on at a time.

presented upon entry into state 3 and is terminated on exit from that state. In fact, transition from one state to another is the *only* occasion upon which stimuli may be changed. However, stimuli *need* not be changed on state transition, as the houselight is shown to be retained when S2 is replaced by S3. State change is considered to be instantaneous so that in the present example the houselight is continuously on (not flickering) despite changes between states 2 and 3. In the present discussion, the word stimulus refers to a physical energy to which the subject is exposed for a finite duration. It refers only to the stimuli manipulated by the experimenter and ignores background energies, either constant (such as properties of the experimental chamber) or variable (such as environmental events including temperature, barometric pressure, *etc.* and subject events such as proprioceptive and interoceptive stimuli).

State changes, or transitions, are notated by an arrow leading from one state and pointing to the next state. For a transition to occur, an input to the system (shown on top of the arrow) must occur. Thus, in Figure 1, which is a state graph of regular reinforcement, CRF in Ferster and Skinner's (1957) terminology, state 1 represents the pre-session state and is replaced by state 2, and its associated stimulus 1, when a "start" input occurs. Conceptually, this input is an instantaneous signal that initiates the experimental session. In practice, this "start" event may involve placing an animal in an experimental chamber or it may be an electric impulse initiated by the experimenter. S2 remains in effect until a response (R) is emitted by the subject. If an R occurs, then state 3 replaces state 2 for 4 sec, and reinforcement (S^R) is presented during S3 and is terminated with return to S2. During S1 and S3, responses have no programmed effects and therefore are not shown in these states.

Figure 2 is a set of partial state graphs presented to clarify the sequential nature of state diagrams. In part *a* of the figure, the potential outcomes of an experiment are diagrammed. This graph may be read as follows:

During state 1, pre-session stimuli are in effect until terminated by a "start" event or input, whereupon S2 is initiated and stimulus 1 is presented. If, in S2, a response of type 1 (R1) occurs first, S3 and stimulus 2 follow. If, on the other hand, a response of type 2 (R2) occurs first during S2, then S4 and stimulus 3 describe the experiment.

In panels *b* through *e*, current states and the transitions that produced them are shown in solid lines and the other potential or preceding states are shown by dotted lines. These graphs emphasize that within a state set, one state and only one describes the conditions in effect at any one instant. Although normally all the possible states of an experiment are graphed, in a particular session not all of these states need occur. For example, in Figure 2a, if an R1 occurs first in S2, S3 becomes current and there is no way shown for S4 to replace S3 under these conditions.

To summarize the basic features of the system then:

(1) Any experiment can be represented by a set of interconnected states.

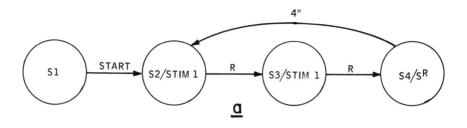

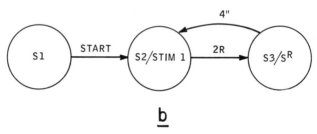

Figure 3. State graphs of fixed ratio. Panel *b* is a reduced version of panel *a*.

(2) Each state may have a specific set of stimuli associated with it, and each state defines the events or inputs necessary for change to the next state. Thus, for psychology, the state is a unit of an experiment that defines the stimuli present and the consequences of responses and time when that state is in effect.

(3) One and only one state can be current within a state set.

(4) Both transitions between states and the inputs that cause them are instantaneous.

(5) If a state has more than one potential next state, then the input occurring first after the state is entered will cause transition to its next state. For example, in Figure 2, if R1 occurs before R2 in S2, then S3 follows, but if R2 occurs first, S2 is replaced by S4.

HIGHER-ORDER DEFINITIONS

Counting. To make the state graph into a practical notational system, it is necessary to develop higher-order definitions based on the preceding rules. Although these simple rules provide for a complete description of reinforcement schedules, the higher-order definitions serve to reduce repetition of common elements in a state graph. The first is in the nature of a simple abbreviation. Figure 3, part *a*, is the state graph of fixed ratio (FR) generated from the previous rules. Before the session, S1 is current; on a "start" input, S2, with stimulus 1, replaces S1. A response in S2 initiates S3 and leaves stimulus 1 in effect. A response in S3 leads to S4 with its associated reinforcement for 4 sec and is then replaced by S2 for another FR2 ratio requirement. If the ratio were much longer than 2, then the state graph would clearly become too cumbersome to draw, with a separate state for each response in the ratio.

To simplify the notation of a series of states that differ only in their distance from the end of the series (the stimulus in the successive states being constant), the abbreviation shown in part *b* of Figure 3 is suggested. In this case the input, 2R, shown causing transition from S2 to S3, represents the sequence of S2 leading to S3 and S3 leading to S4 shown in part *a*. It specifies that the transition from S2 to S3 is caused by the second response emitted after S2 is entered. This abbreviation is equivalent to associating a counter of inputs with a state. The counter is zeroed on state entry and the specified count must be completed before the state is terminated.

The implications of this definition may be clarified by considering a reinforcement schedule reported by Mechner (1958) in which a specified

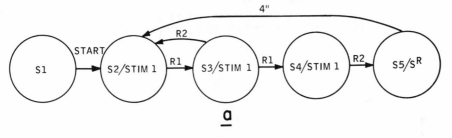

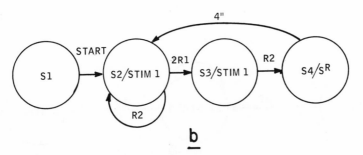

Figure 4. State graphs of a counting procedure. Panel *b* is a reduced version of panel *a*.

number of responses on one lever (R1) must be emitted before a response on a second lever (R2) is reinforced. Premature R2 responses reset the count of R1s to zero. The state graph of this schedule is shown in Figure 4. Part *a* shows a requirement of two R1s before S4 is reached. R2s emitted in S3 reinstate S2, thus requiring at least two more R1s to reach S4. The abbreviation of this schedule is shown in part *b*. The important feature here is that an R2 is shown to reinitialize S2. By our definition, this means that since state 2 is reentered, the counter of R1s is reset to zero, thus requiring two additional R1s to get to S3.

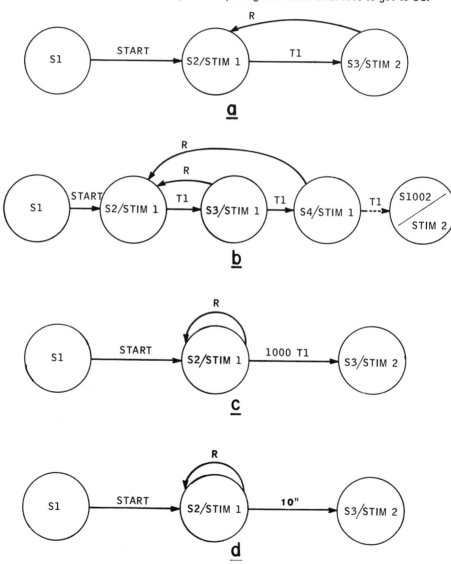

Figure 5. State graphs illustrating development of timing notation.

Timing. The same type of abbreviation can be used to advantage in specifying temporal inputs. The basic rules of the system merely state that inputs are instantaneous, non-simultaneous events. Figure 5a illustrates a state change from S2 to S3 initiated by an external timing input, T1. As drawn, however, the duration of S2 is unknown, since the initiation of S2 could occur at any point between two successive T1 pulses. This means that, on the average, the duration of S2 will be half the interval between T1 pulses and will vary between zero and T1 sec, depending on the time between state entry and the next T1 pulse.

A more useful clock for most behavioral experiments would be one that begins timing on state entry and causes transition at the end of the specified timing interval. This type of timer may be constructed from a free-running repetitive input, such as the 10-msec clock connected to our computer, by defining a time pulse counter associated with each state. For example, the diagram of Figure 5b shows a procedure where a timing pulse, T1, successively advances states from S2 to S1002. Responses return the state set to S2. In this diagram, the variability of the interval between S2 entry and S1002, given no responses, will be merely 0.05%, since all states following S2 are exactly T1 sec

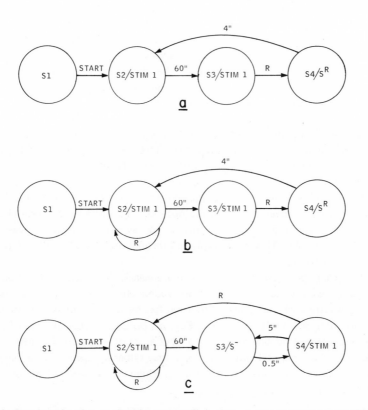

Figure 6. State graphs of a. FI "by the response", b. DRL, c. non-discriminated avoidance.

long. In the same way that the ratio counter was defined, Figure 5c can be considered equivalent to Figure 5b. Thus, Figure 5c shows that 1000 T1 pulses must occur after S2 is initiated for transition to S3. If a response occurs before the 1000 T1 pulses, the count restarts at zero and an additional 1000 T1 pulses must occur, uninterrupted by an R, before S2 is replaced by S3. For convenience, Figure 5c may be rewritten with an absolute time value specified for transition from S2 to S3, representing the necessary accumulation of T1 pulses (*e.g.*, 10" as in Figure 5d).

Figure 6 illustrates three common reinforcement schedules that involve time intervals synchronized with state entry. In Figure 6a, fixed interval (FI) "by the response" (Ferster and Skinner, 1957) is graphed. In this schedule, responses have no effect in S2. Transition from S2 to S3 occurs 60 sec after entry to S2. A response in S3 leads to the reinforcement state, S4, for 4 sec after which S2 replaces S4, and a new 60-sec interval leads again to S3. Figure 6b illustrates differential reinforcement of low rate (DRL) in which responses in S2 reinitialize this state, thus resetting the timer. In this schedule, S2 must be present for 60 sec without a response before transition to S3 can occur. In other respects the schedule resembles the FI of panel *a*.

Figure 6c is a state graph of a commonly used non-discriminated avoidance schedule (Sidman, 1953). In this procedure, responses in S2 reinitialize S2 and reset its timer. If 60 sec elapse in S2 without a response, S3 and associated electric shock follow. Responses during shock have no effect, so shock duration is fixed at 0.5 sec. Following shock, the shock-shock interval starts in S4. Responses during this state lead to S2, but if the 5-sec shock-shock interval elapses without a response, S3 is re-entered.

Parallel State Sets. The temporal values of the preceding examples have been defined in terms of intervals that start on state entry. Although many schedules of reinforcement contain such intervals, others require free-running timers, not starting on state entry, but rather timing independently of responses. Since both types of intervals are required for different procedures, it is desirable to differentiate between them in the notation. To this end, we have chosen to define a free-running timer in terms of the synchronized timer used in the preceding examples. This is accomplished through the use of parallel state sets to describe an experiment.

A single experiment may often be more clearly described by partitioning the contingencies into several sets of interconnected states, each set operating simultaneously with the others. Provision has been made for synchronizing two or more state sets with each other. For this purpose, a special class of outputs may be generated by one state set to serve as inputs to particular states in other state sets. These parallel state sets, then, may either be completely independent, as is demanded by some concurrent schedules of reinforcement, or may be highly synchronized when necessary.

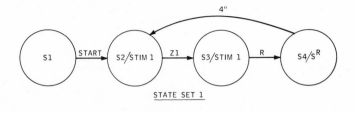

STATE SET 1

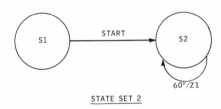

STATE SET 2

Figure 7. State graph of FI "by the clock". Contingencies are controlled in state set 1, and state set 2 represents a free-running clock.

We have chosen to notate the special class of synchronizing pulses as ZN, where N is used as a label for different Zs, since more than one such pulse may be needed. Each Z pulse is considered to be instantaneous, to fit the definition of inputs already stated, and as an input may cause transition from any current state in parallel state sets when so notated. Using this convention, we can now diagram free-running timers of the state-initiated timer developed in Figure 5.

Figure 7 diagrams FI "by the clock", a procedure in which the interval timer is permitted to continue timing the next interval, even after S3 comes on. In the example shown, both state sets 1 and 2 proceed from S1 to S2 on a start input. Sixty seconds later, and every 60 sec thereafter, a timing pulse output, Z1, is generated by state set 2. This output, Z1, can serve as an input in state set 1, and is considered to be instantaneous. If S2 is current, Z1 will produce S3 in state set 1. If not, Z1 will have no effect. Thus, the duration of S2 will vary between 0 and 60 sec, depending on when (with respect to the 60-sec timer in state set 2) it is entered. Responses do not act on the timer shown in state set 2.

The introduction of a free-running timer permits the notation of a session timer. Figure 8a illustrates a 60-min session of regular reinforcement. State set 1 shows the timer that begins the 60-min session with a start pulse and initiates the session stimuli, stim 1. After 60 min have elapsed, a Z1 returns S2 or S3 of state set 2, depending on which is current at that time, to S1, thus terminating the CRF contingencies.

Since, in practice, it is necessary to diagram session duration for every experiment, we have developed a simpler notation for session timing. We always

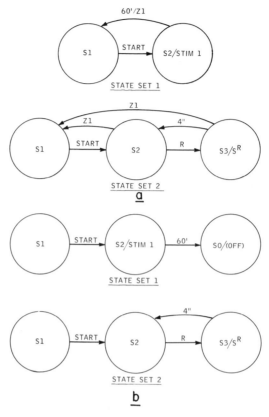

Figure 8. State graphs of CRF with session-timing. Panel *b* represents the session-timing of *a* in abbreviated form.

diagram a session timer, or reinforcement counter, as the first state set. When the desired session criterion has been met, the first state set enters state "zero", which is considered simultaneously to render ineffective all other state sets for this experiment, as is shown in Figure 8*b*. This is a notational convenience that reduces the number of Z-outputs needed and simplifies computer control of session duration.

Outputs. In the initial development of the state system, stimulus outputs were handled in two different but equivalent ways: as instantaneous (zero duration) pulses (Mealy, 1955) or as signals with a finite duration (Moore, 1956). In the latter notation level outputs coexist with states (as in our discussion of Figure 1). The Mealy system, however, did not consider finite outputs, but accounted only for instantaneous pulses. It soon became evident that the Mealy notation could not handle real physical devices that require finite levels. For practical usage, a mixture of the two notations is required. An

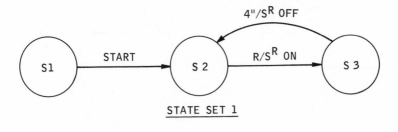

STATE SET 1

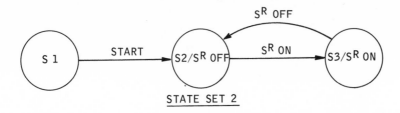

STATE SET 2

Figure 9. CRF represented by two state sets, with reinforcement delivery notated in state set 2.

example of this mixture is shown in Figure 9, which diagrams CRF in two state sets. In state set 1, a response in S2 produces an instantaneous output (S^R ON, equivalent to the Z-outputs of the previous figures) that serves as an input to state set 2, by changing S2 to S3. State set 2 has stimulus outputs associated with S2 and S3, representing the absence and presence of a reinforcing stimulus.

In our computer system, the devices that generate stimuli are contained in the interface, and the program within the PDP-8 generates brief signals that turn these devices on or off. For this reason, we have found it convenient to notate only the onset and offset of a stimulus, as in the upper portion of Figure 9, and to omit the actual description of the level outputs in the lower state set since the latter description refers to permanently connected devices. All further state graphs, therefore, will only show the initiating and terminating pulse outputs.

Recording. State notation can be used not only to describe experimental control but also to diagram data acquisition procedures. The notation of a pulse output can be used to represent the incrementing of a counting device by one. In our computing system, the counter is a specified memory location that can be incremented whenever a particular input occurs. For example, Figure 10*a* contains a state graph of a 60-min CRF session with two parallel state sets. The upper state set shows that on a start signal a stimulus (stim 1) is turned on and remains on for 60 min, at which time stim 1 is turned off and the session ended. The second state set represents a CRF session in which responses in S2 initiate reinforcement and are recorded in counter C1. Again, C1 stands for a device that

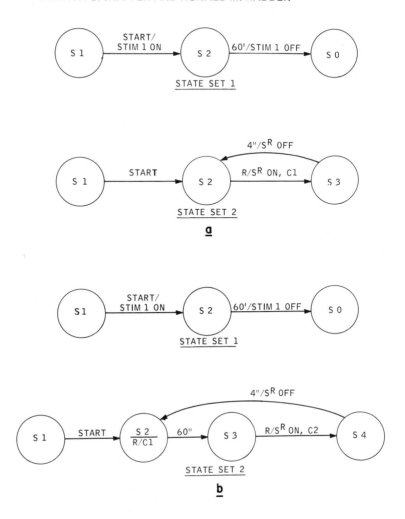

Figure 10. Illustration of data recording for *a*. CRF and *b*. FI "by the response".

accumulates a count of the number of responses during the session. Although not shown in the state graph, it is understood that C1 is at zero at the start of the session and that the accumulated count can be displayed or examined by the experimenter.

Although in this example the response that is recorded in C1 also causes state transition, it is often convenient to record responses in states that are not changed by a response. For example, in FI it is useful to record unreinforced responses that occur before the interval requirement has been met. Figure 10*b* is

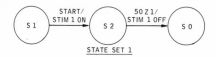

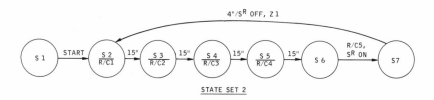

Figure 11. State graph of FI "by the response", as a further illustration of data recording.

a state graph of FI with two state sets, the upper for session duration and the lower for the FI schedule. In this state graph, responses during S2 of the lower state set are recorded as shown by the notation R/C1 inside S2. These responses, then, are recorded in counter 1 but do not cause state change. Reinforced responses, on the other hand, do cause S3 to change to S4. This notation is written: R/S^R ON, C2, on the transition from S3 to S4 in the lower state set.

A slightly more complex but useful notation of FI schedules involves recording responses in successive portions of the intervals to measure the temporal discrimination that often develops under exposure to these schedules. Thus, Figure 11 presents FI with two parallel state sets. In the lower state set, the 60-sec interval state (S2) of the preceding graph has been subdivided into four equal 15-sec portions in S2, S3, S4, and S5. Responses in these states are recorded in C1, C2, C3, and C4, respectively. In this diagram, the session is terminated after 50 reinforcements, by generating a Z1 output at the end of each reinforcement in state set 2 and by counting 50 of these pulses in state set 1.

Similar techniques can be used to notate interresponse-time (IRT) distributions or other histograms. An example of a DRL schedule with separate distributions of IRTs following unreinforced (below criterion) responses and for post-reinforcement latencies is shown in the state graph of Figure 12. State set 1 is the session timer, state set 2 contains the basic schedule contingencies, state set 3 represents an IRT distribution, and state set 4 shows the post-reinforcement latency distribution.

Responses occurring during S2 of state set 2 are unreinforced and they reset the 30-sec timer. Each of these responses also generates a Z1 pulse that advances S2 to S3 in state set 3. Responses occurring 15 sec after an unreinforced response are recorded in C1 and restart the 15-sec timer of S3 in state set 3. If 15 sec elapse without a response, state set 3 advances to S4. Responses in this

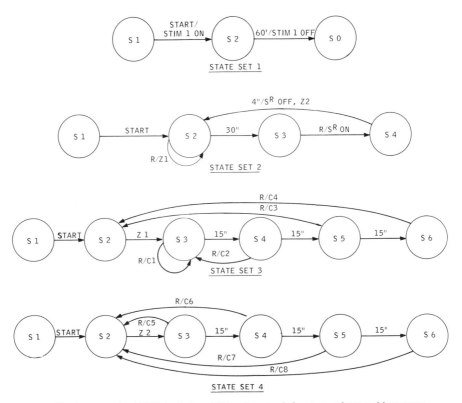

Figure 12. State graph of DRL including IRT and post-reinforcement latency histograms.

state will be recorded in C2 and will lead to S3. If 30 sec elapse without a response, S5 is initiated and responses will be recorded in C3 and will lead to S2, since these responses are reinforced. If 45 sec pass after an unreinforced response, S6 begins and will stay on until a response occurs. Following a reinforced response, state set 3 will be in S2 awaiting an unreinforced response for further recording. On the end of each reinforcement, pulse Z2 is generated by state set 2 and state set 4 will move to S3. Responses here will accumulate in counter 5 and lead to S2. On the other hand, 15 sec without a response will lead to S4, *etc.*

NOTATING VARIABLE CONTINGENCIES

An important set of reinforcement schedules involves variable contingencies, in which some schedule requirement is varied from trial to trial within a session. Simple examples of this sort of contingency are the well-known variable-ratio (VR) and variable-interval (VI) reinforcement schedules, and the variable

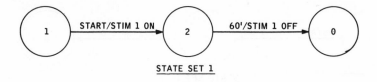

STATE SET 1

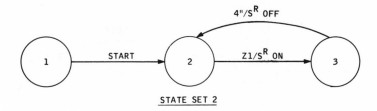

STATE SET 2

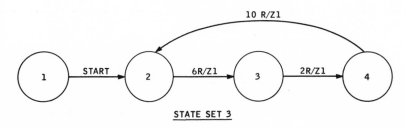

STATE SET 3

Figure 13. State graph of variable ratio.

intertrial intervals often used in trial procedures. Examples of the notation of some variable reinforcement contingencies are presented in this section because they are so often a part of schedules assigned to computer control and because some features of their state graphs may not be immediately obvious.

Variable Ratio.   Figure 13 is a state graph of a variable-ratio schedule. State set 1 turns the session on and times its duration. The salient feature of this procedure is the list of ratios diagrammed in state set 3. At the start of the session, state 2 is entered. Following the sixth response in this state, a pulse, Z1, occurs as an output from state set 3 that changes state 2 to state 3 in state set 2 and delivers a reinforcement. The reinforced response also leads to state 3 in state set 3, with its new ratio requirement of two responses. Any distribution of ratios could be programmed using this technique by simply listing the pre-selected ratio values in state set 3, with one ratio value per state.

Random Ratio.   One of the many possible distributions of variable ratios, random ratio (Brandauer, 1958), involves assigning each response an equal

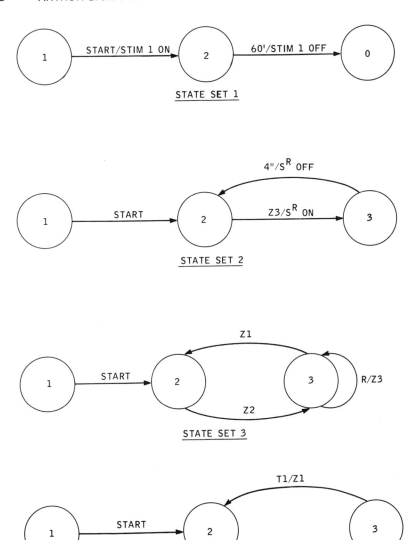

Figure 14. State graph of random ratio.

probability of reinforcement, usually less than unity. Although this schedule could be programmed by selecting a set of ratios from a random number table and entering them in a list as in the preceding example, another approach has been to synthesize ratio contingencies by means of temporally defined schedules of reinforcement (Schoenfeld, Cumming, and Hearst, 1956). In the case of random ratio, there is a free-running probability generator that is examined each time a response occurs. If it is "on" the response is reinforced, and if it is "off" there is no reinforcement. Such a probability generator can be realized by means of a rapid two-state clock, which is "on" for a period of time, T1, and then "off" for some time, T2. If the cycle length of this clock is short compared to the average interresponse time of the subject, the probability of reinforcement for all responses will be equal, and will be given by the ratio $\frac{T1}{T1 + T2}$. An example of this schedule is notated in Figure 14. Once the experiment is started, state set 3 acts as a free-running clock driven by the Z1 and Z2 outputs produced by timing pulses in state set 4. (T1 and T2 cannot be used in state set 3 in place of Z1 and Z2 because responses in state 3 would reset the T1 timer. Whenever a response occurred while state set 3 was in state 3, the re-initialization of state 3 by a response would cause the T1 timer to start again. In fact, further responses in state 3 would each delay the T1 timer, preventing transition to state 2. Therefore, to obtain an independent clock, it is necessary to put the T1 timer in a state set unaffected in any way by responses.) Only while state 3 of state set 3 is current will responses produce a Z3 to initiate reinforcement in state set 2.

This realization of random ratio, both in the notation and the accompanying computer program, is an "ideal" solution, because responses and time pulses are instantaneous: they cannot overlap. When random ratio schedules are programmed by logic modules, responses usually are assigned some finite duration, by a pulse-shaper. There is then a chance that the free-running clock may begin an "on" period during the occurrence of a response and thereby cause a reinforcement to occur even though the response was *initiated* while the clock was still "off". Where this overlapping is possible, the formula expressing the probability of reinforcement must be corrected for the response duration (RD) by adding it as an increase in reinforcement probability: $\frac{T1 + RD}{T1 + T2}$. When T1 and T2 are very small, RD becomes an important factor in determining the frequency of earned reinforcements. Programming this schedule in the present system avoids this problem altogether, since R is treated as an instantaneous event.

Variable Interval. Variable-interval schedules, like fixed-interval schedules, can be divided into two basic categories according to the point at which successive intervals begin timing (*i.e.*, after the end of the preceding interval, as in FI "by the clock", or after reinforcement delivery, as in FI "by the response"). Figure 15 is a graph of VI by the response, since state set 3 shows a "waiting" state that is entered when each interval times out. This state prevents the next interval from timing until the conclusion of reinforcement in state set 2 generates a Z2 pulse. This feature specifies that the minimum interval between reinforcements is equal to the preselected intervals diagrammed in alternate states in state set 3.

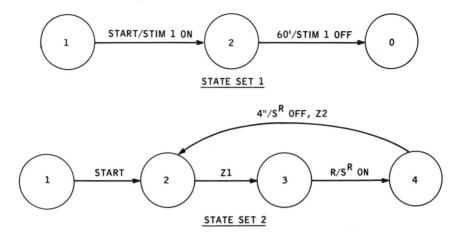

STATE SET 1

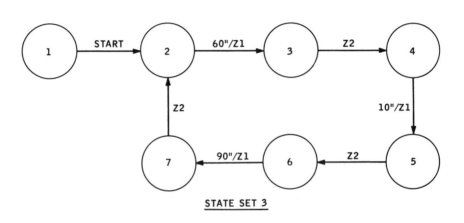

STATE SET 2

STATE SET 3

Figure 15. State graph of variable interval "by the response".

Variable interval by the clock requires that successive intervals begin timing immediately after the preceding interval is completed, so that the maximal inter-reinforcement availability time is specified by the pre-selected interval values. Figure 16 is a state graph of this procedure, and state set 3 contains the list of intervals. Each of the intervals in state set 3 generates a Z1 upon timing out, and initiates the next interval. If the subject does not respond after entering state 3 of state set 2, and before the next Z1 is generated by state set 3, then a potential reinforcement is lost. In other words, the Z1 of state set 3 will have an effect only if it occurs while state 2 is current in state set 2.

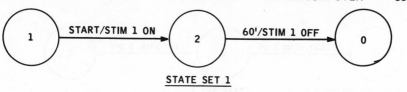

STATE SET 1

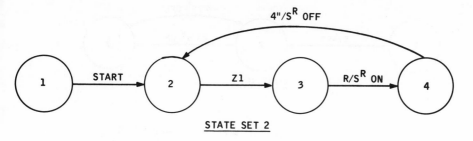

STATE SET 2

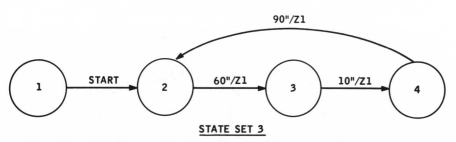

STATE SET 3

Figure 16. State graph of variable interval "by the clock".

Random Interval.   Just as a free-running probability generator can be used in random ratio to replace the sequential list of response ratios required for reinforcement in VR, random interval (RI; Farmer, 1963) makes use of a similar device to replace the list of intervals needed in VI. The RI program is similar to random ratio, except that responses while the free-running clock is "on" are gated through a second clock, which must have completed a specified interval before reinforcement can be delivered. Compare Figure 14, random ratio, to Figure 17, random interval, and note that the first four state sets are identical except for the loop at state 3 of state set 3. In the case of RI, not every response during this state produces reinforcement: only those responses that also occur when state set 5 is in state 3 will be reinforced. State set 5 is driven to state 3 by state set 6, a free-running clock that produces a Z5 every T3 sec. State set 5 waits in state 3 until the next response occurs, which returns this state set to state 2 and also produces a Z4. If state set 3 was in state 3, a Z3 is produced by the Z4 and initiates reinforcement in state set 2. This is a complete description of RI, with two response-independent clocks determining the length of time

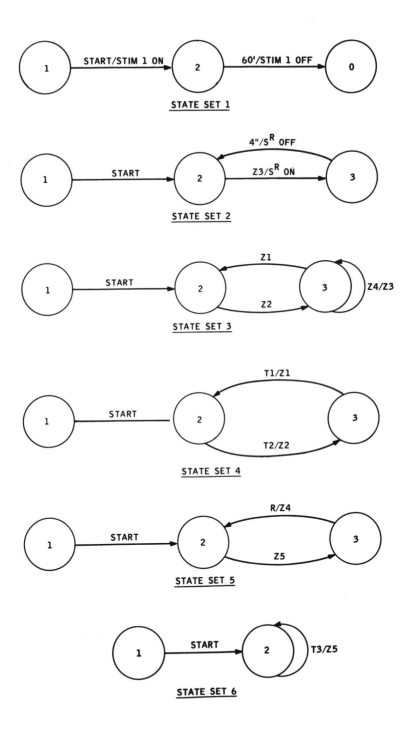

Figure 17. State graph of random interval.

between reinforcement availabilities. Alternatively, the intervals could be selected from a random number table and listed specifically in a state graph of VI by the clock.

THE SYSTEM FOR EXPERIMENT CONTROL BY STATE GRAPH NOTATION

The system used to implement the state graph notation for experiment control consists of three parts: a computer program (the Compiler) for translating state notation into binary coded constant tables; an interface connecting the computer to the experimental stations; and a second computer program that uses the constant tables to control experiments by signals sent through the interface. Programming an experiment in our system consists of producing an appropriate constant table; these tables are the heart of our system. Their format will be discussed first, followed by the other parts of the system that serve to produce and implement them.

THE CONSTANT TABLE

Once the state system had been developed as a precise notation for describing schedules of reinforcement, some way had to be found to represent the state graph of a particular experiment in the memory of the computer. Also, an operating program was required that would use the representation of a state graph to generate stimuli and record data when responses occurred in the experimental stations. Therefore, the present system includes a central executive program, which refers to tables of information containing the details of all the experiments currently being run. These tables contain all the information represented in the state graph of a particular experiment, arranged in a standardized format. For each different experiment, a different constant table must be read into the computer's memory. These stored constant tables are operated on by an executive program (SKED) which is permanent: only the constant table values are changed for different experiments.

In discussing the constant table, consider first the kinds of information it must provide. By way of example, imagine that a subject in an experimental chamber emits a response, R1. What events can be triggered by the occurrence of this response? First of all, the fact that it has occurred can be recorded. If the state during which the response is emitted calls for recording of the response, then the segment of the constant table representing this state will contain the address of a memory location (register), which stores the number of R1 responses that occur during this state. (The contents of all registers used for data recording purposes may be displayed in printed format upon request at any time during or after the session.) Transition from a state may depend upon the completion of a ratio of R1 responses; if so, the segment of the constant table representing the state will contain a counter of R1 responses, which is reset to zero every time the state changes. A second register is paired with the R1 counter to specify the desired number of R1 responses required for transition. Also needed is the address of the segment of the constant table representing the state to which transition leads. This address will direct the executive program to the new portion of the constant table on the next event that causes reference to this state set. Each state's constant table may also contain one register listing Zs that may be put out to drive other state sets, and another register listing output information that will be used to turn stimulus devices on or off.

All of the foregoing information may be required by a single response. The same types of information may be needed by other responses, R2 and R3, as well as by time pulses (there is a 10-msec free-running clock located in the interface that serves as the basic timing source for the system), and by incoming Z pulses generated in other state sets, and each of them will require different recording register addresses, next state addresses, output code words, *etc.*

A number of alternative formats for this information have been developed in several versions of the operating program. The first attempt maximized the speed of searching at the expense of the number of memory locations required. This format involved the use of fixed-length constant tables for each state. Recording counter addresses were always at the beginning of the state, followed by input counters and their paired constants, followed by next state addresses, *etc.* Every item had a fixed location with respect to the beginning of the constant table for a particular state. If an item was not needed, its memory register was still reserved, but set at zero. This was a very wasteful format, because only a few of the many possible events that *could* occur in any one state were required in practice, thus leaving many empty registers.

The format of the present system, although slightly more costly in time, makes for better use of the memory space available in a small computer. This solution employs variable-length constant tables for each state, with only the information actually needed included in each table. This variable format requires that there be code words that tell just what information is available in each state. The "Main Word" is the central code word in each state, and is the only word whose presence can always be taken for granted. It is composed of 12 bit positions, as are all registers in the PDP-8 memory, and each bit can be set independently to indicate various functions. Dissection of the Main Word will show how the constant table would look for any imaginable state configuration. In the course of the ensuing discussion, reference should be made to Figure 18, showing one state in a generalized form: it depicts the relative positions of all information contained in the constant table.

The ninth bit position from the left in the Main Word indicates whether or not there is any recording of inputs in the state. If there is to be no recording, this bit will be zero, and the Main Word will be the first word in the constant table for this state. If the bit is set (to "one"), however, the Main Word will be preceded by a Record Code Word. In this latter word, an appropriate bit will be

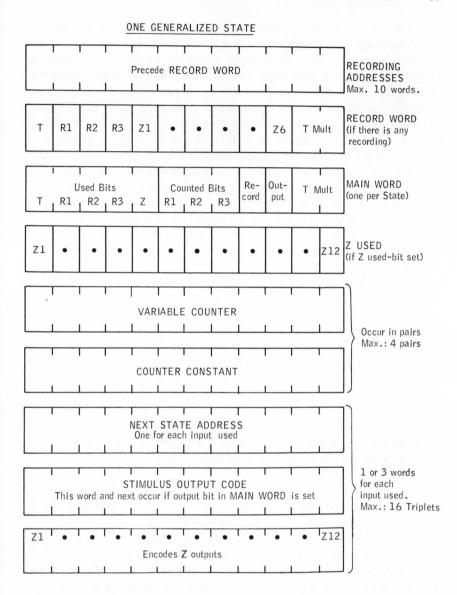

Figure 18. Format of constant table for one state.

set for each input whose occurrence is to be recorded while this state is current. Provision is made for recording the occurrences of clock pulses (notated as "T"), R1-R3, and Z1-Z6 only. For each bit that is set, there will be one register containing the address of a recording counter. These address registers, which begin with the word just preceding the Record Word, will work their way backwards in order of priority determined by the order of the bits set in the

Record Word (*i.e.*, T always comes first, working backwards, and R1 precedes everything except T, but will be first if T is not recorded, *etc.*).

When a response or a clock pulse enters the computer, the operating program must examine each state that is current to determine whether the incoming event is used to cause transition to a new state. For this purpose, several bit positions in the Main Word must be reserved to specify the particular inputs causing transition from each state. These are the first four at the left of the Main Word and are reserved for T, R1, R2, and R3. If any Z, generated in another state set, is to cause transition from this state, the fifth bit position will be set to "one", and the word following the Main Word will have an appropriate bit set for each Z to be used. Altogether then, with the first four bits in the Main Word and the Z bits in the following word (if it is called for), there is a bit position allocated for every possible transition out of a state. Of course it is unlikely that more than two or three transitions would ever be required from a single state, but a unique location had to be reserved for every possible one, since each may be used independently.

In the present system, only responses or clock pulses (but not Zs) may have associated counters. Thus, transition may be programmed to occur after one or several clock pulses or responses counted from state onset, but must follow the first appropriate Z used in a state. The bits indicating whether an input is to be counted before a transition may occur are located to the right of the used bits in the Main Word. If clock pulses are used for transition, they are automatically counted (if only one is needed, the counter is set for "one"); hence there are "counted" bits for only R1-R3. The counters, when called for, occur in pairs: the first word is the one in which the actual counting takes place, and the second stores the total value that must be counted. These pairs will be found directly following the Main Word, or following the Z-Used Word if it appears. Only pairs that are called for will occur, and they will appear in the following order of priority: T, R1, R2, R3.

The maximum value in any counter will be $2^{12} = 4096$. This is more than. sufficient for counting responses, but with a clock pulse repetition rate of 10 msec, this would permit a maximum time of 40.96 sec. To obtain time values up to 11 hr, two T-multiplier bits are provided in the Main Word which will cause counting to occur in 0.01-, 0.1-, 1-. or 10-sec steps when set to 0, 1, 2, or 3, respectively. The counter of clock pulses will therefore be incremented only as often as is indicated by the T-multiplier bits. Recording of clock pulses as data may also occur in these four basic temporal units, so a similar T-multiplier is provided in the Record Word.

The operating program keeps track of the currently active state in a state set by using the address of its Main Word to represent the state. When a state change is to occur, the operating program merely selects the Main Word address of a new state table from a list of "Next State Address" registers found in every constant table. The first of these will follow the Main Word, or if they appear, the Z-Used word or the last Counter Constant. There will be one Next State

Address for each transition that may occur, and those that appear will be listed in the usual order of priorities, T, R1-R3, Z1-Z12. Each one will contain the address of the Main Word of its next state. Each input causing transition to another state will have an associated Next State Address. These addresses will follow one another in succession, unless bit 10 is set in the Main Word. This bit indicates that on at least one transition there is an accompanying Z-Output or a stimulus output. If the "output bit" is set, then each Next State Address is followed by a Stimulus Output word and a Z-Output word, before the succeeding Next State Address. When needed, the Stimulus Output word contains the bit settings that will be used to turn stimuli on or off in the experimental chamber being controlled by this constant table. The Z-Output word will have appropriate bit settings for any Zs that are to be generated on a particular transition.

THE COMPILER

The constant table contains all of the necessary information for the operating program to control experiments. The problem to be considered now is one of translation: how to get the information conveyed by a state graph into the constant table format on a binary coded paper tape that can be entered into the computer. For this purpose, a translator, or Compiler, has been written to translate a modified state graph notation into binary coded constant tables in the proper format, assigned to any desired location in memory. It is the Compiler, then, that performs the tedious job of changing arrows and state numbers into bit settings and memory addresses.

Originally, it was planned to have the Compiler reside in memory along with the operating program, so that new experiments could be programmed while others were being run under computer control. However, the Compiler occupied too much of memory for this to be possible. Although this inability to have both programs in memory together limits the amount of available programming time, compiling usually does not take long and can be sandwiched between breaks in experiments.

The basic principle guiding the design of the Compiler was to keep its notation as close as possible to the state graph description of experiments. The ideal solution would be to enter a state graph, exactly as it appears on paper, into the computer for translation by our Compiler. However, the primary device used to program experiments on our computer is a teletypewriter that transmits information in the form of electrical signals representing the standard alpha-numeric symbol set of a normal typewriter (except that only capital letters are available). The simplest format for writing state graphs on this device is to type transitions, one per line, in sequential order. The circles representing states are omitted, and the notation is thus reduced to a list of transitions. Each line includes the number of the state from which the transition will occur, the input causing transition and any associated outputs, and the number of the state to

```
BOX # (1)     SA (1000)     # STATE SETS 4     1ST RECORDING ADDRESS (200)
STATE SET 1

    S1--- R2/STIM1 ON --->S2        <BEGIN SESSION

    S2--- 60'/STIM1 OFF --->S0      <SESSION TIMED OUT
STATE SET 2

    S1--- R2 --->S2                 <DRL STATE SET

    S2--- R1/Z1 --->S2              <SHORT IRT'S RESET TIMER

    S2--- 30" --->S3                <30" CRITERION MET

    S3--- R1/SR ON --->S4           <NEXT RESPONSE REINFORCED

    S4--- 4"/SR OFF, Z2 --->S2      <REINF. ENDED; RESTART 30" TIMER
STATE SET 3

    S1--- R2 --->S2                 <IRT DISTRIBUTION

    S2--- Z1 --->S3                 <START AFTER UNREINFORCED RESPONSE

    S3--- R1/C1 --->S3              <FIRST RESPONSE BIN

    S3--- 15" --->S4                <SET UP SECOND BIN

    S4--- R1/C2 --->S3

    S4--- 15" --->S5

    S5--- R1/C3 --->S2              <REINFORCED RESPONSES RETURN TO STATE 2

    S5--- 15" --->S6

    S6--- R1/C4 --->S2              <BIN FOR IRT'S LONGER THAN 45"
STATE SET 4

    S1--- R2 --->S2                 <POST-REINFORCEMENT-PAUSE DISTRIBUTION

    S2--- Z2 --->S3                 <BEGIN AT END OF REINFORCEMENT

    S3--- R1/C5 --->S2              <FIRST RESPONSE BIN

    S3--- 15" --->S4                <SET UP SECOND BIN

    S4--- R1/C6 --->S2

    S4--- 15" --->S5

    S5--- R1/C7 --->S2

    S5--- 15" --->S6

    S6--- R1/C8 --->S2              <BIN FOR PAUSES LONGER THAN 45"
```

Figure 19. Teletype record of Compiler-operator interactions, Pass 1, listing transitions of the DRL schedule shown in Figure 12.

which the transition leads. Similar information is repeated for all transitions from each state of every state set. Compiling, then, basically involves typing a list of transitions just as they appear on the state graph, so that the state system notation can be used as the language in which experiments are actually programmed.

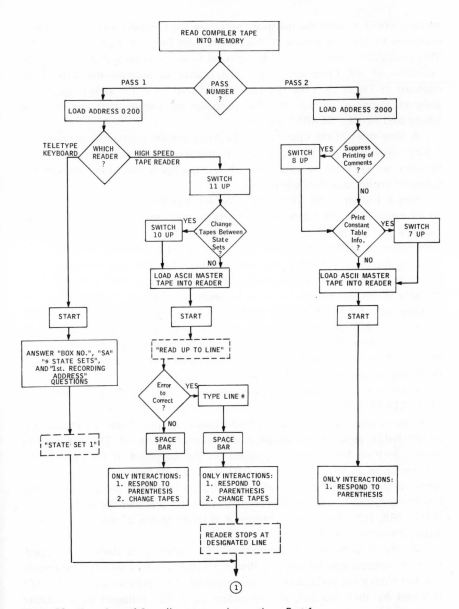

Figure 20. Flow chart of Compiler-operator interactions, Part 1.

Compiler Operation. The Compiler consists of two separate programs that are used in sequence to produce a constant table: the first, Pass 1, produces a paper tape containing a list of all information supplied by the operator, plus certain codes added by the Compiler; the second, Pass 2, reads the tape produced on Pass 1 and punches a complete working constant table in binary code on a second paper tape. During the two passes, the teletype produces a written record of both the questions asked by the Compiler and the operator's responses to them. A sample of this record from Pass 1 is shown in Figure 19. This compilation, which should be referred to in the ensuing discussion of the operation of the Compiler, is the one needed to program the state graph depicted in Figure 12. (The response, R, referred to in the state diagram was assigned response number R1 for purposes of compilation, and R2 was substituted for the "START" input.)

A flow chart of the operation of the two Compiler programs is contained in Figures 20 and 21. In these Figures, all operations or decisions made by the operator are enclosed by solid lines, while those operations or decisions of the Compiler are enclosed by dashed lines.

Pass 1. For an initial compilation, the teletype keyboard is used to provide all information to the Compiler. Once its program tape has been loaded into memory and started (Figure 20), the Compiler asks four questions to obtain information it needs, after which the list of transitions is entered. The first of the four questions is "BOX #", requesting which of the 10 experimental stations the constant table will control. Next, the starting address ("SA"), or location in memory where this constant table is to begin, is requested. Following this, the Compiler asks for the number of state sets to be compiled, and then for the first address of the block of registers in core memory used for recording the data from this station. This question completes the "housekeeping" information, and the rest of the interaction between the programmer and the Compiler consists of the listing of transitions and their associated outputs.

After these initial questions have been answered, the Compiler prints the label "STATE SET 1" and then, on a new line, prints "S1" followed by part of an arrow to begin the first transition (the flow diagram in Figure 21 should now be referred to, as well as the sample compilation of Figure 19). The first input to cause transition from state 1 is typed on the keyboard. If the input is the completion of an interval (between 0.01 sec to 11 hr) following state entry, the specified time is entered (*e.g.*, 30", 2', 0.03", 1 HR) or, if the input is a ratio requirement, the number of responses in the ratio precedes the response (*e.g.*, 30R1, 2R2, R3). The number *following* R refers to one of the three response inputs available for each station.

If any outputs are to accompany this transition, a slash (/) is typed. Stimulus outputs may be listed by their octal codes, or by a six-letter mnemonic selected from a list maintained by the Compiler. Z outputs are specified by "Z" followed by their number, and recording by a "C" followed by a counter number. After all outputs have been specified, a hyphen is typed to initiate completion of the transition arrow. Next, the number of the state to which the transition leads is typed in by the operator, following the "S" that the Compiler prints at the end of the transition arrow. In some cases, the experimenter may wish to record the number of inputs occurring during a state, even though such occurrences do not cause transition. In this case, the input is treated exactly like a transition, except that instead of a next state number, an "X" is entered at the end of the transition line specifying that no state change is to occur on this

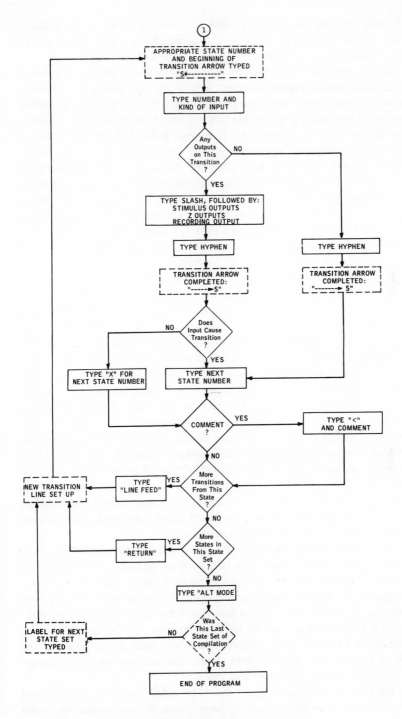

Figure 21. Flow chart of Compiler-operator interactions, Part 2.

input. Finally, it may be desired to add a comment as to the function or significance of this transition. If so, a < is typed, followed by any keyboard characters. Comments may not extend beyond the end of the line.

A line is terminated by one of three non-printing teletype keyboard characters, each specifying a different action by the computer. If more transitions from the present state are to be entered, then "LINE FEED" will be the terminating character, and the next line will retain the present state number. If all transitions from the current state have been entered, then "RETURN" is the terminator and the state number beginning the next line will be one higher than on the present line. If all transitions for the present state set have been entered, then "ALT MODE" will be the terminating character, and then either the next state set number will be typed on a separate line with a new first state, or the program will end if the number of state sets specified at the beginning of compilation has been completed. During Pass 1, a paper tape is punched (with each teletype character represented in a special code called ASCII), recording the interaction between the programmer and the computer.

Modifying master tapes. The output of the initial compilation of any experiment is the master tape, and there are two circumstances under which it might be used as the input source for further Pass 1 processing. The first such circumstance involves the correction of errors or inappropriate entries. The Compiler has been programmed to respond to certain types of errors, mostly illegal characters, by requesting that all transitions for the state currently being entered be repeated. Although the resulting constant table is perfectly valid, the error will be repeated every time this master tape is used, but will be corrected by the information immediately following it on the tape. This will result in a correct, but confusing printed record of the compilation. To avoid this, one should stop compiling as soon as the error occurs, load address 200, and select the high-speed tape reader option for Pass 1, using the ASCII tape generated thus far (refer again to Figure 20). At the "READ UP TO LINE" query, the operator enters the number of the line at which the error occurred. The Compiler will then reproduce on a new master tape what was previously entered (from the old master tape), up to the line specified, at which point it will switch to keyboard mode to allow typing in the remaining transitions.

The second circumstance in which the tape-reader mode is useful on Pass 1 results from the fact that certain state sets, such as reinforcement contingency generators, IRT distributors, *etc.*, are used in many different experiments. Often, a new program can be compiled by typing only one or two new state sets, and then copying, by means of the high-speed tape reader, others from previous programs. To facilitate this, a switch on the computer may be thrown to cause the Compiler to halt after the completion of every state set, to allow for the changing of master tapes when desired. Thus, one can generate a new master tape by "splicing" several older ones together.

One other feature of the Compiler should be noted. Any entry that is typed in by the operator may be enclosed in parentheses. On future readings of the master tape in Pass 1 or 2, the Compiler will change to keyboard mode whenever it encounters an "open parenthesis". This allows the operator to type a new entry in place of what was formerly enclosed by the parentheses, and then switch back to tape-reader mode by hitting the "close parenthesis" character. The reader will skip over the material on the master tape that was within the parentheses. Or, if the operator wishes to retain the material on the master tape between the parentheses, he merely types the letter "Q", which returns the Compiler to tape-reader mode and causes the material between the parentheses to be read from the tape and executed. This provision allows for making a single master tape that can be used in Pass 2, to program the same constant tables for several stations, to vary parametric values for one station, or both. Thus, when one wishes to program an experiment using state sets borrowed from several different previous experiments, one only has to load the proper tape for each new state set, and respond to parentheses with a "Q" or a new entry.

Pass 2. The operation of the Compiler on Pass 2 is even simpler, since the master tape is now read by the second Compiler program to produce a second printed record on the teletype and a punched binary constant table. For rapid processing, all comments (to the right of the <) can be eliminated from the Pass 2 teletype print-out, by means of an appropriate switch setting. A second option slows the teletype print-out on Pass 2 but provides very useful information. If this option is selected, the state graph print-out for each separate state is followed by a listing of the memory location and contents of certain constant table registers. For every state, the address and contents of the Main Word is typed. Following this comes the address and value of all Counter Constants (if any) used in the state, and finally the location and contents are printed for any Stimulus Output words. This information can be useful to someone familiar with the structure of the constant table. Sometimes, parametric changes of an experiment can be made without recompiling, by changing the contents of the appropriate memory registers, whose locations and original contents have been printed.

In Pass 2, after loading the master tape and starting the program, no further action is required of the operator except for responding to program halts at parentheses by typing "Q", or some change in parameter value. At the conclusion of Pass 2, the final address of the constant table and the last recording counter address are listed, specifying the exact memory area occupied by the table.

Compiler Program Description. On Pass 1, the Compiler checks for and identifies errors: illegal characters, or legal characters used inappropriately.

Pass 2 performs the major work of the Compiler. One fixed-length constant table is maintained in memory: it is like the generalized constant table of Figure 18, but has all 69 possible registers, so that every function has a fixed location in this buffer. As each character is read into the Compiler from the tape reader, appropriate bits in the Main Word and the other code words of the fixed-length

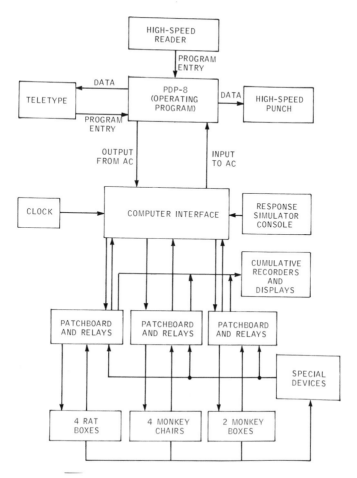

Figure 22. Block diagram of system components.

constant table are set. Recording counter addresses are assigned, based on the given counter number and the first recording address entered at the beginning of compilation. When more than one response is to be counted for transition to occur, the value of the appropriate counter constant is determined directly from the number of responses indicated. For time pulses, which are always counted, the appropriate T-multiplier value is first determined by the Compiler, and then the counter constant value fixed. The Z-Output word and Stimulus Output Code are set directly from the values supplied by the operator, unless the stimulus is specified by a mnemonic, in which case the numerical value for the given mnemonic is found from a list maintained by the Compiler. The Next State Address cannot be specified until all states within the set have been entered. Therefore, the *number* of the next state, not its address, is temporarily entered in place of its address. The information put in this fixed-length constant table is added to by all transitions programmed from each state. When the "RETURN" character is typed, indicating that a new state is to be compiled, the contents of the fixed-length constant table are placed in a storage area. In doing so, registers with contents are stored sequentially; empty registers are omitted, thus reducing the length of the constant table to a minimum. When stored, each register is assigned a memory address, determined by the starting address entered when compiling was begun. The address assigned to each Main Word is saved, by state number, in a special list. When "ALT MODE" is typed, indicating the end of a state set, the Main Word addresses are substituted for the next state numbers that had been temporarily inserted in the Next State Address locations. Then, all the constant tables in the storage area, representing all the states in the state set, are punched on paper tape as a sequence of binary numbers, and the storage area cleared in preparation for the next state set.

After the last state set has been compiled and its constant table data punched, the tape containing the binary constant table is then complete. This tape may be entered into the computer along with the operating program to begin the desired experiment.

SYSTEM HARDWARE

Before the operating program can be discussed in detail, it is necessary to consider the organization of the equipment connected to the computer and the manner in which response inputs and stimulus outputs are transferred between the PDP-8 and the experimental chambers. Figure 22 is the general outline of the entire operating system. Programs are entered into the computer either by paper tape reader or keyboard of the teletype at 10 characters per second, or by the high-speed (300 characters per second) photo-electric tape reader. Data can be printed on the teletypewriter at 10 characters per second, or may be punched six times faster on the high-speed paper tape punch for later printing off-line on the teletypewriter.

The computer is also provided with a hybrid transitor-relay interface that routes signals between the computer and the experimental stations. Additionally, since computer pulses are faster and lower in voltage than devices commonly used in the behavioral laboratory, the interface serves to convert signals from the PDP-8 to appropriate levels for the external devices and *vice versa*. Primarily, however, this interface provides the digital logic necessary for data entry into the computer.

Data enter the interface from a crystal clock (10-msec pulse rate), a response simulator, and from three patchboard relay stations that also receive signals from the interface. The experimental chambers, special devices, and data displays are also connected to the patchboard stations. Each of the 10 experimental stations has been allotted three response lines, R1, R2, and R3, and has 11 different stimulus outputs available to it.

Input-Output Transfers. The PDP-8 has two methods of transferring information into or out of the computer. The first of these, the data break system, is primarily used for transferring large blocks of data between magnetic core memory locations and external data storage devices, such as magnetic tape or magnetic disc units. This procedure, while essential for high-speed transfers of large quantities of data, requires an elaborate set of external logic to implement it.

The second method of communication between the computer and peripheral devices requires less external logic, since it utilizes the computer to control data transfer through a set of appropriate instructions, and a special feature called program interrupt. Because of the slow data rates typical of a behavioral laboratory, this method is more appropriate for interfacing the PDP-8 for experimental control purposes.

Program Interrupt. In the present system, all information transferred into or out of the computer passes through the accumulator (AC), a 12-bit register that also serves as the primary arithmetic register of the PDP-8. Appropriate computer instructions can transfer data from the AC to any specified core memory location (of the 4096 memory cells) or *vice versa*. Other instructions can manipulate data stored in the AC and can make program decisions depending upon the value of the number contained in it. Basic arithmetic operations of addition and subtraction are also carried out between core locations and the AC. Thus, most computer programs involve the AC in every program step (or instruction) to carry out the desired calculation.

Since incoming data must pass through the AC, which may be otherwise occupied by on-going calculations, a special input line, called the program interrupt, is used to signal the computer that data are awaiting entry. When an interrupt signal occurs, the computer will immediately leave the program sequence underway at that time and move to a special location (memory cell 1) for its next instruction. In the process, the address of the next instruction of the interrupted sequence is stored in memory location zero, so that the program may be re-entered when the data causing interrupt have been handled. However, a second circuit within the computer must be enabled by a computer instruction to allow the interrupt signal to trigger this sequence. The interrupt enable, then, can be used to prevent the data-handling program from being interrupted, itself, by new data until the preceding incoming information has been completely treated. If an interrupt signal occurs while the interrupt circuit is off, the signal is stored and will cause a program interrupt as soon as the routine is re-enabled.

Auxiliary to the program-interrupt circuit is a separate function, called program skip, which may be used in conjunction with computer instructions to determine which of the many possible external devices has caused the interrupt. This depends on external circuitry to apply a signal to the skip input line of the computer in conjunction with a computer instruction that tests the information status of the device. When data are entered into a device, triggering a program

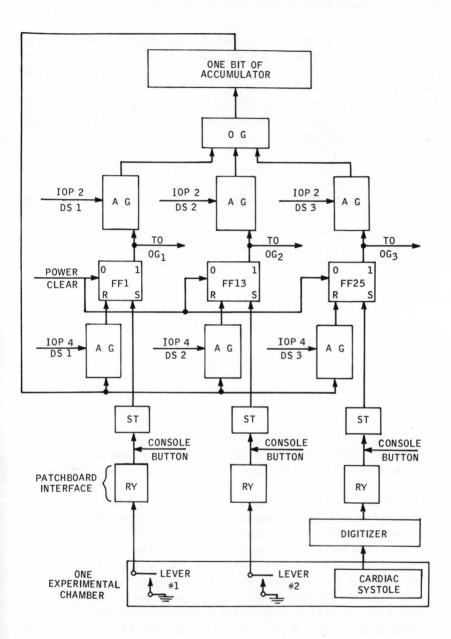

Figure 23. Schematic diagram of input interface: data storage circuits. Signals going to OG₁, OG₂, and OG₃ operate the interrupt and skip circuitry shown in Figure 24.

interrupt, then the program will sequentially request each external device to generate a program skip if the device contains data. The skip pulse causes the computer program to bypass the next instruction and to operate on the following instruction, which will read into the AC. If the device does not contain data, the next instruction is not skipped, and the computer will thereby be directed to another sequence that will test the next external device for the source of the interrupt request.

Computer Interface. The interface contains the digital logic needed to implement data transfer between the computer and the experimental stations. On the input side, a buffer is needed to store incoming data until it can be read into the computer after identification by the appropriate skip instruction. The output side also contains storage registers that are set when a stimulus is to be initiated and reset by a second pulse, when the stimulus is to be turned off. Since all of the information must pass through the 12-bit AC, both the input and output storage registers are most efficiently grouped in sets of 12 bits so that one group may be transferred at a time.

Device selectors. The actual transfer of data in both directions is accomplished by the joint action of computer instructions and some units of external digital logic in the interface. Each input-output (IOP) instruction in the PDP-8 is capable of selecting one of 64 possible sets of 12-bit external storage registers. (Four of these IOP instructions are reserved for high- and low-speed paper tape readers and punches.) Each of these transfer instructions is capable of generating three independent but sequential pulses that can be utilized by means of a digital logic module called a device selector. The device selector (DS) is wired to the computer so that it will pass one or more of the three transfer pulses when that particular DS is addressed by an instruction. Which of the three pulses is selected will also be determined by the same computer instruction that addressed the device selector.

Inputs. The schematic drawings of Figures 23 and 24 show how the three data inputs from one experimental station are entered into the AC. Each station is provided with three separate inputs, R1, R2, and R3, and the interface is organized so that all 10 R1s are contained in a single 12-bit input group, the R2s in a second, and the R3s in a third. (The two extra bits per input group are used for the clock and for five separate inputs that are used to trigger the printing of recorded data.) Starting from the bottom of Figure 23, the fate of a lever closure on lever 1 may be traced to a relay (RY) in the patchboard interface, and then to a Schmitt-trigger (ST) in the computer interface. The ST converts the relay closure to a signal capable of setting a flip-flop (FF1), in the register containing flops for R1 from each station. If FF1 is set and an input-output pulse (IOP) of type 2 (the second in the train of three pulses) is gated through the device selector for the R1 group (DS1), then the and-gate (AG) passes a signal through the or-gate (OG) to the bit of the AC that accepts data from this station.

After data contained in any of the R1 flip-flops (FFs1-12) have been read into the accumulator by DS1, the flip-flops must be reset to prepare for further incoming data. Since the flops containing information from the R1 levers of all of the stations are read into the AC by the same IOP from the same DS, and since this data entry is triggered (via the interrupt and skip routines) by any of the 10 R1 levers, there would be some probability of data being lost when the entire register is cleared. If, after one station requested entry and the register was read into the AC, another station emitted an R1 before the clear pulse was sent by the computer to reset the register, then the flop for the second station would be reset, even though its response had not been entered. For this reason, the IOP4 passing through DS1 is shown to be gated with the bit of the AC receiving information. Therefore, only if this flop has read information into the AC will it be reset by the IOP4 for this group. The "Power Clear" line is used to clear the interface whenever the computer is turned on.

In similar fashion, inputs on response lines R2 and R3 are read into the accumulator. When data in one of these words cause a program interrupt, and are then identified by the appropriate skip routine, the data in the word will be read into the AC in the same manner as was the response buffer for R1.

If any flop from 1 to 12 is set by an R1 (or the two data print commands also contained within this group), this information is sent directly to the program-interrupt circuit, as shown in Figure 24. Each of the three input groups is independently gated with the IOP1 pulse of its own DS before arriving at the skip flag circuit. In this way the computer can separately test which group has

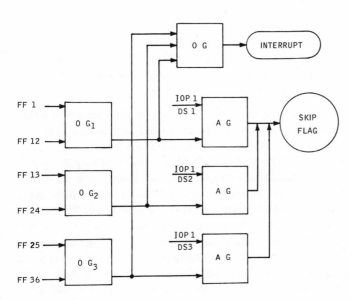

Figure 24. Schematic diagram of input interface: interrupt and skip circuits.

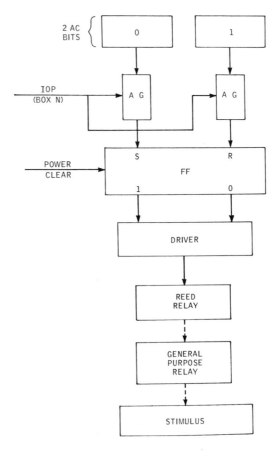

Figure 25. Schematic diagram of output interface: one independent output set. The dotted lines indicate external modifiable wiring.

signalled the interrupt, by going to different routines for IOP1 signals from DS1, DS2, or DS3. (In the same manner, interrupts caused by the tape readers or punches can be determined, using their separate device selectors.)

Outputs. The output interface consists of 11 possible output signals for each of 10 stations. The 11 outputs are divided into two groups: one set of four independent outputs that can be on in any combination, and another set of seven outputs, only one of which can be operated at a time. Figure 25 shows the details of one of the four independent output lines for one station. If bit 0 of the accumulator is set (and bit 1 is not) when a computer instruction generates the appropriate IOP for this station, the flip-flop will be set, operating a reed relay in the computer interface. A cable carries the relay output to the patchboard where a general purpose relay may be operated to produce a stimulus in the experimental chamber. Dashed lines on the figure indicate output paths that can be easily re-routed by patchboard programming. To turn off the

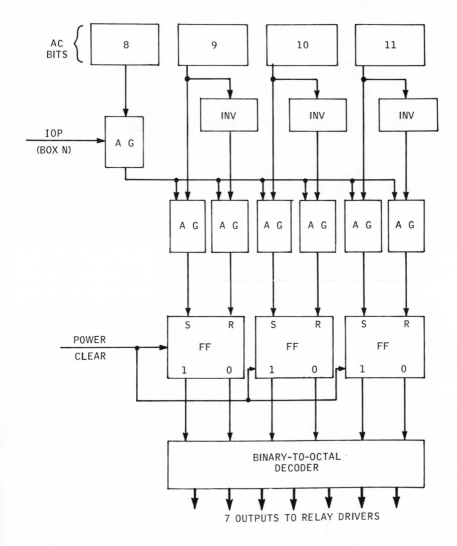

Figure 26. Schematic diagram of output interface: seven outputs, only one of which can be on at a time. The inverters (INV) are used to reset each flip-flop whose corresponding AC bit is at zero.

stimulus, bit 1 of the accumulator must be set while bit 0 is at zero, and the appropriate IOP instructions must be given (the same one as was used to turn the stimulus on).

There is a separate IOP pulse for each of the 10 output sets, each of which is selected by a different computer instruction. This IOP pulse turns stimuli on and off in one experimental box ("BOX N"), and there are nine others, similarly selected, for the nine remaining stations. Bits 0 to 7 of the accumulator are paired in this way to provide four independent outputs. As with the input interface, all flip-flops are reset when the computer is turned on ("Power Clear").

Figure 26 shows the second type of output for one station. Bits 9, 10, and 11 of the accumulator are decoded into seven separate lines, only one of which is operated at a time. The line to be operated is selected only when bit 8 of the accumulator is set, bits 9 to 11 are coded appropriately, and the IOP is generated for this station. In this way, the three flip-flops (set and reset by bits 9, 10, and 11) assume one of eight different configurations, and are fed to a decoder, which drives reed relays in the interface. When bits 9, 10, and 11 are at zero, and bit 8 is set, all seven output lines will be turned off. As with the independent outputs, the reed relay signals are fed to the patchboard for the experimental station. In this portion of the output configuration, when one of the seven lines is turned on, any line that was previously on will be turned off. Thus, a series of stimuli can be programmed with the onset of one stimulus automatically turning off the preceding one.

The output circuits utilize all bits of the 12-bit accumulator, and one-third of a device selector per station. Separate set and reset bits for each of the four independent output lines minimize computer programming and interface hardware, since they permit a device to be turned on or off independently of other devices with a single IOP pulse for each station. The second type of output circuit was designed to increase the number of outputs that could be controlled by the four remaining bits of the AC from two to seven, for use in experiments where several non-simultaneous stimuli are programmed.

The decision to have reed relays in the computer interface leading to other relays in the patchboard interface permits us to use long cables between the computer and experimental stations without electrical noise being introduced into the sensitive computer and interface circuitry from the high voltage devices operated in the running boxes.

Patchboards. The computer interface is connected by cables to three programmable patchboards, each of which is wired to 40 general-purpose relays. The patchboards also receive cables from display devices (cumulative recorders, panels with indicator lights, *etc.*), and experimental chambers (with a set of four rat boxes, a set of four monkey chairs, and a set of two monkey chambers each connected to a separate patchboard).

These patchboards and their associated relays provide for flexibility of the system hardware, in that the addition or modification of display devices or experimental chambers can be easily accomplished by rearranging plug-in connections on the patchboard as desired. Also, cables can be brought to the patchboards from special transducers (EKG, blood-pressure, *etc.*) that can be added to process signals from the testing stations, and their digitized outputs can be routed through the patchboards to serve as inputs to the computer.

The relays in the patchboard system are multi-pole and of higher current capacity than the reed relays of the interface. We normally provide one of these relays for every output of the computer, and also use them to prevent signals from reaching the computer interface before the start of the session. The latter procedure allows us to use an input (R2) both to start sessions (by a switch on the console), and as a regular data input after the session is on. R2s which occur before the switch is thrown are gated out by a "session relay". The only R2 that can reach the computer is from the console switch, whose activation will cause the operating program to generate a stimulus output command ("session on"), turning on the session relay, thus allowing R2s from the station through to the computer.

Response Simulator Console. A console is provided at the side of the computer with a complete set of pushbuttons for simulated entry of any of the 30 response inputs. A row of 11 lights may be connected to any of the 10 sets of stimulus output reed relays for testing new programs or checking for malfunctioning equipment. It is at this console, also, that the R2 switches are thrown for starting experimental sessions.

A special set of five pushbuttons is also located on the console to initiate data print-out. Each button, by feeding into special bits of the response input buffers, initiates a routine that causes all of the memory cells used for recording data from two stations to be punched either on the high-speed punch or on the teletype. The print-commands can also be triggered on regular input lines from the patchboard interface, so that data may be automatically obtained during the session. The output device (high-speed punch or teletype) is selected by a switch on the computer, and a second switch determines whether the recording registers are reset to zero following print-out.

The format of the print-out consists of a station number heading followed by data lines each containing up to 10 four-digit counters. Each counter is differentiated from the next by brackets and they are punched in ASCII code for direct printing on the teletype.

THE OPERATING PROGRAM-SKED

The design of the operating program was determined, to a great extent, by the formats of the constant table and the input and output interfaces. Within these constraints, the operating program itself was written to minimize the time needed to handle each input. In addition, the operating program was made as compact as possible (it occupies 1000 locations or one-fourth of memory) to allow a maximum amount of memory space for the storage of constant tables and data recording registers.

Program Description. A partial flow diagram of the basic features of the operating program, SKED, is shown in Figure 27. It begins with the waiting loop to which the computer returns after processing each clock pulse or response

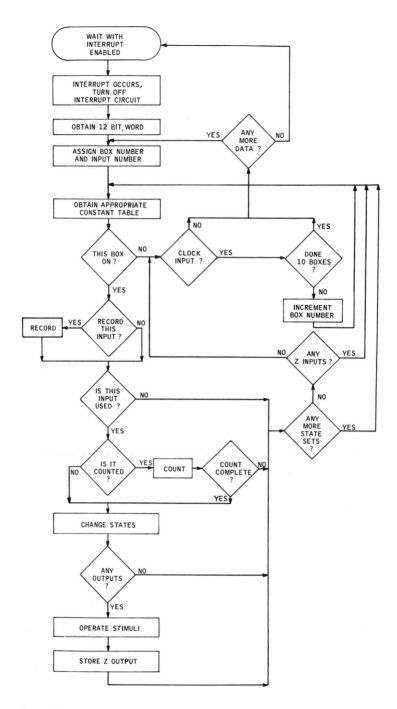

Figure 27. Flow chart of SKED.

input. When the loop is entered, the interrupt circuit is enabled by a computer instruction, and while in the loop, the computer performs no useful functions: it is only waiting for the next input to generate an interrupt signal. When that signal comes, the computer automatically turns off the interrupt circuit so that the intput that caused the interrupt can be completely handled before further inputs will be accepted. The computer also automatically jumps to memory location 1 for its next instruction, where our program begins a routine to determine which 12-bit input buffer contains the signal calling for service. In this routine, all of the input devices in the interface are checked sequentially, until one is found that contains data. The particular input buffer thus selected will determine whether the response is treated as R1, R2, or R3. The selected buffer (that causes a skip to occur) will then be read into the accumulator, and the station in which the response originated will be determined from the position of the bit in the AC set to "one". Similarly, data-print commands and clock pulses are decoded by determining in which of the three input sets they occurred, and which AC bit has been set. In all stages of the input sequence, the clock-pulse bit is tested first to minimize the number of instructions for this input, as it generally has the highest frequency. If more than one bit in the input word is set, the response from the highest-order station is acted upon first and the remaining inputs are stored to be handled one at a time after the first has been completely processed.

After the station number and response number of the input have been decoded, the program then obtains the address of the constant table of the first state set for this box to see if an experiment is in progress. If not, the address of the constant table will be set at zero, meaning that the station is off, and no further computation is necessary. In this case, if the input was not a clock pulse, the program will check if any other data were read in with the present input, and if not, the interrupt will be enabled, and more data awaited. If, on the other hand, the input was from the clock, then each experimental station is examined in turn.

If the register containing the address of the current state of the first state set is not set at zero (*i.e.*, a constant table exists for this station), the program will test the Main Word bit positions (refer to Figure 18) to determine what uses the given input may have. If recording is indicated, this is done first. If the input is not used to cause transition to another state, then no further checking is required. If it is, however, then the appropriate input counter is incremented, if this is required, and if transition is called for (no count of the input was required, or the count criterion has been met), then state change will take place. On state change, the address of the Main Word of the state to which transition occurs on the given input (obtained from the appropriate Next State Address register of the constant table) is inserted in the register containing the address of the current state of this state set. Also, any counters of inputs in the new state are set to zero. Next, any stimulus outputs associated with this transition are generated, and the contents of the Z-output register of the table are stored in a master Z-output storage word in SKED. After the first state set is treated in this fashion, each successive state set for this station is treated in the same way.

Following completion of all state sets for the station, the program checks the master Z-output storage word in SKED to see if any Z-outputs were generated. If there were, then each Z is treated as a new input and the sequence is repeated until all such Zs have been tested against every state set of this station. When this is completed, if the input was a clock pulse, then all remaining stations must be treated in the same way. If it was not a clock pulse, or when all boxes have been handled, then the input word, which was originally read into the AC from the interface, is checked to determine whether any other inputs, in addition to the one just treated, were read in at the same time with it. If so, they go through the same procedure, and if not, the interrupt is enabled and the waiting loop is entered.

New constant tables may be read into the computer or data may be printed while SKED is controlling experiments. These operations are done under SKED control, employing the interrupt system and a feedback feature of the reading and printing devices, in which a signal is sent to the computer interrupt line after a read or print command has been executed. The input lines from these peripheral devices are checked by SKED only after determining that it was not one of the three data input sets that caused an interrupt. Thus, characters are read in or printed out one at a time. While the print or read commands are being executed, SKED returns to its waiting loop, with the interrupt enabled, to handle possible data inputs. When the feedback signal causes an interrupt, the character read into the buffer will be stored in the appropriate place in memory and another read command generated (if the reader is on), or the next character to be printed will be obtained and the print command issued. This will continue, with response and clock inputs being handled while reading or printing occurs, until the new constant table has been read in, or until the data for the two stations controlled by the initiating data-print request have been completely printed out. By the use of switch options, data can be printed on the teletype or punched on paper tape at high speed, and the registers whose data are being printed out can either be cleared (set to zero) or not, following print-out. The registers can be cleared in preparation for an experimental session, or the data can be printed during a session without disturbing the values in the registers.

Timing Considerations and Space Allocation. A computer program that is used to control experiments must be able to respond to the highest input rate likely to occur. Even with the fast cycle time of the PDP-8 (3.0 μsec for the average instruction) this may be quite difficult, since as many as 400 instructions may be needed to handle a response input that changes states in several state sets for one experiment.

The input with the highest rate is the 10-msec clock, which must examine every state set of every box to increment recording counters or to initiate state change. While it is possible in theory to specify the time required by the computer program to handle all of the potential inputs in all of the many possible state configurations, the complete list would be extremely large. For this reason, we have tried to construct a worst case of data rates, number of state sets and number of active transitions, for 10 concurrent experiments, based on our experience in using the system. Calculation of the computer time necessary to handle this example helps to outline the limitations of the system as presently programmed and to structure future programming attempts, designed to reduce these constraints. Following are the assumptions we have made in constructing our worst-case example:

1. The worst case in our system requires that 10 experiments are to be conducted simultaneously. While this is theoretically possible, we usually have had no more than eight operating at once, due to limitations in the amount of memory space available to store constant tables and recording counters. However, it is instructive to calculate program times for 10 stations because a large proportion of the total program time is due to decision-making that is a function of the number of stations that are time-sharing the computer.

2. The second specification for our example is that each station have five state sets, which is about the average we have used in the past for actual experiments. Of these five, one is always the session timer, used to start and stop the experiment. The others consist of contingency controllers and state sets used for recording purposes. (In fact, it is usually the case that more state sets are used for data recording than for actual experimental control.)

3. The third specification concerns data rate. For this we have chosen 10 responses per second for each station (divided in any way among the three inputs), or a total of 100 responses per second for the whole system. Although this rate is much higher than normally obtained in most experiments, it may occur for brief periods, especially when digitized cardiac signals are entered concurrently with lever responses. (Cardiac rate alone may reach six per second or higher in the rhesus monkey or in rats.) In any case, the rate of 100 responses per second is equivalent to one response being entered for each 10-msec clock pulse.

4. The fourth assumption concerns the average number of transitions caused by each clock pulse. As mentioned earlier, each time pulse must address every state set of each active station whenever it is entered. To calculate a typical case, each station was assumed to have a session timer counting to 60 min, two state sets each controlling contingencies with 5-sec interval timers, another state set with 5-sec steps for recording purposes, and an IRT distributor with 0.5-sec steps. The joint probability of any of these intervals causing state change on a clock pulse is approximately 0.026 with a basic timing pulse of 10 msec. This means that, on the average, one state change will occur on every fourth pulse for 10 stations. Most of the time needed to handle each clock pulse is spent establishing constant table locations and counting the pulses, and only a small amount of time is then needed to change states on completion of the desired count in any one state set.

5. The final decision concerns the average effect of an incoming response. In this case, a typical set of operations includes recording of the response in three state sets (of the station in which the response occurs), and state change, with Z and stimulus outputs, in two state sets. In none of these instances is the response counted, so that it automatically changes states when it is used. Of course, the response need be treated only for one station, but the routine identifying which station uses the response input takes a considerable number of instructions.

Using assumptions one, two, and four to test the time taken to handle the clock input, we find that each pulse requires 6.9 msec on the average to be handled. Although this is a considerable percentage of the 10 msec between incoming clock pulses, it is needed to search all the state tables for each box. Of course, the assumption that each state set at least counts every clock pulse may be too severe.

The response input requires, under the assumptions of the example, an average of 1.3 msec to be handled. If the response generates a Z output (which we assumed to be typical), a further 1.1 msec is needed to complete its treatment. These, with the 6.9 msec of the clock, add up to 9.3 msec of program time for each clock pulse. On every fourth pulse, an additional 0.3 msec is required to change one state on the completion of the required count of time pulses.

In fact, the preceding example is based on assumptions that are unlikely to be as severe in practice. Nevertheless, these timing calculations serve to point out the limits of the system. Our experience has been that with eight stations running simultaneously, the program spends most of the time in the waiting loop with the interrupt enabled. This extra time must be made available, however, for the rare instances of extremely high response rates occurring at the same time in many boxes.

A more severe constraint on the system is the limited memory space. Based on the assumptions of the preceding example, it is possible to specify the length of a typical state as 11 counters. This includes (see Figure 18) a Recording Address, the Record Word, the Main Word, a Variable Counter, and Counter Constant for the clock pulse, and two triplets of Next State Address, Stimulus Output Code and Z-Output word for the clock and for the response. A memory location is needed for a recording counter for each state as well, raising the total to 12 memory locations per state. Since the operating program requires one fourth of memory, there remain 3072 locations available for state tables and recorded data. This means 256 of our assumed typical states may be stored in the computer at one time. Since the average state set has six states, this means no more than eight stations can be run simultaneously, if each has five state sets. Of course, if some experiments require fewer states, the variable-length constant table permits other stations to utilize the extra space.

SYSTEM ALTERNATIVES AND IMPROVEMENTS

The system has been in use for two years at the time this chapter is being written. It is the fifth revision in a series of workable programs, each of which represents an improvement over prior versions in terms of speed, convenience, and number of parallel experiments that can be conducted. The evolution of the series is a concrete demonstration of the laws of learning in regard to our programming skills; it is a common experience that complex computer control systems need continual modification as a result of trial-and-error experience. For this reason a number of improvements in the system, not yet programmed, are listed below.

Increasing Program Speed.   The present operating program is relatively slow in treatment of clock inputs. One solution to this problem would be to provide programmable clocks in the interface, and arrange these so that they could be set to required intervals by each state table. It would be necessary to provide one such clock for each state set for each station, since most state diagrams demand different intervals in each state set. To guarantee that enough clocks are available for any configuration of simultaneous on-line experiments that might be conducted concurrently would require at least 50 of these devices (assuming an average of five state sets per station). Even with the low price of integrated circuits, the cost of 50 programmable timers and associated circuitry is rather high.

An alternative method for increasing the speed of the operating program is suggested by an analysis of the present system. The greatest number of computer instructions that follow an input to the computer are involved with decoding the state tables for each station. For example, each clock pulse initiates a number of program steps for each state set of each station to determine whether or not it is recorded, counted, *etc.* Most clock pulses, in fact, are merely counted, after which the count is usually found not to be complete. Most intervals require a considerable number of clock pulses to occur before state change or other functions of a transition are generated. Although state change is the usual consequence of a response input, analysis of this routine and associated output routines establishes that the most computer time is required for decoding and generating needed memory addresses, while the actual functions to be executed require only a few instructions.

We have developed a new version of the system designed to reduce the number of decisions following an input. A new format for the constant table and operating program has been constructed to utilize features of a computer instruction called JMS, or "jump to subroutine". The JMS instruction transfers a program sequence from one portion of core to an addressable subroutine, and it carries the address of the instruction following the JMS to the subroutine. When the subroutine has been completed, this address then can be used to return control to the original program sequence. Special subroutines have been written to perform specific functions of the state system, (*e.g.*, generating a stimulus output) and the same routine is used every time this function is to occur, as demanded by the state diagram. Specific information needed for each operation of the subroutine, (*e.g.*, the output code for the stimulus routine) is stored in the state table immediately after the JMS instruction. This format eliminates the need for coded main words in the state table, since the JMS to a particular subroutine would be placed in the table by the Compiler only when the function generated by that subroutine is required. Consider a response that generates a stimulus output, is recorded in a particular memory location, and changes state. For this case, the state table would begin with a JMS to the stimulus routine in the operating program. Following the JMS would be the 12-bit output code word. The subroutine would first retrieve the output code from the address brought to the subroutine by the JMS instruction, turn on the desired output, and then return to the state table. The next instruction encountered would be a JMS to the recording subroutine, with the address of the recording counter following the JMS. After recording and returning to the state table, the next instruction would be a JMS to the state change routine followed by the necessary information required by this subroutine. Finally, all functions of the response having been completed, the program would encounter an instruction that would transfer control to the next state set for this station.

Preliminary tests of this format yield operating times of 1.6 msec for a clock pulse compared to the 6.9 msec of the older operating program, and 0.9 msec for the treatment of a response compared with the original value of 1.3 msec. These values would permit a clock rate of 3.5 msec between pulses instead of the old rate of 10 msec for 10 stations.

A second advantage resulting from the new format is the ease with which the program can be revised to provide for new functions when necessary. All that need be done, in effect, is to add new subroutines to SKED and to add the new JMS instructions to the Compiler. Furthermore, the new format would facilitate adding subroutines written in standard machine language as part of a state table.

Decreasing the Number of Cells Needed by a State Set.   A more important modification of our system will reduce the number of memory locations required for a state set by a factor of five at the least. This improvement depends upon adding two new operations to those already performed by transitions, and by reorganizing the new state table. A sizeable number of states are currently required to program repetitive functions (*e.g.*, interresponse-time distributions with one state per recording interval of the histogram). These functions often consist of a sequential string of states, advanced by one input (T in the case of IRTs), and differ only in the address of the memory location in which the response will be recorded. By adding a Fortran-like output statement, such as $C_i = C_i + 1$, specifying that a counter address is to be incremented on each transition, and a second statment such as $C_i = C_1$ to reset the location to the first of the series, an entire state set may be reduced to a single state. (For more details see Snapper, Knapp, and Kushner, 1970). Although the addition of these output functions will create larger single states, it will considerably reduce the number of states for most experiments.

More Extensive Editing in Compilation. The present Compiler permits a certain amount of editing of master tapes by "splicing" tapes and by reading up to and skipping errors. However, the correction of typographical errors is somewhat cumbersome, since it involves reading portions of programs already punched on tape. Future versions of the Compiler will utilize the symbol tape editor program provided with the PDP-8 to produce the first version of the master tape. This will permit far more flexible and quicker editing than is now possible. (The only reason that the tape editor is not being used now is that our present Compiler uses some characters considered illegal by the standard PDP-8 editor.)

Auxiliary Equipment. Two very useful additions to the system hardware would be an expanded (8K) memory and a magnetic tape or disc storage device. The expanded memory (much more economically feasible in the newer PDP-8s than in our older one) would permit the simultaneous use of the operating system and the Compiler. Alternatively, if necessary, the available amount of memory for state tables and recording counters could be more than doubled. Magnetic tape or disc storage devices would also greatly reduce compilation time. Other advantages of expanded storage would include more rapid data print-out and increased efficiency in entering both the operating program and the constant tables into memory.

Special Cases Requiring Additional Programming. Although the state system adequately describes the sequential properties of reinforcement schedules, some procedures may require extensive manipulation of input data in order to specify a response in the binary (on-off) format required by the rules of the notational language. For example, if an analog signal is measured, representing the force applied to a lever by the subject (Notterman and Mintz, 1965) a response may be (and in most cases actually is) defined in terms of a threshold value of force exceeded for a specified duration. If the computer has an analog-to-digital converter as an accessory, it may be convenient to convert the analog signal, test the digital numbers, and then specify that a response has occurred when certain criteria have been met. At this point, it would then be reasonable to use the state system to control the consequences of the response. Of course, since the input conversion and data manipulation may require the full-time attention of the computer, the number of stations that could be controlled simultaneously may have to be reduced.

Another type of reinforcement schedule requires extensive mathematical manipulations of the incoming response rate to decide whether reinforcements should be delivered following a response. For example, Weiss and Laties (1965) described a schedule in which reinforcement probability depends upon the value of the ratio between each interresponse-time and its predecessor. Since this type of decision requires arithmetic routines not available in SKED, a special-purpose machine language or FORTRAN program is required. However, a sub-routine may be inserted in SKED to generate the ratio and to identify each categorical value as a separate digital response. Once the assignment of a response category has been made, then SKED may use this information to control the experiment. As was the case for analog conversion, however, the time required by each response may be greatly increased by the input routine, thus reducing the total number of parallel stations.

Rearrangement of Input-Output Allocation. In the present configuration, each station has three inputs (R1, R2, and R3) and 11 outputs available to it. Modification of this arrangement is possible by revising SKED so that one box could have all 30 inputs and 110 outputs. Of course, intermediate arrangements could also be achieved.

CONCLUSION

The present system is very easy to use both in terms of programming and operating experiments. On first glance, the notation system may seem to be difficult to learn, but in fact, in our experience, it has been quite easy to train graduate students in its usage. The major advantages of the system lie in the speed in which new experiments can get underway after original design. Our usual programming time rarely exceeds an hour for several parallel stations, and mistakes in state diagrams are the exception rather than the rule.

For these reasons we feel that the present system is useful even when it has to be supplemented by special programs for special cases (none of our studies has yet required this), and would be our choice with only one station to operate. In fact, we have even applied the notational system to the older methods of programming by constructing state modules from relays (Snapper and Knapp, 1969) so that it is possible to program experiments by wiring the modules to mimic the state diagram of the procedure.

Finally, it should be noted that the present organization of the Compiler and operating programs is only one of many possible alternatives. Other computers and other system requirements could lead to different methods for translating state graphs into actual operating programs.

REFERENCES

Brandauer, C. M. *The effects of uniform probabilities of reinforcement upon the response rate of the pigeon.* Unpublished doctoral dissertation, Columbia University, 1958.

Farmer, J. Properties of behavior under random interval reinforcement schedules. *Journal of the Experimental Analysis of Behavior*, 1963, *6*, 607—616.

Ferster, C. B. and Skinner, B. F. *Schedules of reinforcement.* New York: Appleton-Century-Crofts, 1957.

Mealy, G. H. A method for synthesizing sequential circuits. *Bell Systems Technical Journal*, 1955, *34*, 1045—1079.

Mechner, F. Probability relations within response sequences under ratio reinforcement. *Journal of the Experimental Analysis of Behavior*, 1958, *1*, 109—121.

Mechner, F. A notation system for the description of behavioral procedures. *Journal of the Experimental Analysis of Behavior*, 1959, *2*, 133—150.

Moore, E. F. Gedanken-experiments on sequentail machines. *Automata studies.* Princeton: Princeton University Press, 1956.

Notterman, J. M. and Mintz, D. E. *Dynamics of response.* New York: Wiley, 1965.

Schoenfeld, W. N., Cumming, W. W., and Hearst, E. On the classification of reinforcement schedules. *Proceedings of the National Academy of Sciences*, 1956, *42*, 563—570.

Sidman, M. Avoidance conditioning with brief shock and no exteroceptive warning signal. *Science*, 1953, *118*, 157—158.

Snapper, A. G. and Knapp, J. A multi-purpose logic module for behavioral experiments. *Behavior Research Methods & Instrumentation*, 1969, *1*, 264—266.

Snapper, A. G., Knapp, J., and Kushner, H. Mathematical description of schedules of reinforcement. In W. N. Schoenfeld (Ed.), *The Theory of reinforcement schedules.* New York: Appleton-Century-Crofts, 1970.

Weiss, B. and Laties, V. G. Reinforcement schedule generated by an on-line digital computer. *Science*, 1965, *148*, 658—661.

CHAPTER THREE

DIGITAL COMPUTERS
AND THE MICROANALYSIS
OF BEHAVIOR [1]

BERNARD WEISS

The University of Rochester School of Medicine and Dentistry

[1] The preparation of this chapter, and collection of the data described in it, were supported in part by NIMH grant MH 11752 and in part under contract with the USAEC at the University of Rochester Atomic Energy Project, and has been assigned Report No. UR-49-*1471*.

INTRODUCTION

It takes no more than a quick scan of the *Journal of the Experimental Analysis of Behavior*, from the early issues, beginning in 1958, to the current ones, for a reader to detect some clear-cut trends in the experimental analysis of behavior. Investigators are turning their attention to the fine details of behavior, both in the sense of control and in an analytical sense. There is also a pronounced tendency toward quantitative (mathematical not statistical) treatment and more attention to a precise control of the experimental organism's history. Parallel trends are also apparent and perhaps even magnified in behavioral pharmacology. When confronted with all the added complications introduced by chemical agents, the serious investigator finds himself forced to grapple with the most minute details of control and analysis in order to interpret his data adequately.

There is no doubt that these trends will be accelerated by the availability of the laboratory digital computer. The on-line computer permits an unprecedented degree of interaction with a behaving organism. Responses may be detected and environmental events initiated in a matter of microseconds; the topography of the response may be specified with arbitrary degrees of complexity and subtlety; contingencies of reinforcement and other experimental parameters can be changed quickly during the experiment and as a consequence of the performance itself.

The digital computer offers not so much a new approach to instrumentation as new dimensions in understanding. The experimental analysis of behavior, from its earliest history, spurred psychologists toward greater and greater automation and finer and more profound analyses. Automation, of course, is an answer to the numerous sources of bias and distortion that afflict behavioral research. It is so easy for adventitious variables to slip into an experimental setting that even the most alert investigator must make the fullest possible use of automation. This is one reason why psychologists have been among the most diligent users of the laboratory computer. Twenty-five percent of the original LINC computer evaluation group (Blough, Boneau, Weiss) were psychologists. As I suggested in a recent article (Weiss, 1969), the pervasive influence of the operant approach probably owes a great deal to Skinner's talent as an apparatus designer and to the later development of automation with relays.

I foresee the computer making contributions to the analysis of behavior at many levels. Although we now know a great deal about shaping and maintaining operant behavior, and schedules of reinforcement, computers permit us to fabricate contingencies impossible to duplicate by conventional methods. Moreover, they also facilitate detailed and novel analyses of the behavior. Microcontrol and microanalysis are twin aspects of digital computer technology with implications more profound than simply expanding our ability to control many experimental chambers at once. Eventually, as in my laboratory, we will probably find experimenters doing fewer experiments, perhaps with fewer animals, but working more intensively. The analysis of data will be a much more empirical and searching enterprise, calling for as much originality as planning the experiment itself. With the possibilities inherent in easily manipulated, detailed records of behavior, processes are amenable to analysis that otherwise would have to be explicitly planned for in an experimental design. This increases the likelihood of fruitful accidents.

In this chapter, I will discuss the ways in which computers are used in a laboratory devoted to the experimental analysis of behavior and, in particular, to assessing the effects of drugs on behavior. Since my point of view was forged largely by the experience with the LINC computer, I will begin by a discussion of that experience.

THE LINC CONCEPT

The LINC, originally conceived by Wesley A. Clark, was created at the Lincoln Laboratories by a group that recognized that computer technology had not adequately served the needs of biomedical research. Large machines, and the requisite administrative structure of the typical computer center, made it impossible for an investigator to use computers as an experimental tool. The LINC was designed to maximize the degree of control over the machine by the individual researcher. Clark and Molnar (1965) gave as their goal a machine (1) small enough for the individual laboratory, (2) providing direct communication with the scientist via the console and the display, (3) fast enough for on-line work, (4) flexible with respect to the connection of external devices, and (5) with an instruction set easy to learn and use.

It had a number of useful features for the laboratory scientist. One was an extremely informative console, which made it easy to test and correct programs. It had many index registers and many logic instructions. It came with an oscilloscope display, analog inputs, and simple instructions for programming displays—even instructions for making it easy to display alphanumeric information. The input-output structure was easy to interface. The LINC also came with a relay register, with input sense lines, and with output pulse and level lines. In certain respects, the key to the LINC lay in the magnetic tapes. These were premarked into "blocks" of standard size, addressed by simple instructions. The tape logic enabled one to walk up to a machine with no bootstrap program in the memory and, using a simple console procedure, load any block of tape into memory. They enabled complex but easy-to-use programming systems to be written (LAP 3, 4, and 6), and made it easy to segment long programs on tape. Because of the type system, it was deceptive to consider the LINC merely as a 2048-word machine.

My introduction to computer technology took place by way of the LINC Computer Evaluation Program. Having designed and built two prototypes of the LINC, the LINC design group, supported by a number of interested agencies

(NIH, NASA), decided to perform the crucial experiment, namely, to see whether or not life scientists could incorporate small computers into their laboratories, could learn to program them effectively, and could keep them working. Those of us selected to take part in the program spent a month learning about computers in general and the LINC in particular. Part of our education consisted of assembling the LINC from individual components and getting it to run. This month proved to be an invaluable experience. Not only did it teach us the fundamentals of computer technology, and tell us something about how to troubleshoot the LINC, build interface for it, and program it, but it also taught us not to stand in awe of computers—not to feel it necessary, for "economic" reasons, to press them to their limits, and, above all, to treat them as laboratory devices.

On the basis of this experience, and my further observations, I believe that if an investigator turns to a computer as a laboratory tool, he must learn the technology in order to use it most effectively. Few, if any, of the productive behavioral investigators in past years were unfamiliar with relay logic and allied technologies, and certainly did not rely wholly on technicians or other technical assistance. The *Journal of the Experimental Analysis of Behavior*, for example, was filled in its early years, and still is, with technical notes of various kinds. A computer is not like a centrifuge that you turn on and off. It should engage the experimenter as closely as the electron microscope, say, engages the histologist. It demands a mastery of new techniques. Lacking an understanding of how computers work, and of programming, an investigator is limited to experiments within the bounds set by access to people capable of serving his needs. If he is lucky, he will find them. Even if he does, what may still elude him is the originality that the computer makes him able to exploit.

Another reason that we try to get along with a minimum of professional programming assistance, and that we also encourage investigators to wire their own interface circuitry, is that we are also in the business of training graduate students. Especially when funds are limited, the new Ph.D. should be able to do things for himself. If that means programming and interfacing a small computer, he should leave our laboratories with the appropriate skills.

CURRENT USE IN THE LABORATORY

Since this laboratory began its ventures into computer technology with the LINC, a prototype machine, troubleshooting occupied a substantial portion of the first few months. In addition, I had to teach myself programming and to design interface circuitry. Programming for only one man made things easier, and progress was probably faster because of it. But it would have been useful, for more recent years, to write programs for more general use. This problem will be discussed later in more detail.

A present, the laboratory possesses three machines. A PDP-8 was added in 1966 because the expansion of the laboratory made the LINC an overburdened machine used day and night. More recently, a PDP-12 was added.

The LINC is connected to various kinds of experimental chambers and peripheral devices. These include an IBM-compatible tape transport (Datamec 2020), a digital plotter (Calcomp 565), and a teletype. The LINC typically controls between one and four chambers at once, depending upon the experiment. The bulk of these are behavioral experiments, asking questions about schedules of reinforcement and their interactions with drugs. The PDP-8, which has 4096 words of memory, is equipped with two DECtape units, an oscilloscope display, and an analog-to-digital converter. All experiments now running on the PDP-8 use the analog equipment in conjunction with a polygraph. The programs, for the most part, deal with single organisms, mostly because of the specialized nature of the experimental chambers, although the programs themselves are rather complex, too. The limiting factor, however, is not the computer itself. The PDP-12, which has 8192 words of memory, is used both for on-line control and complex analytical procedures.

Even before the LINC experience, my interests had turned towards a microanalysis of behavior. This is the main reason that we do not use the machine to study large numbers of animals at once. Although limits were placed on such an application with the LINC because of memory space, and our desire to record all events on tape, large numbers of animals would have limited our ability and opportunities to analyze the data from many different vantage points, in a manner that we will describe later on. Being able to manipulate data is useful and exciting with an on-line machine, and is something that current terminals do not yet allow you to do for a reasonable price. Because of the other computer facilities in our department, we find it possible to perform complex calculations elsewhere, for example, on our IBM 360/44. This saves time on the laboratory computers and, for certain kinds of problems, particularly mathematical ones, makes programming easier.

PROGRAMMING

Perhaps the main reason that digital computers have not yet produced the impact that we expected earlier is that many investigators are reluctant to set aside the time to learn programming, an indispensable skill in using the computer. Programming a small computer to conduct on-line experimentation is not the arcane, subtle art that many hold it out to be. At that level, it nowhere approaches in difficulty the effort required to learn a foreign language. To overcome some of this reluctance, as the reader will observe from some of the other chapters in the book, some laboratories have developed special languages to make the task of programming easier. In this laboratory we have not, although we have made use of William Simon's SNAP and TRUW languages (cf, Chapter 11), and Grason-Stadler's SCAT system.

One reason arises from the LINC and my history. With only a single person involved, a prototype machine, an eagerness to apply the computer, and the need to develop interface hardware, a special language for behavioral experiments seemed too much of an undertaking. Also, realizing that the computer would alter the operation and orientation of the laboratory, it was impossible to be sure if settling on a special approach would be useful.

A second reason was that the LINC is not particularly onerous to program in machine language. This has little to do with one's talent as a programmer, but a great deal to do with (1) the LINC instruction set, which is versatile and easy to use, (2) the ease of debugging programs on-line because of the console design and some other features, and (3) perhaps most of all, the programming system, originally LAP-3, now well into advanced versions of the LAP-6 system designed by Mary Allen Wilkes Clark.

A major problem with machine-language programming is the awkwardness of the assembler and editor provided with the typical small computer. For example, to make more than minor changes in a program on a PDP-8 equipped only for paper tape, the programmer must first enter a bootstrap loader, then load in the Binary Loader, then the Editor, then the paper tape that contains the symbolic program or manuscript, then punch a new symbolic tape after making the corrections, then read in the assembly program, then the edited symbolic tape, and, finally, punch a binary tape. The binary tape constitutes the program. This is a maddeningly long and tedious process, one which might well have driven me to an interpretive language had I been forced to contend with it. Even high-speed readers and punches, although they shorten this process, are tedious to use. With a Disk or DECtape, the process is less time consuming, but even with these aids, tends also to be tedious. For example, the DECtape version of the PDP-8 Monitor System is comparatively inefficient and difficult to use, and requires an exceptionally long time to compile machine code.

The LINC programming system possessed none of these disadvantages. Operating in a conversational mode, via the oscilloscope display and keyboard, it permitted the programmer to type in his manuscript, automatically numbered manuscript lines, permitted instantaneous deletions and insertions, and assembled a binary version in a very short time. The newer version, spawned by experience with the earlier one, constitutes a complete programming system, allowing on-line editing, compiling, searching, and calling up and storing programs. But even with the earlier versions, it was easy enough to make a few changes, additions, or deletions, recompile, and test the assembled program once more. With the latest version of LAP-6, for example, it requires 70 sec on the LINC and 30 sec on the PDP-12 to assemble a program with 904 lines. This version, called the Wisconsin Assembly Language (LAP6W-WISAL), and developed by the Laboratory Computer Facility at the University of Wisconsin, incorporates all of the earlier features of LAP-6 and adds a few more. Table 1 lists many of the programming features of LAP6W-WISAL.

Another feature that made machine language programming on the LINC easier than on other machines was the console. The LINC console has two 12-bit sets of switches to correspond to the LINC word, and a number of control switches. They permit easy examination and modification of registers, execution

Table 1. LAP6W—WISAL

Manuscript Display and Location Commands

Forward 1 page
Forward 1 line
Forward 1 character
Backward 1 page
Backward 1 line
Backward 1 character
Split line
End line
Delete page
Delete line
Delete character

Assembler Displays and Commands

Next display
Forward 1 frame
To first display
Begin display
Return to
Print display
List manuscript
Print reference table

Index Display and Location Commands

Forward 1 frame
Forward 1 entry
Backward 1 frame
Backward 1 entry
Delete entry
Return
Reread index
Write index
Print index

Meta-Commands

Locate display at specified line
Add manuscript by block number
Add manuscript by name
Assemble LINC code
Copy file
Copy manuscript
Copy program
Copy block numbers
Continue search for character string
Display index (file)
Exit from LAP6W
Issue file-only label
Load binary by name
Load binary by block number

List LINC code
Print manuscript
Print reference table of LINC program
Save binary conversion on tape
Issue system label
Save manuscript on tape
Save program on tape
Search for specified character string
Switch tape unit
Assemble PDP-8 code
Load PDP-8 binary by name
Load PDP-8 binary by block number
List PDP-8 code
Print reference table of PDP-8 program

of instructions coded by the 12-bit switches via a "DO" lever (which is helpful for interface debugging), an "AUTO" mode switch and potentiometer to execute instructions at speeds ranging down to one instruction every *n* sec (also useful for interface debugging) and, especially, I STOP and XOE STOP. When I STOP is on, the program stops at an instruction location matched by one set of the 12-bit switches, at which point one can examine various registers, modify them, resume the program, or step through the program one instruction at a time. XOE STOP gives the option of stopping at an instruction that references that address, with again, the same options. Although software routines have been written (for example, PDP-8's DDT) to allow the same kind of debugging and modification, they do not permit the easy step-by-step examination that the LINC affords through the console.

Still another reason for not adopting a language was the wide variety of uses to which the machine was put. Although the applications began with operant experiments, we have also used the LINC in neurophysiological experiments, for example, evoked potential averaging (Lowy and Weiss, 1968), stereotaxic instrument control (Siegel, 1969), and with various peripherals such as the Calcomp digital plotter and the Datamec tape transport. In addition, more than I even expected, we have used the LINC for interactive data analysis. By this, I mean analysis of the kind that requires the investigator to burrow into the data, and involves everything from editing the data to twisting and manipulating it in numerous ways. For these purposes, programming skills are perhaps even more essential than for on-line work. It would be difficult to envision a language flexible enough to fulfill all our needs, especially since we continually make new demands. Many times, while sitting at the console and, in a sense, "playing" with the data, we have often revised programs on the spot in order to enhance some aspect of the analysis or the display. Someone who relied solely on professional programmers to carry this out could progress only very slowly as new aspects, dimensions, and modes of analysis occurred to him.

My views of programming are also molded by the belief that the scientist must possess enough familiarity with his equipment so that he is sensitive to sources of distortion. A scientist who uses computers should be ready to undertake programming simply because that job is part of his job as a scientist. With the digital computer, to a very great extent, the program is the experiment.

In the experience of this laboratory, what is most useful is not one grand programming system, but specialized and well-documented subroutines and program "packages", such as the "Question and Answer" routine devised originally by M. B. McDonald of Washington University, which uses an interactive oscilloscope display to obtain data from the keyboard. This subroutine is especially useful to us and is widely used in both off-line and on-line programs. It allows one to specify a statement or question and the number of blanks to be filled in. These blanks, filled in through the keyboard, contain information stored in a designated part of the memory where they can be recaptured by rather simple programs. Another set of especially useful routines have been those that control the operation of the IBM-compatible Datamec tape transport, which we obtained from Dr. William Talbot and others at Johns Hopkins (see Chapter 7), and later modified to suit our own needs. We also make use of subroutines for overcoming some of the disadvantages of the non-buffered LINC tapes, for emitting teletype signals and characters in various formats, for making oscilloscope graphs, for producing Calcomp plots, for carrying out fixed and floating point arithmetic, for generating random numbers, and so on. With conventional paper tape machines, stringing these subroutines together with a new program would be a very unpleasant job. With the LINC, all one has to do is to string together the tape-stored subroutine manuscripts with the LAP-6 programming system, and then issue the command to assemble.

The specialized languages and systems developed for experiments on behavior, such as Millenson's ACT (*cf,* Chapter 1) and Grason-Stadler's SCAT, take one beyond the level of the subroutine package. They make the jobs of on-line programming, and even analysis, much easier than writing the equivalent in machine language. Also, for a laboratory anxious to begin computer-controlled experiments, they represent a quick and flexible mode of entry. But it must not be overlooked that they do not permit the full variety of manipulations that many laboratories find necessary both for control and analysis. No language can.

ON-LINE CONTROL

From the very beginning, the computer in this laboratory was envisaged as a tool to permit the microcontrol and microanalysis of behavior. It was also envisaged as a tool for constructing rather complex relationships or contingencies between behavioral events and associated environmental events. For such goals to be achieved meant attention to a number of factors that we had not had to consider before. We will begin this section of the chapter by discussing a series of decisions it is necessary to make before actually beginning to code a program.

Table 2

*Instruction
location*

L	Skip the next instruction if clock input is ON
L+1	Jump to L+3
L+2	Jump to Timing Routine at L+10
L+3	Skip the next instruction if Lever 1 input is ON
L+4	Jump to L+6
L+5	Jump to response servicing routine
L+6	Skip the next instruction if Lever 2 input is ON
L+7	Jump to L+9
L+8	Jump to response servicing routine
L+9	Jump to L
L+10	Load a "1" in the accumulator
L+11	Add the accumulator to the timing register

.
.
.   ETC.
.

L+N	Jump to L

TIMING REQUIREMENTS

One immediate choice that has to be made is the degree of temporal resolution the experimenter requires for control and analysis. Although advances in technology may eventually make it a minor consideration, the problem will never totally disappear simply because computer speeds, memory size, and long-term storage capacity will always be finite. For the present, the scientist must carefully trade off temporal resolution against other requirements, mainly the complexity of on-line processing and the number of experiments or animals conducted or studied simultaneously.

When the requirements for temporal resolution are not particularly stringent for the speed of the machine and the complexity of the contingencies, a very simple scheme for measuring inter-event times can be employed. Suppose, for example, that the experiment handles four input lines, three from response devices and one from a multivibrator used as a time base. Assume that each event sets a flip-flop in the interface that can be reset under program control. The following sequence of instructions (Table 2) can then be used to increment the registers set aside in memory for timing.

Such a scheme, as we stated earlier, is adequate for many applications. It requires only a rather simple interface and presents a minimum of programming problems. Sometimes, however, more complicated schemes are made necessary by certain inescapable program complexities, or by the need to service many inputs, or by the need, say, with simultaneous EEG processing, to hone temporal resolution to a much finer degree. A solution to problems of this kind may lie in an external clock register whose contents can be read by a program command. Such a register is incremented periodically by a time-base generator such as a crystal-controlled multivibrator. The program can then be written to examine the clock register only when a response event has occurred. Usually, the clock register is preset with a certain negative number. Each pulse from the time base advances the clock register. When the clock register reaches zero, a register in the memory is incremented by the program. With the time base set to 1 msec and the external counter set to -1000, the clock register in memory will contain the number of seconds elapsed, and the interface clock register will contain the number of milliseconds minus 1000. If millisecond resolution is required, two words can then be used to represent the time in a 12-bit word length machine that gives a resolution of 1 msec in nearly 17 million msec.

ON-LINE VERSUS OFF-LINE PROCESSING

The experimenter must also weigh how much on-line processing he needs to do against the amount that he wishes, or can do, off-line. This decision also must take into account the amount and detail of the raw data the experimenter desires to preserve, which involves deciding on the resolution of the stored data. Suppose, for example, that during the course of the experiment the investigator wishes to compile inter-event time histograms for each subject, and means and standard deviations for various behavioral parameters. The program must then be written not only to exert on-line control, but to provide, with each response processed, appropriate increments in histogram bins, and entrance to arithmetic routines. If the experimenter chooses on-line arithmetic processing, he must then decide whether to conduct it in fixed-point or floating-point format. Fixed-point formats are those in which the values in the registers are treated as integer values. No fractions are possible. The floating-point format permits the manipulation of fractions. On 12-bit machines, the typical floating-point format sets aside one word for the exponent and two words (24 bits) for the mantissa. The numbers are represented as logarithms to the base 2. Floating-point routines, without special hardware to facilitate their use, require much more time than fixed-point routines. On the PDP-8 for example, floating-point division and multiplication require about 3 msec. The accessory hardware may cut this time in half. When several experiments are being handled simultaneously, with complex calculations initiated for each response, it is apparent that off-line processing is a better solution than undertaking a very complex programming project to accommodate all of these demands.

PERMANENT DATA STORAGE

Whatever the experimenter decides about the extent of on-line processing, there still remains the question of how, what kind of, and how much data to keep in a permanent file. Our point of view is that the experimenter should preserve as much as he can of the information necessary for later analyses, should additional questions seem relevant or new analytical techniques be developed. We stressed this point earlier but it must be stressed again, because one should not, in a concern for efficient on-line control, neglect the role of analytical procedures. Devising elaborate schedules of reinforcement without being able to examine the resulting data in fine detail, including its sequential aspects, may make these procedures largely irrelevant. The grosser the data, the grosser the conclusions.

Given a requirement for convenient, efficient long-term storage, one must then decide on a medium. Paper tape is bulky, difficult to access, and slow. Disc systems do not afford sufficient storage capacity. The most reasonable solution is magnetic tape. LINC tapes offer special advantages in this respect. Their operation, which is directly under program control through simple instructions, allows the experimenter to include all the information he requires of a single response and save it for later processing. Industry compatible (IBM format) tape decks have the advantage that the data are more accessible to the large computers available in computer centers, but they are more awkward to use, both mechanically and from the standpoint of programming, especially if the analyses are conducted on the laboratory computer itself. Many manufacturers now are also offering small cassette-type recorders, in which data are recorded bit-by-bit in serial fashion. Although the speeds do not match those attainable by LINC tape, or IBM format transports, they still are faster than high-speed paper tape and much more compact and accessible. On the average, they seem to cost no more than the high-speed paper tape punch and reader. It is also useful to point out the great advantage of buffered tapes. The classic LINC pauses while tape transfers are being made. The Spear MicroLINC and the PDP-12 can make these transfers without interfering with the running of the program. When input and output events are occurring at rather high rates, this can be an important or even a crucial convenience.

Permanent storage also requires that some decisions be made about format. First, the experimenter must decide how many bits to preserve if, say, he is interested in inter-event times. Second, he must decide how much of the ancillary information is necessary. We typically use a two-word format (24 bits) to carry the information in a single IRT when we are content with 40-msec resolution. Eleven bits of one 12-bit word are used to represent the IRT. The leftmost bit, the sign bit, is set to 1 if the response has been reinforced. Even with only 11 bits, a 25-Hz clock can provide inter-event times up to 82 sec. The second word of the two-word format is used to represent animal number, box number, response device, schedule, etc. Thus, a typical set of code words might have the following format:

Word One: Bit 0 = reinforcement
             Bit 1–11 = interresponse time

Word Two: Bit 0—2 = Chamber number
            Bit 3—5 = Lever number
            Bit 6—8 = Schedule component
            Bit 9—11 = Animal number

If this is inadequate, a three-word format could be used, with 23 bits representing time. This would give 1-msec resolution up to about 280 min. As long as permanent storage is conveniently addressed, the amount of data recorded for one response event can be quite large without producing any undue convenience.

ON-LINE INTERVENTION AND PARAMETER FLEXIBILITY

The less an experimenter tries to do with a single program the easier it is to write. Most on-line programs in our laboratory evolve by accretion. A basic program structure is typically developed first. Once the basic structure has proven adequate, it is made into a more elaborate system, sometimes by design from the beginning, sometimes because new tasks for the computer or inadequacies in the basic treatment have to be dealt with. But before beginning to write code, the experimenter must decide how many options, how many parameters, and how much flexibility he will build into the program. Suppose, to take a simple example, the experimenter writes a program to control a fixed-ratio reinforcement schedule so that the subject is presented with the reinforcing stimulus after every N responses. In writing the program, the experimenter has to decide how easy to make it to change the required number of responses. The simplest solution is not to bother, and assume that simple console manipulations before the session begins will suffice. Another possibility is to set it at the beginning of the session by using a question and answer display via the oscilloscope and keyboard. This value, as described later, can be saved and inserted into the program. A more complicated solution makes it possible for the experimenter to change the ratio during the experiment. If the experiment is not to be interfered with, provision has to be made to accept an external input and put it in its proper location. On the LINC, a simple solution would be to employ one of the six sense switches on the console. They are directly addressed by instructions of the following kind:

"Skip the next instruction if sense switch N is up."

The program might specify that if the particular sense switch were up, the number appearing in the left bank of 12-bit switches would be inserted into the register that sets the fixed-ratio requirement. With more complex programming, the entry could be made via the keyboard.

The essential point is that the amount of flexibility in the program must be traded off against the ease of programming. The more provision one makes for alterations, the greater the number of programming problems to be solved, the longer the program, and the more difficult it is to perfect.

Table 3

Memory Location	Instruction Mnemonic	Effect
1	SETi 16	Put −30 decimal (= −36 octal) in 16
2	−36	
3	OPR 1	Reset response flip flop
4	SXL 1	Is response flip flop set?
5	JMP 4	No. Return to location 4
6	XSKi 16	Yes. Increment 16 and skip location 7 if 16=0
7	JMP 3	Not zero. Return to location 3
8	OPR 2	Fixed ratio fulfilled. Operate feeder
9	JMP 1	Return to location 1
.		
.		
.		
16	−36	Peck counter

ACTUAL PROGRAM CODING

If all one demands of a program is the equivalent of a few relays, counters and timers, the necessary programming is rather simple. Suppose, for example, that the program called for reinforcing the pecks of a pigeon on a fixed-ratio 30 reinforcement schedule. Table 3 shows how this would be done with LINC instruction code. The first instruction, a two-word instruction, puts the fixed ratio, as a negative number, in a designated register (16). The next instruction, located in memory location 3, issues a pulse that turns off the response flip-flop. At location 4, input line 1 is examined to see whether or not a response has set the flip-flop connected to it. This line is continually searched by the set of instructions in locations 4 and 5 until a response is made. The next instruction has two functions. First, it increments location 16. The first response, for example, will change 16 from −30 to −29. If the incrementing operation has changed location 16 to 0, which means that the fixed-ratio requirement is fulfilled, the program will skip to location 8, at which point a pulse is produced to operate the feeder. If the fixed-ratio requirement has not been fulfilled, the response flip-flop is reset and the searching procedure begins again.

With a few simple instructions, then, one can duplicate a resettable counter, the main program module that would be used in conventional relay or solid-state programming. But suppose the situation is somewhat more complex from the standpoint of recording. For example, suppose that counters are set aside to record total number of responses, and total number of reinforcements. These simply require two more registers in memory to be set aside as counters. Suppose, in addition, that the experimenter wishes to compile an interval histogram on-line. This is a relatively simple problem also. As in Table 2, a timing register is incremented on each clock pulse. Suppose 250 locations are set aside in memory for the histogram, from, say, location 1000 to 1249, and that the resolution required is 100 msec. The timing register would then be incremented 10 times per second. When the timing register reached a count of 250 (the first pulse marking time zero) no further increments would occur. All IRTs longer than 25 sec would fall into the last bin. It is then a simple matter to take the IRT, add 1000 to it, and use this number as the address of the register to be incremented. All of these additional refinements cost very little in time. Depending upon the machine, they may add between, say, 30 and 100 μsec.

But again, the computer is capable of a great deal more, even with a simple fixed-ratio reinforcement schedule, because of its ability to store data easily recaptured for later processing. As an example of the refinements possible, we will use an experiment conducted by C. T. Gott, whose aim was to conduct a microanalysis of the transition from continuous to fixed-ratio reinforcement (Gott, 1969). Gott developed a programming system that would allow him to control and record from three pigeon chambers at once, with each chamber capable of being controlled independently. In our early experiments, even when more than one chamber was connected to the LINC for the same experiment, programs were written in a rather linear fashion. By this, we mean that programming elegance and compactness were sacrificed for speed and for ease of debugging. For example, with three chambers connected to the LINC for a single experiment, each with one lever, programs simply scanned the inputs in sequence, then went to appropriate subroutines if the response has been made. For some experiments this was sufficient because all animals were on the same schedule at the same time. For Gott's purposes, an approach closer to the concept of time sharing was necessary. His solution was to set aside a parameter "field" for each subject or for each input. All the basic housekeeping chores for the program were regulated by the main program. Individual subject fields were transferred into place in sequence, and serviced by the master control routine.

The advantage of such an approach lies in the flexibility it affords in individualized treatment. With the central program assuming all housekeeping duties, the sequence and parameters of schedule components are designated by a series of control words in each field. Table 4 is a section of a LINC program showing the elements of such a field. Gott describes it as follows (Gott, 1969, p. 34–35):

> In the Box-Check Subroutine, each schedule of reinforcement is treated as a sequence of schedule components, and represented by a corresponding sequence of program subsegments. The number and nature of subsegments in the sequence depends on the schedule to be implemented. Each schedule component in turn becomes the current one. The corresponding program subsegment is executed on each service cycle (approximately every 40 msec) until its programmed criteria have been satisfied. Control then passes to the next member of the sequence. The successive satisfaction of all components which are relevant to a given schedule of reinforcement constitutes a "schedule cycle." Three independent schedule cycles, one for each subject, are in progress at any given time.
>
> Nine program segments are provided in the control structure of the BCS. Three of these segments are standard, permanent features of the control program, while the remaining six are available for construction of any schedule components desired by the individual experimenter. The constant segments are those for "initial time-out"

Table 4. Arrangement of Control Words in a Field

LOCATION	OCTAL	TAG	CONTENTS
			(WORKING FIELD
44	1000	#1A	1000 (BIRD CODE
45	0001	#1B	1 (BRANCHER
46	0000	#1C	(BRANCH CONTROL
			(CONTROL PARAMETERS
47	0000	#1P	(PAUSE
50	0000	#1S	(S1
51	0000	#2S	(S2
52	0000	#3S	(S3
53	0000	#4S	(S4
54	0000	#5S	(S5
55	0000	#6S	(S6
56	0000	#1F	(FEED
57	0000	#1O	(TIMEOUT
60	0000	#1D	(DURATION
61	0000	#1N	(REINF NO
			(COUNTERS
62	0000	#2P	(PAUSE RESP
63	0000	#2T	(TOTAL S+ RESP
64	0000	#2O	(TOUT RESP
65	0000	#2N	(NO REINF
66	0000	#2D	(ELAPSED TIME
67	0000	#2F	(FEEDTIME
70	0000	#2B	(HOLDTIME
71	0000	#2R	(SCHEDULE WORD
72	0000	#2C	(1-SEC COUNTER
73	0000	#2E	(1-MIN COUNTER
74	0000	#3F	(PAUSE,FEED,TO COUNTER
75	0000	#3U	(IRT2
76	0000	#3T	(IRT1
			(3T IS ENDMARK FOR NEXTBIRD
			(HOMEFIELD 1
			100
100	2000	#2A	2000
101	0001		1
102	0000		0
			(HOMEFIELD 2
			134
134	3000	#3A	3000
135	0001		1
136	0000		0

(PAUSE), "feeder cycle" (FEED), and "time-out after reinforcement" (TO). The construction of the other components is simplified by virtue of modular provisions for response checking, recording of IRTs, *etc*. Each of these functions is programmed as a subroutine; the function is performed whenever the subroutine is entered by means of a single JMP (Jump) instruction. Since all timing and housekeeping functions are performed elsewhere in the control program, the individual schedule components usually may be succinct combinations of appropriate subroutine jumps, plus short programming segments to specify the distinctive characteristics of the respective component.

The greatest flexibility ensues when each schedule component is written in a general way, with unspecified parameter values. The JUNEBIRD system was designed with this in mind, and provision was made to supply the needed parameter values to the various schedule segments. For each subject one control field is provided in core storage. For each schedule component, one word in this control field is reserved for a parameter value, and a second word is reserved for a schedule counter. Parameter values are initialized before each run, as described above in the discussion of "Identification Records."

The information required by the control words in the system is supplied through the keyboard in response to oscilloscope displays. This is a good example of one of the less-obvious advantages of the laboratory computer. It eases considerably the task of keeping track of the mass of information the experimenter has to record along with his actual data. Among these are, animal number, weight, experiment number, schedule, schedule sequence if a multiple schedule, time, drug and drug dose if relevant, session duration, *etc*. With the LINC, such information can easily be preserved on magnetic tape by employing the "Question and Answer" display.

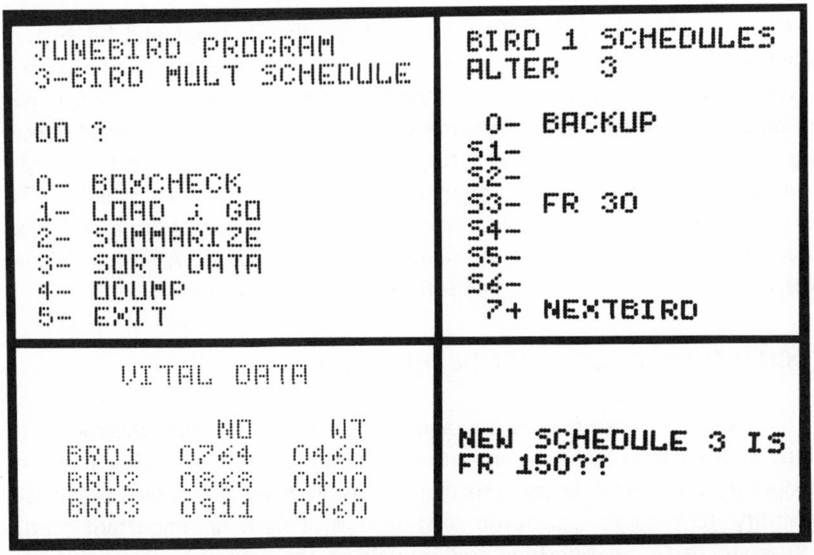

Figure 1. Four LINC oscilloscope displays that are part of a programming system that controls three pigeon chambers simultaneously. The top left panel asks the experimenter to specify an operation. The top right panel displays the current schedule components. If any are to be altered, the display at bottom right appears. The bottom left display requests bird numbers and body weights; these data are written on tape. (From Gott, 1969).

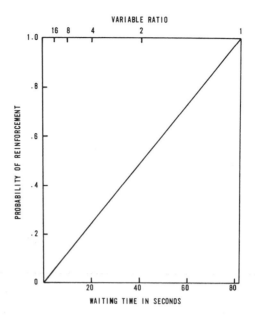

Figure 2. Schematic representation of a linear SRW schedule with maximum probability of reinforcement (P = 1.0) at 82 sec. Note that at the top of the figure, equivalent variable-ratio values are given.

Figure 1 shows the first four frames from the set employed by Gott to collect and store the relevant data. In the first display, the experimenter is asked to collect one of six options via the keyboard. The response to this display goes into an answer field and relevant parameters are used later by the master control program. The second frame asks for the bird weights. The third display is presented three separate times, one for each bird, to show the schedule. The fourth permits schedule alteration. Succeeding displays asks for drugs and doses, conditions for termination of the experiment, and so on. All such data are preserved on tape in conjunction with the experimental session.

STOCHASTIC REINFORCEMENT SCHEDULES

Gott's system is an excellent example of the flexibility and convenience the computer affords in studying conventional reinforcement schedules. From the standpoint of a control device, a further extension of the computer's potential is its ability to program stochastic relationships. This is an important feature because stochastic relationships predominate in the natural environment. One simplified stochastic reinforcement schedule that has engaged our interest is the SRW schedule (Stochastic Reinforcement of Waiting), which is diagrammed in Figure 2. The following relationship is illustrated here: the longer the IRT, the higher the probability of reinforcement. Such a function is revealing because it makes contact with several other reinforcement schedules. One can conceive of it as a stochastic DRL schedule if the conventional DRL schedule is pictured as an instantaneous change in probability of reinforcement from 0 to 1 at a specified IRT. It also corresponds to a variable-interval schedule in that the longer the IRT, the higher the probability of reinforcement. Note also, along the top of Figure 2, the correspondence with a variable-ratio schedule. IRTs of 20 sec are reinforced on the average of one time in four, representing a variable ratio of 4.

Programming the linear relationship in Figure 2 is relatively simple. The random number is generated by a subroutine using iterative multiplication of the form

$$X_r = KX_{r-1}$$

where K equals 8t-3 and t is a small odd number (Hamming, 1962). On a 12-bit machine, this algorithm generates a set of numbers between 0 and 2047 before repeating. The sequence then, is pseudo-random, as are all deterministic subroutine-generated numbers. Although this scheme gives a rectangular distribution, which is useful, it possesses the defect of peculiar serial dependencies that may cause a slight departure from the parameters described by the experimenter. Such a fault can be attenuated by generating a new random number on each clock pulse, so that many numbers typically are generated and discarded between responses. Various other schemes exist for generating random numbers distributed according to various models. All such subroutine generated numbers are pseudo-random or quasi-random but possess two advantages. First, the sequence is reproducible, making it possible to reconstruct a condition without also storing the sequence of random numbers. Second, a pseudo-random distribution may make it easier to specify or control the contingencies.

For the linear function shown in Figure 2, the program generated a random number whenever a response occurred. Since both the IRT and the random number were limited to values between 0 and 2047, we merely set the criterion so that if the IRT exceeded the random number, reinforcement was programmed. During experiments that required a limit to be set at 40 sec, which meant doubling the slope of the function, the random number was divided by two simply by shifting it one bit position to the right.

Suppose, however, that instead of the linear function, we require something more complex. Figure 3 is a function that relates the uniformity of IRTs to the probability of reinforcement, a function that governs the Autoregressive reinforcement schedule (Weiss and Laties, 1965). Each time a response is made and terminates an IRT, that IRT is compared to the preceding IRT. The quotient of the larger over the smaller is then computed. As shown in Figure 3, the closer the quotient lies to 1.0, the higher the probability of reinforcement. This function is exponential. Instead of trying to produce a random-number distribution with an exponential form, the following solution was adopted. The

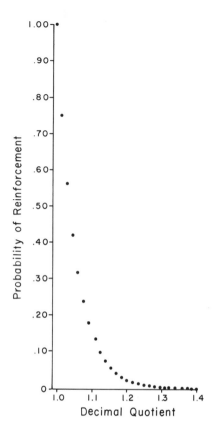

Figure 3. Schematic representation of the ARG reinforcement schedule. The probability of reinforcement for any response is a function of the similarity of the just-ended IRT and the IRT directly preceding it.

same kind of random-number generator used for the SRW schedule was employed. The function relating probability to quotient was stored as a table in the memory. When a quotient was computed, it was used to pick a location from the table. Since the random-number generator produces numbers between 0 and 2047, the location in memory corresponding to a reinforcement probability of 0.5 contained the entry 1024. If reinforcement occurs only when the random number is less than the number in the table, quotients that extract the table entry 1024 will be reinforced half the time.

ADJUSTING SCHEDULES

As indicated earlier, it is possible to provide for on-line changes by the experimenter in reinforcement schedule parameters. There is no reason why this

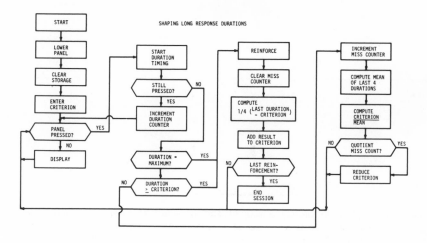

Figure 4. Flow chart of the SHAPE program used with dogs. The response duration specified as criterion must be exceeded for reinforcement to occur. At that point, the criterion is raised by one-quarter of the difference between the current criterion and the duration that exceeded it. The criterion is lowered as a function of the duration of the misses. The closer these are to the criterion, the fewer misses required to reduce the criterion.

can not be an internal feature of the program. That is to say, some aspect of the behavior itself can be employed to change certain parameters. Such an example is given in Figure 4, which is a flow chart of a program designed to control response duration. The response, studied with dogs, consists of pressing a panel with the snout. Response duration had shown itself to be sensitive to certain drug effects (Weiss and Laties, 1963). In an attempt to increase sensitivity to drugs, we decided to use the computer to shape long-duration responding. As shown on the flow chart, a session begins with an arbitrary minimum duration criterion. When the dog exceeds the criterion it receives dry dog food reinforcers and the criterion is raised. Note that this is a shaping process, a process of gradual approximation. If the criterion were to be raised too swiftly, we run the risk of losing control over the response by producing extinction. The criterion is therefore raised only by a fraction of the difference between the old criterion and the response that exceeds it. We now employ a value of 0.25. With such a value, responding does not extinguish. Provision is also made for reducing the criterion. This is a more complicated problem because we do not wish to reinforce short-duration responses. Therefore, the decision is made on the following basis. The program examines the last four response durations. If they are very short, then a long string must be emitted before the criterion is lowered. If, however, they fall just below the criterion, the latter will be decreased in order not to lose the behavior further.

During a session, the LINC oscilloscope display, as shown in Figure 5, indicates the progress of the experiment. The left side of the oscilloscope shows

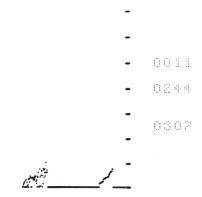

Figure 5. Oscilloscope display during SHAPE program. The leftmost group of points represents successive response durations. The rightmost group represents the corresponding criteria. Scale markers represent 10-sec intervals. From top to bottom, the displayed numbers represent (as octal numbers) the number of remaining reinforcements, the duration of the last response (as number of 40-msec units) and the current criterion.

the successive response durations as heights. The function on the right shows the criterion associated with each response. The numbers represent, from top to bottom, the number of reinforcements still available, the most recent response duration, and the current criterion. This arrangement of contingencies is rather sensitive to chemical manipulation (Weiss, 1970).

Once such a flow chart is devised, and certain logical decisions are made, writing the machine code for such a program is mostly a matter of following a few well-defined sequences. For arithmetic computations, several shortcuts were taken. The mean of the last four durations is computed by fixed-point routines. Since the time resolution in this experiment is 40 msec, the 11 bits of the word used for recording duration encompass a range from 0 to 82 sec. With long-duration responses, the accumulator register, where the addition is performed, might overflow; but, since we do not require extreme precision in these calculations, we do the division beforehand. Each response duration is shifted right by two bit positions. Since each shift means a division by two, each duration is then divided by four. These scaled numbers are then simply added to give the mean. The amount of precision lost, for our purposes, is negligible, but the gain in convenience and speed is not. The ease of such manipulations leads us, in situations like this one, to choose powers of 2 when we must decide on, say, how many responses to use in calculating some function based on a trend.

ANALOG-CODED RESPONSES

One aspect of computer technology that we believe will assume a larger role in operant research is its ability to handle information that originally was in analog form; that is, a continuously varying electrical signal. For instance, a

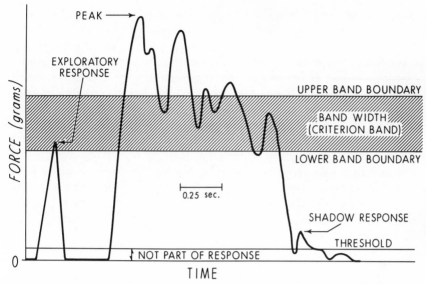

Figure 6. Diagram of typical response that might be made by monkey required to emit response force between specified limits for specified minimum length of time (from Koepke, 1970.).

growing number of publications (Notterman and Mintz, 1965; Falk, 1969) attest to the many interesting facets of variations in response force. Hefferline's pioneering studies (*e.g.*, 1956) exemplify how fine a degree of control can be exercised by operant procedures provided the instrumentation is available for detecting, as Hefferline did, minute changes in muscular contraction. The digital computer equipped with an analog-digital converter, so that the continuously varying electrical signal can be changed into a numerical quantity, makes the logical instrumentation much easier and simpler.

As an example, we will choose a project in this laboratory by U. C. Koepke (Koepke, 1970) designed to measure discriminative motor control in squirrel monkeys. The monkeys were seated in a restraining chair and trained to extend a hand to touch a lucite plate attached to a strain gauge. The output of the strain gauge was amplified by a polygraph whose output, in turn, went to the analog-digital converter attached to the PDP-8. Our aim in this experiment was to train monkeys to emit responses with a force between prescribed limits for a minimum duration. A schematic response is shown in Figure 6. Without a computer, the experimenter would need instrumentation to record when a response was above threshold, when it had entered the criterion band, and how long it remained in the criterion band. Even so, a great deal of information would be lacking. Since the numerical quantities from an analog-digital converter can be treated as any other number, programming can take the place of a tremendous amount of instrumentation. Thus, a program can decide, first, whether or not the input is above threshold, that is, whether a response is in progress. It can then decide whether the value is below, within, or above the criterion band. It can set limits to the criterion band; it can decide whether or not the response has been within the band for a long enough period of time. It can decide whether or not a response ought to count in the force computations by setting a certain minimum duration. It can calculate the force peaks, and the number of crosses into and out of the criterion band. In addition, if a convenient permanent storage medium is available, these and other features of the response can be kept for further reference and analysis.

Analog signal processing has another advantage. By using appropriate response devices, shaping can become an easier process. When a rat, say, is introduced to a new chamber containing microswitch levers, it often makes tentative movements, briefly touching the lever, but not depressing it enough to close the circuit. The animal can be shaped to give a firm, definite response by gradually raising the force criterion for reinforcement. Such a criterion can even be put on an adjusting or titration schedule so that the experimenter's decisions about when to change the criterion are made beforehand and incorporated into the program.

As computers become more and more common in behavior laboratories we will find that the variations in response topography typically disregarded, such as location, duration, force, displacement, *etc.*, will be better appreciated. These dimensions of operant control are not irrelevant to our understanding of behavior. It makes a lot of difference to our prescriptions for modifying behavior if a given class of response events is relatively uniform or relatively variable, and over how many measurable dimensions the uniformity or variability extends. Moreover, certain applications will have a fundamental impact on our understanding of other kinds of processes. For example, our studies with monkeys are concerned with motor impairment produced by exposure to mercury. Falk's experiments (1969) analyzed the effects of certain drugs on motor control. Evarts (1968) described a very important application— recording from single pyramidal tract cells in monkeys during trained movements of a response device with specified force and distance parameters.

THE ANALYSIS OF OPERANT BEHAVIOR

The conventional reinforcement schedules offer few problems in programming with traditional relay equipment mainly because they were framed in relay terms. Their analysis, however, presents formidable problems. Numerous features of behavior, even on simple reinforcement schedules, can not be captured except by recording the behavior in fine temporal detail and by preserving sequential order. And much of the necessary analysis, if the experimenter is going to grapple with the data on its own terms, has to be descriptive or semiquantitative. For these purposes, the large machine, with its intervening operating systems and typical geographical remoteness, may be far from the optimal solution. A laboratory computer under the scientist's own control that is equipped with an easily accessible permanent storage medium offers much more convenience and flexibility. With the addition of an oscilloscope and a plotter, it should meet all of the experimenter's needs except for massive volumes of complex numerical analyses.

EXAMINATION OF INDIVIDUAL RESPONSES

Skinner's *The Behavior of Organisms* (1938) and Ferster and Skinner's *Schedules of Reinforcement* (1957) are two excellent examples of how perceptive behavior scientists are able to extract immense amounts of information simply from an examination of cumulative records. For many schedules of

Table 5. General Display Program

Analog input	Function
Knob 0	Shift display along X-axis
Knob 1	Shift display along Y-axis

LINC Keyboard input	
0	Clear sign (reinforcement) bit
DEL	Delete (set to 0) IRT > ???
i	Remove IRT > ???, pack remainder
−	Set minimum to ???
+	Set maximum to ???
B	Draw bar graph
C	Clip data with respect to mean
D	Differentiate
E+	Compute successive differences (absolute)
E−	Compute successive differences (preserve sign)
F	Three-term moving average
G	Read in programming system
H	Seven-term moving average
I	Integrate
K	Write data
L	IRT /.5
M	Display data with mean
N	Cancel mean
O	Restore original data
P	Change polarity of data
R	Read data
S	IRT/2
VF	Deviations from three-term filter
VH	Deviations from seven-term filter
W	Deviations from mean
X	Expand X axis
Y	Compress X axis
Z	Random shuffle of order

reinforcement, this kind of analysis can be carried one step further by examining the features of individual IRTs. With an oscilloscope display and the easily addressable LINC tapes, an investigator can scan an experimental session response by response, at the same time producing transformations of the data that enhance one or another feature. One of the most useful programs in our library, called GENDIS, was developed by Louis Siegel from some basic routines originally written by A. J. Hance. Table 5 is a list of options incorporated into the program. The experimenter can call in specified blocks from the tape, subject the data to various transformations, recapture the original data, compute means, write the transformed data, expand and contract the display, and so on. Figure 7 is a panel showing various options in operation. The data come from monkeys controlled by a DRL 20-sec reinforcement schedule. Panel A shows 256 successive IRTs from Session 8 as a bar graph. Panel B shows the same data transformed by a smoothing function that consists of subjecting the points to a moving average of the form

$$X_i = X_{i-3} + X_{i-2} + X_{i-1} + 2X_i + X_{i+1} + X_{i+2} + X_{i+3}/8$$

Such a smoothing operation is equivalent to filtering with a low-pass filter. Removing some of the sharp reversals in the display makes it easier to grasp some of the long-term trends. A three-term filter is also incorporated into the program. Panel C shows a display of the mean IRT superimposed on the string of IRTs. Panel D shows one way of examining serial effects. This is an option that plots IRTs simply according to whether they lie above or below the mean. Alternating trains above and below the mean are evidence of a long wavelength drift.

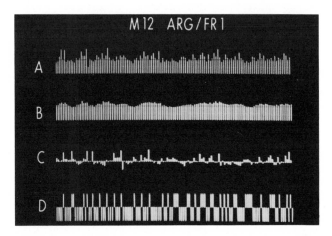

Figure 7. LINC oscilloscope display of various options available for GENDIS program. A, 128 successive IRTs represented as height. B, successive IRTs after smoothing by seven-term moving average in order to make fluctuations more visible. C, mean IRT imposed on display. D, IRTs represented simply as above or below mean in order to show drift.

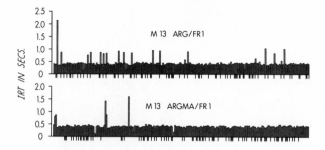

Figure 8. Plot of individual successive IRTs (top) from the regular ARG schedule and from the modified version that compared the current IRT to the mean of the last eight (bottom).

All of the different options are under keyboard control. To smooth the data by the seven-term moving average, for example, requires only that the experimenter depress "H" on the keyboard. The new function appears on the oscilloscope screen promptly. Parameters for the display can be obtained through the use of knobs controlling potentiometers connected to the analog-digital inputs. By varying these, the observer can scan through the data, looking for analytical possibilities, or arrange for more convenient positioning of the display.

Permanent records of response-by-response changes can also be plotted on the Calcomp digital plotter, using the data accessed by GENDIS, transformed by it, or by a number of self-contained options. Figure 8 shows successive individual IRTs from two versions of the ARG schedule. The top display is a sample from the regular ARG. The bottom display is based on a schedule modification that compared the current IRT to the mean of the last eight IRTs, rather than the just preceding one, in order to reduce pausing.

LONG-TERM TRENDS

Sometimes it is easier to grasp the effects of a particular experimental variable by looking not only at the unit events, but also at gradual changes over long periods of time. Many of these can be computed quite simply and plotted. For some of our data, for example, we have found it useful to plot mean IRT/100 responses and mean reinforced IRT/100 responses. Figure 9 depicts the development of performance on a stochastic reinforcement schedule with a function that rose in Gaussian fashion from a reinforcement probability of zero at short IRTs to a maximum of 1.0 at 40 sec. The function therefore was much like a conventional DRL 40-sec. The left side of Figure 9 shows that mean IRT rose with exposure to the schedule contingencies, as expected. The mean reinforced IRT provides an additional interpretation of the data. Early in the subject's exposure, most reinforced IRTs came from long pauses interspersed

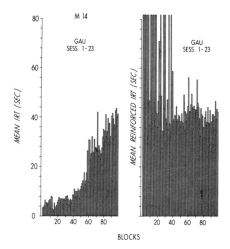

Figure 9. Comparison of mean IRTs, mean reinforced IRTs, and mean post-reinforcement intervals for 30 sessions on a Linear SRW 40 schedule after transition from a SRW schedule that differentially reinforced long IRTs.

with periods of high response rates. As the contingencies gained control, a more uniform distribution of IRTs appeared that had the effect of increasing mean IRT but decreasing the mean reinforced IRT because the long pauses were absent.

By permitting an experimenter to view in one display a rather large section of an experimental history, three-dimensional plots play a similar role. Figure 10 describes the acquisition and maintenance of DRL 20-sec performance. Each tracing is a frequency histogram for a single session. Successive sessions run along the X axis, frequency is represented on the Y axis, and IRT duration is represented on the Z axis. Several stages are apparent in the development of DRL performance. The control exercised by the schedule first appears as a small peak near the minimum IRT required for reinforcement. With continued

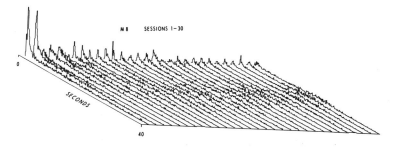

Figure 10. Isometric plot showing development of DRL 20-sec performance in one monkey over 30 sessions. IRT length is represented on the Z axis, frequency on the Y axis, and successive sessions on the X axis. (From Weiss, 1970).

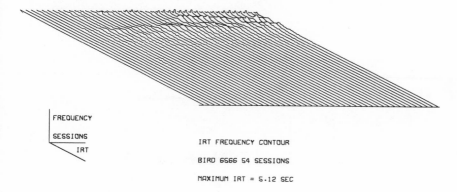

FREQUENCY

SESSIONS

IRT

IRT FREQUENCY CONTOUR

BIRD 6566 54 SESSIONS

MAXIMUM IRT = 5.12 SEC

Figure 11. Isometric plot showing development of multimodal IRT distribution in pigeon exposed to VI 2.5-min schedule for 54 sessions after switch from CRF (courtesy of Ronald W. Wood).

practice, the bimodality becomes more and more prominent and eventually the second peak dominates the distribution.

Figure 11 is another demonstration of how such a plot can reveal long-term trends. These tracings are based on pigeons subjected to a VI 2.5-min reinforcement schedule. The most interesting aspect of this plot is its multi-modal character, and how different peaks arise and fade with time. It is important to note that the bulk of these IRTs are shorter than 2 sec; recording

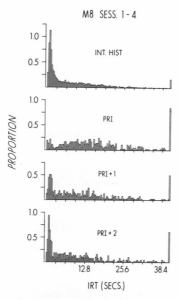

M8 SESS. 1 - 4

INT. HIST

PRI

PRI + 1

PRI + 2

PROPORTION

IRT (SECS.)

Figure 12. Performance of monkey (also shown in Figure 10) during first four sessions on DRL 20-sec. The topmost histogram is a conventional interval histogram. The succeeding histograms represent the distributions of the post-reinforcement intervals and succeeding IRTs. (From Weiss, 1970).

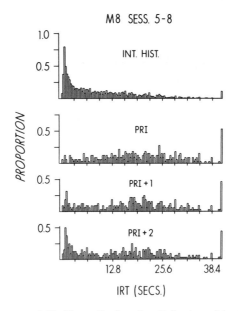

Figure 13. Performance on DRL 20-sec, Sessions 5 to 8. See legend for Figure 12.

IRTs in categories that wide would have missed completely the character of the performance. Although response rate may remain nearly the same throughout this entire process, it is apparent from charts such as Figure 11 that a VI baseline is constant only in the grossest sense.

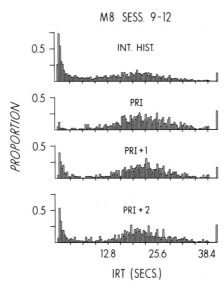

Figure 14. Performance on DRL 20-sec, Sessions 9 to 12. See legend for Figure 12.

DISTRIBUTIONS AND TRANSFORMATIONS

More and more operant experimenters are presenting IRT distributions as indices of performance. This is a relevant behavioral dimension because the distribution is so sensitive to reinforcement variables. For certain schedules, the conventional interval distribution of all responses can profitably be broken down into a number of components. An example again comes from the development of performance on the DRL schedule. Figure 12 shows histograms compiled from the first four sessions on DRL 20-sec for Monkey M8. The four distributions are based on all intervals, the post-reinforcement intervals, the IRTs following the post-reinforcement interval, and the next IRTs. Figures 13 and 14 present equivalent distributions for Session 5 to 8 and 9 to 12, respectively. These distributions suggest that the post-reinforcement interval is the key to DRL performance. During the first four sessions, the distribution of the post-reinforcement interval is quite different from that of the histogram of all IRTs. Even PRI + 1 is different. A reinforcement tends to lengthen the next IRT even when the consummatory response, as in our case, occupies a negligible amount of time. Given that it is longer, it is more likely to be reinforced. Such an effect will tend to propagate into the next IRT. This is one reason for the trains of reinforced IRTs in DRL performance remarked on by several observers. In Sessions 5 to 8, this is even more apparent because the PRI and PRI + 1 distributions indicate the schedule to be coming into firm control. One would not reach such a conclusion simply by examining the interval histogram. In

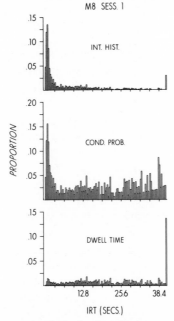

Figure 15. Comparison of the interval distribution, the corresponding conditional probability distribution (or IRTs/OP), and the corresponding dwelling time distribution for Session 1 on DRL 20-sec.

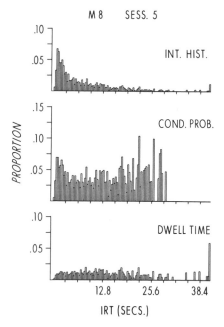

Figure 16. Histograms representing performance on DRL 20-sec, Session 5. See legend for Figure 15.

Sessions 9 to 12, the discrimination is already well advanced, and the peak around the minimum reinforced IRT of 20 sec is quite clear.

Some further aspects of how DRL performance develops are shown in Figures 15, 16, and 17. These show certain characteristics of performance in Sessions 1, 5, and 10 for the same monkey. In addition to the interval histogram, these figures contain a distribution labelled "Conditional Probability," which is equivalent to Anger's IRTs/OPS (Anger, 1956). Such a distribution shows the probability of a response in time bin *i* provided that the pause since the last response has extended to time bin *i-1*. The distribution at the bottom represents a transformation we call the Dwelling Time. It represents the proportion of the session occupied by IRTs of various length. Ten 6-sec IRTs would occupy 1/60 of a one-hour session. Sixty 1-sec IRTs would occupy the same proportion of the session.

These additional transformations illuminate some further aspects of DRL schedule control. During Session 1, a tall peak dominates the conditional probability distribution, indicating that we are not dealing with a random process; the latter would give a constant conditional probability. By Session 5, the short IRTs no longer predominate. The conditional probability distribution now is relatively flat, as is the dwelling time distribution, showing little precise control by the schedule contingencies. By Session 10, however, marked changes are apparent in both the conditional probability and dwelling time distributions; these are reflected less clearly in the interval histogram. The conditional

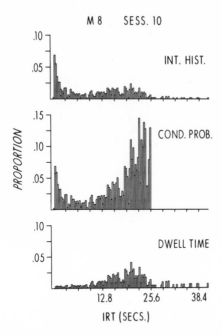

Figure 17. Histograms representing performance on DRL 20-sec, Session 10. See legend for Figure 15.

probability distribution indicates a steeply rising probability beyond 6 sec. The grouping in the dwelling time distribution indicates that a large part of the session is occupied by IRTs long enough to result in reinforcement.

These graphs were produced by a set of routines containing a number of different plotting options. Like most of our programs, they evolved from a relatively circumscribed aim and then expanded as we changed and expanded our questions. To use them now, the experimenter loads his program tape and his data tape on the LINC or the PDP-12, each of which is equipped with two transports. Once the appropriate set of routines are in memory, the experimenter specifies the tape blocks he wishes processed, then depresses a key on the keyboard, which corresponds to the desired option. Many of these options, we might add, have been modified several times for different purposes. Some of them were written to deal with rather specific kinds of data, others did not include what turned out to be important ancillary parameters. They are good examples of the evolutionary development that programs subjected to constant scrutiny by investigators often undergo.

SERIAL PHENOMENA

Many of the effects produced by different contingencies of reinforcement are expressed in behavior as changes in serial patterning or serial dependency. An excellent example comes from Gott's work on the development of fixed-ratio

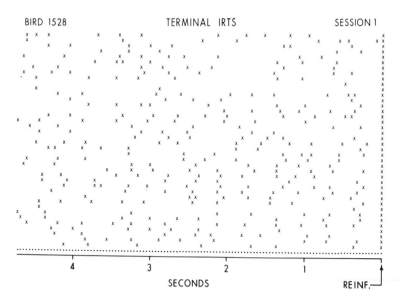

Figure 18. Successive responses on FR 30 plotted backwards from reinforcement. Forty ratios were completed in a session. From right to left, each x represents the temporal position of a response. Each dot represents 40 msec. The end of the first ratio is at the top of the chart, the end of the fortieth at the bottom. Figure 11 is from the first session on FR 30 after the transition from CRF. (From Gott, 1969).

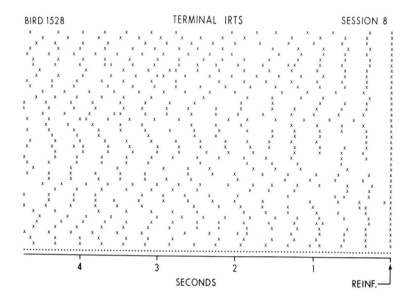

Figure 19. Terminal IRTs aligned on reinforcement for Session 8, FR 30. Compared to Session 1, Figure 18, these show much more regularity in spacing. (From Gott, 1969).

performance. By examining the individual IRTs within the early fixed ratios after the transition from continuous reinforcement, it became apparent that continued exposure to the schedule produced not simply a shortening of IRTs (in fact sometimes a lengthening of the mean took place), but a change in their uniformity. Although this might be reflected obliquely in an ordinary interval histogram, it seemed necessary to examine the uniformity in a more direct way. For this, a measure was developed called, "Terminal Response Convergence." Gott used the printer on the IBM 360/44 for the plots shown in Figures 18 and 19. Figure 18 is for Session 1 on FR 30 and Figure 19 is for Session 8. The last response of the ratio, the reinforced response, is shown to the far right as an X. Forty separate lines of Xs represent the 40 ratios within a session. Counting back from reinforcement, the dots along the abscissa represent clock

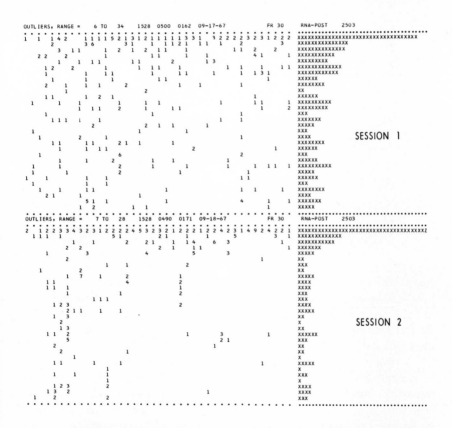

Figure 20. Distribution of pauses more than 1 sec long ("outliers") with ratios during Sessions 1 and 2 on FR 30. Columns left to right represent successive ratios (40 per session). Rows represent ordinal position within the ratio, with the post-reinforcement interval at the top and the thirtieth at the bottom. Numerals appear in positions where outliers occurred, the duration in seconds being represented by the numeral ($Z \equiv 10$). The right hand section of the chart sums the outliers by ordinal position, each x representing a pause. (From Gott, 1969).

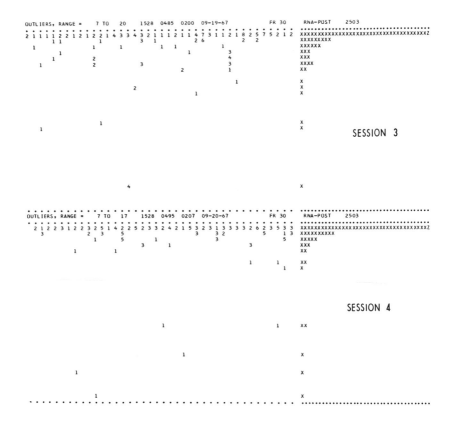

Figure 21. Distribution of outliers during Sessions 3 and 4 on FR 30. (See legend for Figure 20.) Note the progressive decrease in incidence of outliers from Sessions 1 to 4. (From Gott, 1969).

pulses separated by 40-msec intervals. Thus, we scan backwards for approximately 5 sec before reinforcement. An X appears in each clock pulse position in which a response was recorded. Contrasting Session 1 with Session 8, it is easy to see that responses are spaced much more uniformly in the later session than in the earlier one.

A close inspection of Figures 18 and 19 also suggests that a large proportion of response-rate variability is contributed by occasional long pauses. These pauses can also be plotted, as in Figures 20 and 21. This time, each horizontal line represents a single ordinal position within the fixed ratio. Thus, the top line for Session 1 represents the post-reinforcement pause. The second line represents the second IRT, and so on. There are 40 vertical positions on the left side of the graph corresponding to the 40 fixed ratios within the standard session. Each number represents an "outlier", defined as an IRT larger than 1 sec. Their duration in seconds is given by the numbers that correspond to the position in which they occurred. The histograms at the right are sums of the number of

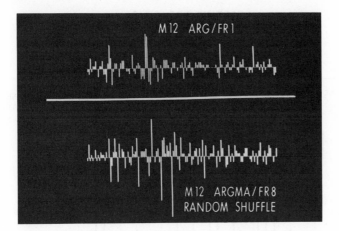

Figure 22. The left side shows 128 successive differences on the ARG schedule after smoothing by a seven-term moving average. The schedule demanded eight successes for reinforcement rather than one, as on the regular ARG schedule. An upward deflection indicates that IRT_i was greater than IRT_{i-1}. A downward deflection indicates the opposite. The right side of the figure shows an equivalent display after a random shuffle of serial order. Note that the magnitude of the differences is greater.

outliers in each ordinal position. During the first four sessions, the number of outliers diminished rapidly. But note how this disappearance took place. One might have predicted that those IRTs closest to reinforcement would be affected before those furthest away. This does not seem to be the case. Once beyond the first few IRTs, outliers seem to vanish at a rate independent of position within the ratio. Finally, a pattern is achieved during which long pauses are most frequent in the post-reinforcement interval and diminish sharply beyond it.

Another facet of serial IRT uniformity is provided by successive differences between IRTs. Recall that on the autoregressive reinforcement schedule, as depicted in Figure 3, the criterion for reinforcement is a function of the similarity of two successive IRTs. When serial uniformity is of particular interest to the experimenter, as here, he can examine the magnitude of successive differences, as in Figure 22. The left side of the figure shows successive differences after smoothing by a seven-term moving average. The random shuffle option in GENDIS can be used to determine to what extent such a plot is a function of serial uniformity or simply due to a narrow distribution of IRTs. If the distribution of successive differences, with serial position preserved, is narrower than the distribution after random shuffling of serial order, a serial relationship must exist. The right side of Figure 22 indicates that a serial relationship was present.

The Expectation Density (Huggins, 1957) is a useful method for examining periodicities, provided the data are statistically stationery. Figure 23, adapted from Poggio and Viernstein (1964), shows how the Expectation Density is computed. Assuming responses to be discrete events in time, and assigning the

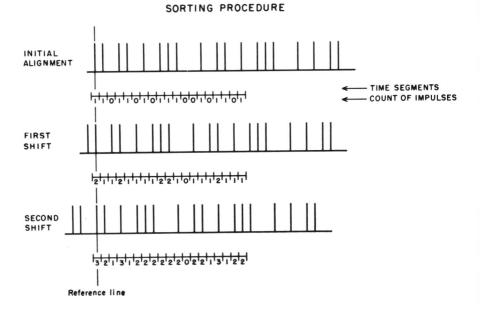

Figure 23. Schematic of the Expectation Density sorting procedure. Event 1 is first aligned with time zero. Every bin (scanning right) in which an event has occurred is incremented by one. Event 2 is then aligned with time zero and the process repeated. In this way, a frequency distribution is built up that indicates the frequency of events at specified intervals after an event at time zero. (From Poggio and Viernstein, 1964. With permission.)

first event to Time T=O, succeeding events are then scanned in turn and 1's added to the time bins in which they occur. When a predetermined section of time has been scanned, event 2 then becomes T=O, and the process repeated. Huggins (1957) showed that the Expectation Density is equivalent to an autocorrelation coefficient for unit events, corresponding to the function based on continuously varying quantities. A random process will produce a flat Expectation Density function while one containing periodic components will show peaks.

An application of the Expectation Density to behavior is exemplified by Figure 24. Early in DRL performance, the Expectation Density is characterized by an early peak followed by a relatively flat distribution from that point onward. This indicates a random process except for an excessive number of short IRTs. Later, the function is characterized by almost complete randomness. Finally, it becomes dominated by two frequencies, one high and one low, corresponding to very short IRTs and IRTs close to the criterion. Similar inferences could be made from the Conditional Probability distributions in Figures 15, 16, and 17. The conditional probability, however, does not take into account the serial relationship. It is entirely possible, that is, for interval distributions to indicate that they have been produced from a random process,

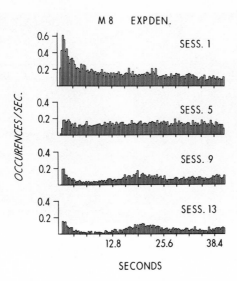

Figure 24. Expectation Density function from M8, DRL 20-sec. A flat function indicates a random distribution of inter-event intervals, as in Session 5. The right ends of these functions indicate the average frequency of responding. Thus, in Session 13, it represents about 0.1 response per second, or a rate of 1 response/10 sec.

yet display a significant serial dependency. This is especially true if long-term trends are present.

The joint interval histogram is better known to psychologists as a scatterplot. We use it here as a reflection of serial dependency. Figure 25 shows a joint-interval histogram from one session on DRL 20-sec. IRT_j is plotted on the abscissa, IRT_{j+1} on the ordinate. The time scale covers a range from 0 to 20 sec. There seem to be two distributions in this figure. One could draw an ellipse to

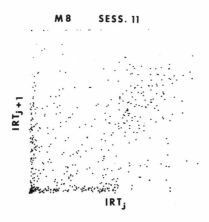

Figure 25. Joint interval histogram (scatterplot) showing the correlation between successive IRTs on DRL 20-sec. Both axes extend from 0 to 40 sec.

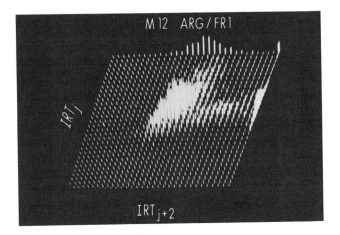

Figure 26. Joint interval histogram from the ARG schedule with density represented as height. Axes run from 0 to 1 sec. Note the elliptical shape of the function.

enclose the points plotted in the upper right quadrant, which indicates that if IRT_j is long, then IRT_{j+1} will tend also to be long. The margins of the display encompass another concentration of points. These indicate that if IRT_j is short, then IRT_{j+1} will range from short to intermediate in length. Thus, for IRTs 10 sec or shorter, no significant serial relationship exists.

The joint interval histogram may be very difficult to interpret as a two-dimensional plot if the distribution of intervals is narrow, since only brightness differences can indicate density. To deal with such a situation, one can prepare an oscilloscope display in which the number of points occupying one position is represented as height. Such a display appears in Figure 26. It reflects performance on the ARG schedule. A slight serial relationship is deduced from the fact that the total distribution is elliptical in shape.

Figures 25 and 26 were photographed from the LINC oscilloscope. Since it is convenient to be able to specify the separation and offset of the cells, and the height of the bars within each cell, for the display in Figure 26, we employ the parameter knobs of the LINC system to vary these values.

More complex quantitative measures of serial dependency generally are easier to program and faster to perform on a large machine, provided one has the necessary equipment for making the transfer. Computing time series measures such as autocorrelations and power spectra may sometimes be useful for analyzing subtle serial dependencies (for example, see Weiss, *et al.*, 1966). This should not, however, discourage the owner of a small machine who has no easy access to large machine facilities. Numerous programs have been written to perform similar kinds of analyses on the LINC and its progeny. Autocorrelation and power spectrum routines, fast Fourier transforms, and related treatments are available. In fact, they probably are more efficient if the volume of data is not too great, or access to large computer facilities not relatively convenient.

SUMMARY

I have tried to present the reader with a point of view about the use of computers in behavior as well as some possibly useful techniques. This point of view was shaped by my experience in the LINC evaluation program, and by events and experiences in our work since then. I aimed to stress two main points. First, the digital computer is an elegant experimental tool. Although it is of great utility in large-scale drug screening, for example, I believe its most important contribution will be to put behavior under a microscope—to provide more profound analyses and finer control than has ever been possible before. Second, I believe that behavioral scientists should equip themselves as well as possible to understand computer technology and, especially, programming. The program is the experiment to such a great extent that much of the potential of computer technology can be lost by scientists who fail to equip themselves with the necessary skills.

REFERENCES

Anger, D. The dependence of interresponse times upon the relative reinforcement of different interresponse times. *Journal of Experimental Psychology*, 1956, *52*, 145–161.

Clark, W. A. and Molnar, C. E. A description of the LINC. In R. W. Stacy and B. D. Waxman (Eds.), *Computers in biomedical research*, Vol. 2. New York, Academic Press, 1965. Ch. 2.

Evarts, E. V. Relation of pyramidal tract activity to force exerted during voluntary movement. *Journal of Neurophysiology*, 1968, *31*, 14–27.

Falk, J. L. Drug effects on discriminative motor control. *Physiology and Behavior*, 1969, *4*, 421–427.

Ferster, C. B. and Skinner, B. F. *Schedules of reinforcement*. New York, Appleton-Century-Crofts, 1957.

Gott, C. T. *A microanalysis of fixed-ratio performance*. Doctors' thesis, University of Rochester, 1969.

Hamming, R. W. *Numerical methods for scientists and engineers*. New York, McGraw-Hill, 1962.

Hefferline, R. W., Keenan, B., and Harford, R. A. Escape and avoidance conditioning in human subjects without their observation of the response. *Science*, 1956, *130*, 1338–1339.

Huggins, W. H. Signal-flow graphs and random signals. *Proceedings of the Institute of Radio Engineers*, 1957, *45*, 74–86.

Koepke, U. C. *A computer-based method to study discriminatory voluntary muscular control in small primates*. Masters' thesis, University of Rochester, 1970.

Lowy, K. and Weiss, B. Assessing the significance of averaged evoked potentials with an on-line computer: the split-sweep method. *Electronecephalography and Clinical Neurophysiology*, 1968, *25*, 177–180.

Notterman, J. M. and Mintz, D. E. *Dynamics of response*. New York, Wiley, 1965.

Poggio, G. F. and Viernstein, L. J. Time series analysis of impulse sequences of thalamic somatic sensory neurons. *Journal of Neurophysiology*, 1964, *27*, 517–545.

Siegel, L. A computer-controlled stereotaxic system. *IEEE Transactions on Bio-medical Engineering*, 1969, *16*, 197–204.

Skinner, B. F. *The behavior of organisms*. New York, Appleton-Century-Crofts, 1938.

Weiss, B. and Laties, V. G. Effects of amphetamine, chlorpromazine, pentobarbital, and ethanol on operant response duration. *Journal of Pharmacology and Experimental Therapeutics,* 1964, *144,* 17–23.

Weiss, B. and Laties, V. G. Reinforcement schedule generated by an on-line digital computer. *Science,* 1965, *148,* 658–661.

Weiss, B. The fine structure of operant behavior during transition states. In W. N. Schoenfeld (Ed.), *The theory of reinforcement schedules,* New York, Appleton-Century-Crofts, 1970. Ch. 9.

CHAPTER FOUR

A FORTRAN-BASED CONTROL
AND DATA-ANALYSIS SYSTEM
FOR BEHAVIORAL EXPERIMENTS[1]

DEREK P. HENDRY

University of Illinois, Chicago Circle[2], and

WILLIAM J. LENNON

Center for Computer Sciences, Northwestern University

[1] The work was supported by special grants and contracts awarded the Bioengineering group through Presbyterian-St. Luke's Hospital and the University of Illinois, Chicago, Illinois, from the W. Clement and Jessie V. Stone Foundation; the Smith, Kline, and French Foundation; the General Research Support Fund of Presbyterian-St. Luke's Hospital (S01-FR05477); the Office of Naval Research (N00014-67-A-0185); the National Institutes of Health (1-R01-HE10246-01, 1-R01-G, 14221-01, 1-R01-GM14221-02, 1-R01-GM14221-03, 5-R01-NB-06197-02, 5-R01-NB-06487-02, 1-T01-GM01436-01); the National Science Foundation (GK-885); and the Air Force (AF0SR-978-66).

[2] Present address: University of California, School of Optometry, Berkeley, Calif., 94720.

INTRODUCTION

This chapter reviews our experience at the University of Illinois at Chicago Circle in creating an on-line control system for psychological experiments. We had available a medium-sized, relatively old computer which was being used for on-line physiological experiments. Many of the problems that had to be overcome no longer warrant consideration because of advances in computer technology. Nevertheless, the philosophy we have evolved is applicable to present-day laboratories embarking upon the relatively new methods of computer control of experiments. The most important aspect of our approach was to take advantage of the existence of considerable laboratory experience and existing teaching facilities by building both our control and analysis around the FORTRAN language programming system available on our computer. With this approach, we were able quickly to get experiments running, minimize the time needed to train new people, begin evolving improved control and analysis procedures without jeopardizing previous work and experiments in progress.

In working with an obsolete computer with many different users, we were incapable of predicting when the equipment might be upgraded or replaced. Therefore, we wished to remain as flexible and machine-independent as possible.

It would be misleading not to acknowledge the importance of personal history in the decision to adopt a computer for control and analysis of experiments. I (the senior author) take the opportunity of describing here what seem to me some relevant personal experiences that disposed me to embark upon this odyssey of computing.

While I was a student in the richest nation in history, expenditures for scientific research were growing at an unprecedented rate. I remember the news of Sputnik and the concern voiced in some quarters that universities would be unable to spend all the money that was being pressed on them for the sake of science. At that time, and since, I worked in the most strongly supported laboratories in my discipline, in association with men whose scientific work is known and respected throughout the world. In such situations, one might think, the essentials to carry on research could be had for the asking, or would be lying around ready to be used by the lowliest graduate student. How different the reality! No matter how "rich" the institution by repute, it was always destitute in terms of moveable assets. My academic career seems to have been a continuous round of soldering, milling, drilling, glueing, and ordering components. One always needed more things than one could afford to buy and therefore one made the things instead of buying them, labor being cheap. Things I made were often copies of things I (or someone) could have bought, and the making was drudgery with no creative component or satisfaction. I made panels of relays, stepping relays, timers, counters, response mechanisms, feeders, cumulative recorders, whole experimental chambers, and mazes. I made snap leads to save 10c a lead. I even made snap studs, at the rate of about eight a minute, turning each one down from a cheese-head screw with a special home-made cutting tool.

I always regarded this manufacturing activity as an absurdity and I made several vows, which I was unable to keep, to kick the habit. My colleagues were evidently in the same trap. I was appalled to hear Professor Skinner relate how, as a young man, he had fashioned his own relays, thinking it a marvellous convenience, if somewhat extravagant, that he could buy the coils.

When I moved to Chicago in 1965, I resolved to make a fresh start and to build nothing that could be bought. There was only one other way to establish a viable laboratory without any money and that was to use an available computer for control. This required making the experimental interface, but that could not, at that time, be bought. I have stuck to my resolution fairly well. Although I have done a good deal of soldering and milling and drilling, most of the output consists of things that could not be bought. I can therefore recommend the establishment of a computer-based laboratory as a potentially liberating experience for experimental psychologists, who have nothing to lose but some old chains.

Having referred to the whole enterprise of establishing a computer-based laboratory as an odyssey, I may be forgiven for hoping that those who read this book enjoy a revelation comparable to that which Keats experienced on being properly introduced to Homer:

> Then felt I like some watcher of the skies
> When a new planet swims into his ken;
> Or like stout Cortes when with eagle eyes
> He stared at the Pacific . . . .

CONTROL OF EXPERIMENTS

GENERAL NEEDS OF A RESEARCH LABORATORY

In working with both very large and very small computers, it has become clear to us that there are different functions that are best performed with the two different classes of computers. In the "perfect" laboratory, we feel that the computer can best serve the researcher by completely controlling, robot-fashion, the daily conduct of experiments, assisting in the specification of data analysis, performing that analysis, and, finally, displaying the results to guide the experimenter in decisions about the next direction his research should take. While it is possible to attain most of these objectives in some form, using a combination of available computers, we were forced to simulate this desirable mixture by treating the different functions as separate problems, with properly defined communications between programs that performed the different tasks. Thus, we used the FORTRAN language as an aid in precise specification of experiments. We controlled the experiments using the FORTRAN-coded programs. We designed data-taking subprograms that created data records from all experiments using a general coding system. This uniform method of data-acquisition permitted us to write special-purpose analysis subprograms that we could use in a modular fashion to perform analyses tailored to individual experiments. Throughout our developing system we have constantly emphasized modularity. When designing an analysis program, it has always proven expedient in the long run to divide the analysis into sections that could be coded independently of one another; consequently, the inevitable minor changes did not require rewriting of the entire program. The results thus represent an intermediate plateau in a continually evolving system approach toward effective combination of machine and experimenter capabilities. We will return to this point after discussing the capabilities attained and reviewing some of the arguments leading to our individual decisions.

The remainder of the chapter is divided into four main sections. The first section concentrates on the specification and control aspect of the laboratory. We present the rationale behind our selection of FORTRAN and detail our techniques for specifying the control of individual experiments. The second section illustrates on-line recording of data, and the third summarizes our modular approach to off-line recording and analysis of data. The fourth section deals with questions arising when the introduction of a computer into a behavioral laboratory is being first considered.

GENERAL REQUIREMENTS FOR A BEHAVIORAL EXPERIMENT

The control of a behavioral experiment can be described in terms of specific contingencies relating numbers of responses, stimuli, and temporal durations. Complicated schedules can be described in terms of simple, logical functions of the form.

"If A *and* B *but not* C then *do* D, otherwise . . ."

A, B, C are true/false measurements like "a reponse has occurred", "the time interval has elapsed", or "the green stimulus light is on". D would be some control action like turning off the stimulus or initiating reinforcement or punishment.

These logical relations are generally established using electronic or electromechanical *and* gates, *or* gates, and inverters. Counting, timing, and probability functions provide the experimenter-specified control conditions. In general, the control systems have to react faster than the subject's minimum interresponse time (of the order of 100 msec), but in practice the immediacy of the controlled stimulus changes is limited by the response time of the stimulus generators, which are light bulbs, solenoids and electromechanical devices. This basically irreducible time to turn on a stimulus often makes it possible to ignore the time required for conventional relays or solid state logic equipment to make even quite complicated decisions. However, this conventional equipment is very slow by computer standards.

Because solid-state logic modules react faster than relay equipment, special-purpose components are more readily introduced so that complicated control systems are generally easier to construct using these higher speed modules. However, both systems produce the problem of the "hanging lead": a snap lead or banana plug is accidently pulled loose—where does it belong? Hard-wired systems using patch panel boards are the general solution to this problem. Flexibility is sacrificed to some extent for reliability.

POWER AND FLEXIBILITY OF DIGITAL COMPUTERS

If an experimental laboratory builds such a hard-wired, patch-panel system, it is in essence building a special-purpose computer similar to the early IBM accounting machines. Just as accounting facilities have evolved into computing facilities, experimental control facilities can also. The advantage of this evolution for business applications was the ability to use one piece of equipment to perform the functions formerly requiring several machines. Once established, it could do calculations and reports that were previously impossible. This approach has been ours as well. The computer was first integrated into the running of experiments and then new functions were investigated.

The computer we have available is a GE225. It is a 20-bit parallel arithmetic machine with parity checking. The basic timing cycle of the machine is 18 μsec, a very slow machine by today's standards. Usable groups of instructions take between 300 and 800 μsec. For example, the calculation of a pseudo-random number uniformly distributed between 0 and $\pm 500,000$ takes 500 μsec or 0.5 msec, The computer is thus capable of registering a change in the state of the experiment (environment) say, the occurrence of a peck on a key, and performing a complicated decision function within 1 msec.

The computer operations of addition, subtraction, and bit-by-bit, 20-bit logical calculations are performed at a rate of about 20,000 per second. Thus, any decision function required by the experiment that can be broken down into 50 or fewer separate, parallel logic, or serial arithmetic steps can be easily performed in less than 1 msec. As with more conventional equipment, the time required to turn on or off some electromechanical device will be the longest delay in reacting to a subject's response. In a later section, specific ways of calculating decision functions will be shown. At this point, we should be aware that the potential exists to fulfill the general requirements for controlling a behavioral experiment.

OUTLINE OF THE COMPUTER-BASED SYSTEM

Figure 1 is a schematic representation of our system for running experiments. Subjects are pigeons, but the same system, with different input and

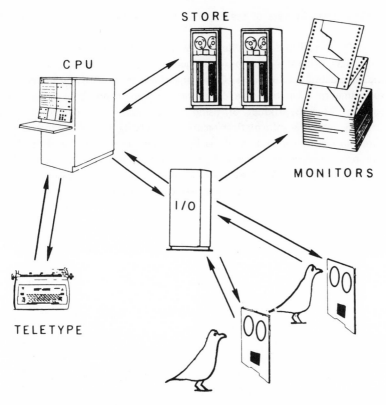

Figure 1. Schematic diagram of control system. The GE 225 computer communicates directly with the teletype, the digital magnetic tape controller and the experiment input/output interface equipment. At the interface, logic levels from the computer output register are converted into driving signals for lights and feed magazine solenoids. Subjects' responses (optionally) drive local monitor equipment while setting flip/flops in an input register in the interface. The input register levels are then converted to GE-compatible levels that can be read into the computer under program control. All changes of subjects' environment are controlled by the computer, while the behavioral data are stored on digital magnetic tape.

output devices, would be used with other subjects, including humans. We have a standardized experimental environment consisting of two illuminated pigeon keys, a "houselight" and solenoid-operated feeder. Two standard cumulative event recorders monitor responses. The interface equipment serves to change the control voltages used for driving the experimental chamber into the logic levels used within the computer and *vice versa*. Data are recorded on one digital magnetic tape while specific experimental programs are called from the other digital tape using a communication program that interacts with the teletypewriter. There is one data line connecting each bit of a special storage register in the computer to each possible stimulus in the chamber. Similarly, one line runs from each bit of a response storage register near the chamber into the computer.

All of the changes in state of the experimental chamber are initiated within the computer.

We have introduced great flexibility and eliminated the "hanging lead" problem. New programs may be debugged and tested without disrupting the running of existing experiments. Given the characteristics of the interface and the experimental chamber, the computer program completely describes the experiment. As a byproduct of using the computer for control, we may permanently store the information we are manipulating to create a record of the experimental events for later analysis by the same computer. We thus have an information-processing experimental system for the specification, running, and analysis of experiments. The key to making effective use of this flexible system lies in the ease with which the computer operations can be specified by the experimenter.

A DEFINITION OF SOFTWARE—ASSEMBLERS AND COMPILERS

Software is the term that refers to the efforts made to ease the programmer's task in specifying computer operations. The computational power of the computer is applied to the problem of easing communication by translating more natural-looking process descriptions into the complicated-looking instructions needed by the computer. The individual commands for computer operation are themselves very simple, so that many commands are generally needed for performing routine functions. Keeping account of the large quantity of instructions requires extensive bookkeeping operations that tax the abilities of the most sophisticated professional programmer. To assist the programmer, special translation programs exist that let him use names for computer operations and data storage cells. The simplest of this class of programs, called Assemblers, performs the bookkeeping necessary for the creation of specific computer instructions and data cells. Specific mnemonic code words are (usually) translated one for one into actual machine instructions. The individual operations of the computer must be well understood in order to write programs using assembly language.

A more complicated set of programs for easing communication are called compilers. Program specifications written in the language translated by the compiler bear no obvious relation to the individual operations of the computer. More bookkeeping operations are assumed by the compiler so that fewer details must be specified by the programmer. The language used is thus closer to the general outline of operations an experimenter would put down as he designed the experiment. Ideally, he would use a language that directly expressed the operations he used. For example, the language APT describes the operations a machine tool would perform in cutting a piece of metal into a specific shape. When a special purpose language does not exist for describing the control functions needed by a programmer, he can generally use some algebra-like language to specify the desired computer operations and take advantage of its bookkeeping actions and relative simplicity of specification as compared to machine or assembly language.

FORTRAN

For our operation, we decided to use the FORTRAN II (+) language distributed by GE for the 225. FORTRAN is designed to facilitate the specification of algebraic operations and makes little reference to the specifics of how the operations are carried out in the computer. It is a procedure-oriented language where groups of commonly used operations can be programmed as independent subroutines or procedures and named for later uses as building blocks in larger programs. There were four main reasons for our selecting this particular language:

(1) Suitability for Data-Analysis. FORTRAN is a logical choice for performing data analysis. Nearly all data analysis programs written by lab personnel for the past three years had been written in FORTRAN, with special FORTRAN-compatible machine language subroutines for analog input-output.

(2) Compatibility with Other Users. Other experimenters in the lab were controlling experiments in neurophysiology, electrocardiography, motor control, *etc.*, using FORTRAN and special analog input-output subroutines. We were able to specify most of our control functions in FORTRAN and needed only machine language input and output subroutines to drive and sample our newly installed binary lines and clock register.

(3) Generality. Potential experimenters would have to learn only one set of rules for both specifying experiments and later analyzing the data. They could count on being helped by virtually any other member of the lab when faced with a perplexing programming problem because everybody was using the same language. This is particularly important with small computers, where the unwritten rules learned while working with the machine can often mean the difference between successful interaction and frustrating failures.

(4) Prompt Feedback during Development. We were not sure what we needed for efficient control of behavioral experiments. Several languages exist for the 225 which could easily have been used. Alternatively, we could have devised a special control language designed to express the main types of procedure used in behavioral experiments. Any of these alternatives, however, would have required extensive systems programming before language could be used by GE 225, at which time we would have owned the language and felt obliged to defend it from all dissenters. APT, FORTRAN, and some other

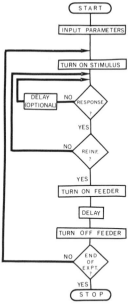

Figure 2. Organization of simple control program. After parameters are read in, the program "loops" once for each trial of the experiment. Within each trial, one "tight" loop constantly tests the input register for a response. After each response, a calculation determines whether the conditions for reinforcement are satisfied. When satisfied, the output register is changed to initiate reinforcement and a small delay is calculated to time reinforcement availability. The optional delay depicted for the "tight" loop when no response is detected is included to demonstrate how one might control an experiment even through the computer has no externally controlled clock. This delay is usally unnecessary since most modern computers do have a clock of some kind.

languages have suffered in their development because they were defined to solve a problem for a specific computer only to become standardized and demanded for machines that came later.

By gaining experience with FORTRAN-coded experiment control, we felt we would avoid false starts, get some experiments running, and learn exactly what aspects of control and control-specification would benefit most from incorporation into a specially designed, problem-oriented language.

(5) Minimum Risk from Obsolescence. While it is impossible just to take FORTRAN-program decks and compile them on other computers, it is far easier to modify a FORTRAN system than to rewrite a machine-oriented system if we would have to move to another, newer machine. This consideration was particularly relevant inasmuch as we were working in an expanding laboratory with an outmoded computer that was being used day and night and could be replaced at any time.

The five reasons reflect our two goals in using the computer: (1) we wanted to utilize the flexibility and power of the computer and (2) simultaneously to study the best approach in achieving that power and flexibility without requiring exotic computer skills.

SPECIFYING EXPERIMENTS IN FORTRAN

Figure 2 is a flow chart of a typical experiment-control program involving a single decision schedule, and represents the outline of a simple fixed-interval or fixed-ratio experiment. Initially, identifying information and data such as subject number and weight would be read into the computer and stored on the permanent storage medium identifying the experimental data to follow. The input parameters specify the ratios or intervals desired, the number and duration of feedings, and the order of stimulus presentation.

All of the bookkeeping cells are initialized (set to zero) and the experiment is started. The stimulus is presented and a short testing loop awaits the occurrence of a response. When the response occurs, the bookkeeping cells are updated and the decision calculation is carried out. Is the fixed-ratio complete? Is the interval time past? If the schedule is not complete, control is returned to the test section that awaits the next response. At schedule completion, the stimulus is extinguished and the feeder activated. A small test section then awaits the desired delay for feeding. After feeding, the number of feedings is compared to the number specified by the experimenter and control is either transferred back to start another trial or the experimenter is notified that the experimental session is complete.

We will discuss in detail the programmed testing for schedule completion. It should be clear that nearly any logical or arithmetic calculation can be specified and that schedule completion can initiate any new condition, such as the change to the next component of a chain schedule, as well as the indicated reinforcement phase.

Two types of decision-making are represented by this example: subject-precipitated and experimenter-specified. A response will initiate the calculation of a decision function involving ratios and intervals. However, stimulus (or feeding) timing must be determined independently of subject behavior. These two types of control have to be handled differently.

DECISION-MAKING: FIXED RATIOS AND INTERVALS

A fixed ratio is complete when a specified number of responses have been made. The number in a cell is initially set at zero and increased by 1 for each response. After each increment, the number in this cell is compared with the desired ratio. If the count has reached the value of the ratio, the schedule is complete and control is transferred to the next section of the program, usually the part that controls operation of the feeder. Figure 3a indicates the action performed, along with some typical FORTRAN coding, for the decision making. Two aspects of the FORTRAN coding should be noted. First, in order to take

(A) FIXED RATIO

(B) FIXED INTERVAL

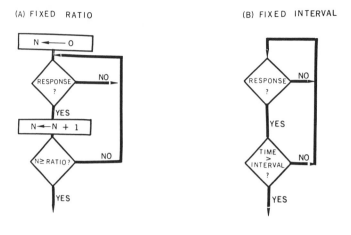

10	N=0	50	IF (KEYPRESS(1)) 50,60,60
20	IF (KEYPRESS(1)) 30,20,20	60	NOW = IREADCLOCK (1)
30	N=N+1		IF (NOW−INTERVAL) 50,50,70 .
	IF (N−ISRATIO) 20,40,40	70	... schedule complete
40	... schedule complete		

Figure 3. (A) Logic required for FIXED-RATIO decision making. (B) Logic required for FIXED-INTERVAL decision making. At each response during a FIXED-RATIO calculation, a cell storing the number of responses is incremented by one after each response. When the required number of responses have been made, control passes to the next section of the program, a new schedule in a chain, or the reinforcement subprogram. For the FIXED-INTERVAL schedule, the current time is compared with the duration of the FIXED INTERVAL. In the example, KEYPRESS is a function subprogram that has a negative value if key 1 (in these examples) has been struck by the subject. Its value is positive otherwise. ISRATION and INTERVAL are cells containing the specified ratio and interval values, respectively. IREADLOCK is a function subprogram whose value is the current time count for timer 1 (in these cases).

advantage of computer speed, integer arithmetic is generally desired and this version of FORTRAN demands that cells assigned for storing integers must have names beginning with the letters I, J, K, L, M, or N. Second, this version of FORTRAN requires that a conditional test be expressed as a calculation producing a result less than, equal to, or greater than zero. These aspects illustrate the inconvenient compromises one has to make when using the bookkeeping and communication power of a high-level language for a job it was not designed to handle.

Deciding whether a fixed-interval schedule is completed is even simpler to program than the case of the fixed ratio. One cell is reserved to contain the count indicating time from the beginning of the current trial. At each response, this current time count is compared with the specified interval count. Figure 3b illustrates the coding for reading the interval timer with one of the machine-coded subroutines, IREADLOCK, and the subsequent IF statement test. Note that the current time must be greater than the interval for completion of the schedule.

These two tests are quite simple and are performed very rapidly. Few instructions are required for performing the additions and zero tests so that the program can initiate output based on these decisions within 1 msec. Coding these instructions in machine language would only improve the reaction time by a factor of two or three unless some anticipatory tricks were used. For example, for a fixed ratio, FR n, instead of performing the decision to reinforce after the response has been made, the decision could be made at the $n - 1$ th response to reinforce the next (nth) response. In this fashion, the program would respond within the reaction time of the input-output equipment. For our computer, and others with a similar instruction set, such techniques would speed up computer response only by a factor of six or so. Since it is unlikely that the experiment will be degraded for delays on the order of milliseconds, it is possible to have more clear, understandable programs without the cost of "wasted" time being significant.

PROBABILITY: MONTE CARLO DECISIONS

Hardware Approaches.   Many behavioral experiments require the specification of probabilities, and many manufacturers of behavioral research equipment offer a device whose output is a random function of the input. We therefore incorporated probabilistic decision-making in our computer programs. Fortunately, mathematicians interested in simulation, linguistics or game theory also have requirements for making statistical decisions in computer programs; as a result, this problem has had a great deal of attention given to it and several simple techniques have been developed. One of the earliest was a hardware register that counted radioactive emissions. Similarly, the probability function modules designed for behavioral experiment control can be included as special computer hardware. A third hardware possibility is to look at a few low-order digits in the clock register whenever a response has been made. These three approaches all permit probabilistic decisions of the same order of complexity as may be obtained using conventional equipment. The third approach, which utilizes the randomness of the subject's responses to sample a regular counting function like a clock, is the most straightforward and requires no additional special-purpose hardware.

Software Approaches.   There are two popular software methods for specifying probabilities. One method is to use tables of random numbers that have been stored on magnetic tape and thus serve as a source of uniformly distributed random numbers. The other method is to calculate a sequence of integers that pass stringent statistical tests for randomness. These pseudo-random

MONTE CARLO DECISION MAKING

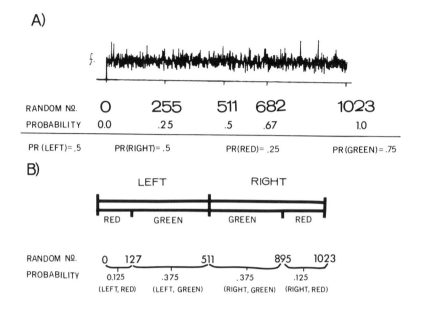

Figure 4. Monte Carlo decision making. (A) A computer-generated plot of the frequency of 10,000 pseudo-random numbers produced by an algorithm that calculates a sequence of integers that appear uniformly distributed between 0 and 1023. Approximately one quarter of the numbers generated lie to the left of the integer 255 so that, over a long run, "coin-flip" decisions will appear random, with the relative frequency of success approaching the specified probability of success. (B) Illustration of the combination of two independent decisions by generating a single random number. A color (red or green) has to be projected on a key (left or right). If two independent random events are to be selected, they can be combined into one decision where the outcome of the decision will be determined by the segment of the divided line that the pseudo-random number falls into. A decision made by this method is random, provided the random numbers satisfy the desired statistical criteria for being uniformly distributed between two values that can be made to cover the range of probabilities from 0.0 to 1.0.

numbers are deterministic but have such a long cycle before the sequence repeats that they generally pass the statistical tests for randomness. We used this method to obtain numbers that appear to be uniformly distributed between zero and about one million. This technique works better for some machines than for others and, in general, the high-order digits are "more random" than the low-order ones. We thus take the high-order 10 bits and work with a pseudo-random number distributed over the range 0 to 1023. Figure 4a is a histogram of the first 10,000 numbers generated with this subroutine. In performing probability decisions, we represent probability 0.0 as the integer zero and probability 1.0 as the integer 1023. We then select an integer in this range that corresponds to the desired probability. For example, 1/4 would be represented by the integer 255, 1/2 by 511, and 2/3 by 682. We then generate a pseudo-random number and if it is less than the integer we selected, we consider the decision outcome a "success". We can see in the histogram that the distribution is not perfectly uniform. but if we choose a probability of 1/4 and consider the numbers generated either side of the line between the integers 255 and 256, approximately 1/4 lie to the left of the line and 3/4 to the right.

The calculation we use takes about 0.5 msec so that we can make about 2000 probability decisions a second. The power of this form of probability decision technique is not in randomly determining the outcome of a single decision but in combining several decisions into one calculation. For example, to select one of two colors to appear in one of two locations requires only a single calculation to produce one random number. The outcome is then determined by comparison of the random number with the numbers (0 to 1023) selected to specify the respective probabilities. The integers between 0 and 1023 are divided into four segments that are proportional to the four probabilities. The range in which the random number falls then determines which of the four possible conditions will be selected.

The preceding example is illustrated in Figure 4b, where the outcome of the random number calculation determines whether the stimulus is red or green and whether it appears on the left or the right. In actual experiments, left/right referred to key position and red/green referred to key color.

VARIABLE RATIOS

It should be clear from the preceding discussion that we can generate a random number at each response, compare it with the integer representing the probability of reinforcement, and then decide whether the schedule requirements have been satisfied. In considering the effect of timing upon an experiment, we can see that the addition of 0.5 msec for the calculation of a probability to the decision time required for every response would be a significant increase over the time required in the case of a fixed-ratio schedule. Therefore, we have found ways to reduce the decision time before reinforcement.

There will usually be long time periods during reinforcement or between trials when no response is anticipated. During these periods, the number of times the subject must respond before reinforcement may be calculated. This calculation can either be in the form of repeated "coin-flips" using the above random decision technique or using the fact that the distribution of repeated failures prior to a success is geometric. Whatever the calculation is, the number of responses needed to achieve the first success can be used in a fixed-ratio decision function for the upcoming trial. In this fashion, the speed of a fixed-ratio decision is retained while the desired variable-ratio schedule is in fact being used.

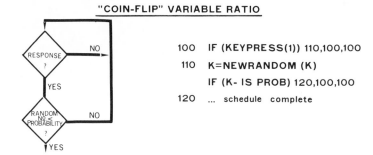

"COIN-FLIP" VARIABLE RATIO

```
100   IF (KEYPRESS(1)) 110,100,100
110   K=NEWRANDOM (K)
      IF (K- IS PROB) 120,100,100
120   ... schedule complete
```

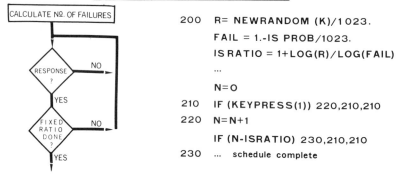

PRECALCULATED VARIABLE RATIO

```
200   R= NEWRANDOM (K)/1023.
      FAIL = 1.-IS PROB/1023.
      IS RATIO = 1+LOG(R)/LOG(FAIL)
      ...
      N=O
210   IF (KEYPRESS(1)) 220,210,210
220   N=N+1
      IF (N-ISRATIO) 230,210,210
230   ... schedule complete
```

Figure 5. Two techniques for calculating VARIABLE RATIOS. For the "coin-flip" decision, a pseudo-random number generator function, NEWRANDOM, provides an integer uniformly distributed between 0 and 1023. ISPROB is a cell containing an integer such that ISPROB/1023 is the probability of reinforcement for each response. This decision is carried out after each response and adds 0.5 msec to the time required for making a corresponding fixed-ratio decision. The binomial distribution describes the relative frequency of reinforcements using "coin-flip" decisions. The geometric distribution thus describes the number of successive failures (or successes) before a success (failure). In the precalculated version, the uniformly distributed random number (g) by the calculation: g = 1 + log (R)/log (probability of failure). Note that both log calculations will be negative and thus the calculated ratio positive. If the log of the probability of failure is calculated in advance, this algorithm will take about 65 msec. The real-time decision is then a standard FIXED-RATIO decision like the one in Figure 3a.

As indicated earlier, the calculation of a pseudo-random number takes about 0.5 msec. Thus, if the repeated coin-flip procedure is used, the prior calculation of the number of responses before the next reinforced response will take time proportional to the calculated ratio. For example, the schedule VR 102 would be implemented by specification of the pseudo-random number 10. The distribution of times to calculate the ratios would then be geometrically distributed with a mean of 51 msec (102 x 0.5 msec). The actual ratios would be the numbers of calculations of random numbers between each successive random number < 10.

VARIABLE   INTERVAL

EXPONENTIAL

K=NEWRANDOM (K)

R=K/1023.

TIME=AVERAGE * (-LOG(R))

INTERVAL=TIME

...

UNIFORM

K=NEWRANDOM(K)

INTERVAL=(MAX-MIN)*

K / 1023.

...

```
300     IF (KEYPRESS(1)) 310,300,300
310     NOW =IREADCLOCK (1)
        IF (NOW-INTERVAL) 300,300,320
320     ... schedule complete
```

Figure 6. Two techniques for precalculating VARIABLE INTERVALS. In both cases, a statistically distributed duration with specified average is precalculated for use by FIXED-INTERVAL decision-making as shown in Figure 3b. For the uniform distribution, a minimum and maximum time are selected such that the average interval for the experiment is half way between them. The minimum interval will be MIN and the maximum MAX with any interval between MIN and MAX equally likely to occur. The exponential distribution describes the times between Poisson-distributed arrivals like telephone cells or radio-active particle emissions. The Poisson-distributed times are similar to those generated by a "coin-flip" module set for a very small probability of success. Note that the exponential pre-calculation is in floating point with a final conversion to fixed point for the later decision making. The exponential calculation takes about 70 msec, the uniform about 2 msec.

However, the same result can be achieved more simply, more quickly, and without variation in the calculation time. All that is required is the calculation of a geometrically distributed random number whose mean is chosen according to the desired variable ratio. Note that the probability of reinforcement after one response is $p = 1/r$, where r is the mean ratio of the variable ratio. The probability of reinforcement at the second response is $(1-p)p$. The probability of reinforcement at the nth response is $(1-p)^{n-1}p$. It turns out that we may calculate a random number, U, uniformly distributed between 0.0 and 1.0 and, given p, solve the equation $U=(1-p)^m$ for m, the number of successive failures. If we then reinforce the $(m+1)$st response, the distribution of reinforcements will be as if determined by a fixed probability on each response. The calculation involved is then $m=\log(U)/\log(1-p)$. This algorithm and the individual coin-flip algorithm are presented for comparison in Figure 5. The coin-flip decision takes the 0.5 msec additional computing time over the fixed-ratio time while the geometric distribution pre-calculation takes a fixed time equal to the 0.5 msec and the calculation time for a division and two logarithm calculations. If the log functions are calculated in floating point on our computer, the time used will be about 65 msec while a hand-coded machine-language version will take about 5 msec. Because the calculation will take place during some feeding or intertrial time involving several seconds, and because the hand-coded version requires numerical analysis sophistication if the routine is not available for a desired computer, we prefer to use the slower floating point function distributed with the FORTRAN running system and then decide for a given case whether to do the individual coin flips or the lengthy pre-calculation of the ratio. While this form of prior calculation is straightforward, we prefer to use the random decision at each response in an effort to retain the simplicity of specification possible with FORTRAN, provided the time for the decision calculation is not too large; for most experiments, a delay of up to about 50 msec is acceptable.

VARIABLE INTERVALS

Variable intervals, where reinforcement is a probability function of time, are probably the most difficult decisions to define mathematically. Two possible calculations mimic current hardware practice. First, a minimum and maximum are selected and a uniform distribution is used to select a time between these limits. This is the simplest approach and is analogous to the time-selection behavior of a tape timer. The second approach approximates the discrete binomial distribution obtained when independent "coin-flips" determine whether an additional time increment will be added to the interval.

Calculating the Poisson-distributed times that approximate the binomial is straightforward. It can be justified as the usual intent in VI schedules for at least two reasons. First, most random time-related events from radio-active emissions to supermarket arrivals are accurately described by this distribution. Second, the times between such events are exponentially distributed. Many experiments will prefer an exponential distribution because it makes for a kind of unpredictability that a uniform or Gaussian distribution does not. With an exponential distribution the failure of the event to occur up to any given time is of no value in predicting its next occurrence; that is, "events-per-opportunity" is constant.

For all interval calculations, the most straightforward method is to calculate the next time period, selected from the desired distribution and to use the fixed-interval decision machinery already described. In that case the value of "INTERVAL" in Figure 3b would be specified afresh after every reinforcement, according to the outcome of the calculation. Figure 6 illustrates the coding for uniform and Poisson (exponential) distributed random intervals as pre-trial calculations. Note that the final calculation is equivalent to that in Figure 3b.

TIMED INTERVALS

The programming examples discussed so far have all dealt with subject-precipitated decisions. We have shown in the flow chart for Figure 2 one example of stimulus timing—timing feed hopper presentation. We indicated in discussing the figure that the program would continually loop through a test section that compared the advancing clock count with the desired feed interval. While this type of timing is straightforward, it assumes that only one monitored time interval is to occur at any given time. In general, we must assume that several parallel timing calculations will be proceeding simultaneously and we need an easy method of specifying these time durations.

There are two major approaches to implementing several parallel time measurements. The simplest, conceptually, is to have as many different, parallel timing devices as there are durations. The second method is to break up the parallel time durations into segments of overlapping and non-overlapping intervals that can be timed by a single series timing device. The first approach is analogous to having separate timer modules for each duration defined for a conventionally controlled experiment. This particular approach could be applied to computer control as well. A special piece of hardware can be selected and activated by presenting it with the desired duration using some binary code. In general, the unit cost for such a device exceeds $700 and we would still run the risk of not having enough individual timers.

A simple series timing routine is possible with some modern computers that have the capability of performing one instruction, which is a decrement count and test. For these machines, a basic oscillator periodically interrupts the normal flow and transfers control to a subroutine that decrements and tests all of the counting cells in computer memory. The advantage of this approach is that, in theory, the entire core memory of the computer can be assigned the task of maintaining individual counts so that there is no incremental hardware cost for adding additional timers. As each additional time is requested, the interval count is set aside in a temporary cell and the additional decrement and test instructions are added. At each count, all of the active cells are decremented and tested. Whenever one of them counts out, the equivalent of an experiment-precipitated interrupt is generated, simulating the effect a response would have. It should be clear that updating will require computer time in rough proportion to the number of active counts. Further, since the most recently requested durations will generally bear no relation to already active ones, keeping track of which cells are active (timing) and which are idle (not timing) will prove a significant programming problem, which, while not apparent to the experimenter writing in FORTRAN, will add still more computer time as cell lists are updated.

The approach taken in some early time-sharing systems was to allow the programmer the concept of independent timing functions that were translated into serial requests. The software would behave like the taxi dispatcher who is given several timed taxi requests. He sets an alarm clock for the earliest time that his attention is demanded and sorts the outstanding requests in order of demanded times—first come, first served. When the alarm clock sounds, he resets it for the next demanded time and dispatches the requested cab. From a system programming point of view, we have the same time-consuming problem we had earlier, but we need perform the calculations only whenever a request is made or the alarm clock sounds. Given that the computer is fast enough, it may even be possible to sort and update the desired times using FORTRAN coding with a machine language function for reading the clock.

From our experience in simulating the various possible modes of operation, we favor a compromise between the last proposed technique and the first plan using independent timing hardware. In particular functions like feeder timing are fairly constant so that we prefer to initiate the feeding cycle and have an interrupt occur as the food hopper drops back into its standby position, thus achieving the timing function as well as automatic equipment function monitoring. While we have not run any experiments requiring special stimulus-timing that was not related to an interval schedule, we would generally decide for each experiment whether to include passive stimulus-timing at the site of the experiment or in the computer. The decision would depend on whether the presentation would remain constant throughout the entire set of experiments. If control is to remain flexible, it is preferable to do most, if not all, timing under the explicit control of the computer; moreover, safeguards and monitoring are then byproducts.

SUMMARY OF DECISION-MAKING TECHNIQUES

A great deal of detail has been given about specifying the simple program steps used to realize the five basic building blocks of most behavioral experiments. This description should serve to illustrate the ease with which experiments can be specified. In particular, the time required for control decisions has been given, and if we make the assumption that we prefer ease of specification and understanding to program efficiency, we can summarize decision timing considerations with our rather slow machine as follows:

(1) A fixed-ratio or a fixed-interval decision can be executed in less than 1 msec.

(2) A probability decision takes about 1 msec.

(3) A variable-ratio decision using a probability decision at each response takes just over 1 msec.

(4) A variable-interval decision is divided into two parts with a random interval calculation taking either less than 1 msec or more than 50 msec as a calculation in "free" time. A fixed-interval decision is then made for each response. Since achieving the 5-msec calculation requires writing a machine-coded logarithm function, the longer calculation serves as a more accurate

indication of normal requirements.[3] Thus, it appears that the GE225 is theoretically capable of reacting to 500 to 1000 responses per second.

When some form of control of different experiments is introduced, the reaction time of the computer programs will suffer from the added burden of assigning individual responses to different control programs. A rule of thumb for calculating this degradation would be doubling or tripling the time needed, since the calculation to assign responsibility is comparable to the decision function for a fixed ratio. Thus, 200 responses a second is a conservative estimate of the upper limit decision capability of the GE225. We must bear in mind, however, that specification of the computer system will depend on the delay we can tolerate for those cases in which several independent experiments "simultaneously" demand attention. If 10 msec is the maximum tolerable delay, we cannot consider parallel control of more experiments than we anticipate will generate these 10 events. We will discuss this further as techniques for parallel control are considered.

THE ADEQUACY OF THE COMPUTER

So far in this section of the chapter we have justified the use of the FORTRAN language and demonstrated with simple examples of code how the individual decisions that make up the control of an experiment might be programmed in FORTRAN. We in fact do use coding similar to that shown, although minor modifications have been introduced as our technique has evolved. Figure 2 is a representative flow chart of an early experiment demonstrating our use of computer timing before the real-time clock was installed. The later figures represent isolated segments of code demonstrating a particular decision technique presented under the assumptions that we have just detected a response and that we have a real-time clock for measuring time intervals.

In all of the examples, communication with the experiment or the real-time clock is accomplished through the use of FORTRAN-linked subroutines and functions. As far as the experimenter is concerned, these functions behave as if he were the sole user of the computer. We mentioned that we encouraged simplicity over timing optimization in the interests of aiding communication between experimenters. This attitude has paid off whenever new people have become involved in the laboratory. In the worst cases, they had to learn FORTRAN from scratch, as well as our coding conventions. They have usually survived to produce their own control and analysis programs. For people familiar with computers and in particular with FORTRAN, our preceding remarks and

[3] If enough space is available, variable ratios and variable intervals can be generated by consulting a stored table of exponentially distributed numbers. This would greatly reduce the calculation time.

examples probably prompted innumerable suggestions for different approaches. A major problem is that for every desired computer application there are many possible approaches. We initially wrote heavily parameterized programs that could serve to specify entire families of experiments. After several rewrites, because we had failed to ancitipate all possible variations, we wrote simpler and simpler programs, thereby saving considerable programming time by not trying to anticipate changes we were gradually learning to accept as unpredictable.

It is also quite clear that the use of one computer for controlling one experiment, even with today's decreasing prices, is a luxury few can afford, if for no other reason than that we are interested in performing more than one experiment at a time. We thus turned our attention to the control of several simultaneous unrelated experiments.

RUNNING EXPERIMENTS IN PARALLEL

In anticipating the need to perform several experiments at one time, we tried to retain all of the advantages sought when we initially decided to use the FORTRAN language and running system. We did not want to invest a great deal of time in writing a time-sharing monitor system and yet we wanted to ensure the independence between programs that would preserve the ease of experiment specification and update we were used to. We were faced with a need to compromise the needs of the experimenter with the desires of the system programmer, both of whom must be happy for such a system to succeed.

There are many designs for operating a computer for simultaneous users. Most of them suffer from being designed for all possible contingencies. Students of computer science will discuss for many years the problems of the manufacturers who promised "all things to all people simultaneously—using one computer". Rather than review these possible approaches, which are either becoming outdated or operational as new hardware improvements are introduced, we will introduce a programming philosophy amenable to parallel programming on the class of computers we are likely to encounter in the laboratory. We will discuss this philosophy in terms of the GE225 because it is representative of what can be expected in this area. The major improvements over its design will be in the area of improved hardware handling of interrupts generated by experiments together with the introduction of inexpensive mass storage devices like magnetic disks or drums.

Simplifying Assumptions and Constraints. The first assumption is that we will be satisfied to update experiments within 5 msec of the event or time that precipitates a possible change. The second assumption is that the experimenter will not be overburdened by the requirement that he use decision functions that take about 1 msec. In this fashion, if two events occur "simultaneously", the later-serviced one will still be updated in the minimum time desired. Further, we assume that the experimenter knows in advance which experimental chambers he will use and that the communication lines are uniquely defined. This requirement could be better stated by specifying that the control program assigned for an experiment to a particular experimental chamber is unique and that a different program will be residing in computer memory for each active chamber per experiment.

Organization of Control Programs. An experiment-control program will be written as a subroutine subordinate to the main control program, the system monitor. The experiment-control program will be divided into three parts with radically different characteristics. The first part, *experiment-specification*, will be concerned with reading in control parameters for defining the values of variable specifications of the experiment and identifying data such as subjects' number and weight. This part will be substantially like the initial portions of the example in Figure 2. It would be given control at the initiation of each new running of the experiment and would serve completely to define the experiment to follow. (The optional fourth part would be similar in nature and would permit storage of experimenter's comments concerning the recently run experiment.)

The second part of the program, *pre-calculation*, would be given control during each inter-trial/feeding time to calculate the specific parameters for the upcoming trial. For fixed ratios and intervals, this section would be minimal: however, for variable ratios, intervals, and random stimulus or schedule decisions, this section would be complicated and time-consuming. The only constraint on this section of the program is that it should consume much less computer time than the normal inter-trial time for the experiment being controlled.

The third part, decision-making, is the time-constrained decision section that is given control each time there is a response in the experiment or an interrupt generated by the completion of a time-delay calculation. This is the section that decides which response took place in the experimental chamber and then performs the decision calculation outlined earlier. In general, there are four possible outcomes from such a decision calculation. (1.) Control can be returned to the monitor program with no change in the environment requested. (2.) Change in environment can be requested, such as changing key color. (3.) An interval calculation can be requested. (4.) Finally, the inter-trial interval and pretrial calculations may be initiated.

Figure 7 is a flow chart illustrating this organization. We can appreciate that there will be few time constaints on the segment of the control program that accepts the input parameters before running the experiment. Minimal time constraints are placed upon the pretrial calculation section while the most stringent constraints are placed upon the decision-making response-analysis segment. These constraints are dictated by the hardware features of our computer.

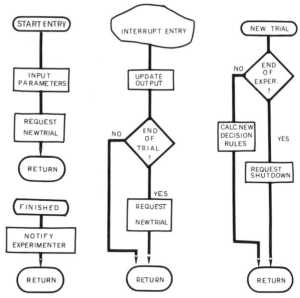

Figure 7. Organization of control program for multiprogramming. The diagram represents one FORTRAN subprogram with a "four-way branch" statement at the beginning of the program. An argument in the subroutine serves to select which segment of the program will get control at a particular call to the subroutine. For clarity in the figure, this logic is eliminated and the subprogram displayed as though it were four separate programs with some means of communicating between sections. The "interrupt" section is used with the interrupt facility for the computer inhibited. Thus, response-precipitated parts of the program (in the interrupt section) will operate without risk of being delayed by any other experiment. With this freedom goes the responsibility to make decisions as rapidly as possible. For this reason, the "new trial" section is used to precalculate time-consuming decision rules between trials so that the interrupt section can use the more rapid decisions for FIXED RATIO and FIXED INTERVAL when a response occurs.

Whenever a response or clock alarm occurs, the normal sequence of processing is interrupted and control is given to a small program that reads in the data, stores it on tape, and decides which experiment has generated the interrupt (the alarm clock being treated at this level like an experiment). The working registers of the computer are saved and control is transferred to the response segment of the appropriate control program.

After the decision-making is carried out, control is returned to the monitor program. A check is made for simultaneous requests and then the working registers are restored and control returned to the calculation that was interrupted. At this point, the interrupt hardware equipment is turned on again so that subsequent requests will be serviced. In the event that a response has occurred while the interrupt hardware has been turned off for the decision-making, it is "remembered" by the hardware and another interrupt is immediately generated.

The machine language program that saves the working registers and assigns responsibility needs about 0.5 msec on the GE225. Another millisecond is required to check for simultaneous events and restore the *status quo*. By deferring servicing of control requests until after the interrupt has been reestablished, it is possible to handle two or three simultaneous interrupts within the desired 5 msec.

The other segments of control programs and most segments of the monitor are then run in a mode where they can be interrupted by subjects' responses and clock alarms. This mode of operation is reflected in the timing constraints established.

Details for Programming in the Parallel Environment. The success of this organization lies in the use of co-routines and computed go-to statements. A subroutine is a modular piece of coding that has been given a name so that it may be called by a program needing that particular operation performed. Implicit in the use of subroutines is the convention that the subroutine returns control after it is finished to the main program from which it was called. A co-routine, however, is called just like a subroutine but instead of returning, it calls another routine, which may in fact be the routine that called it. The name co-routine is derived from the fact that neither routine involved is subordinate in the traditional sense of main programs and subroutines. Computed go-to statements are already standard statements in most FORTRAN compilers and have the function of transferring control to one of several listed statements according to the computed value of a switching variable.

The experiment-control program is thus a co-routine that is called by the controlling co-routine, the monitor. When control is given to the experiment-control program, the first statement is a computed go-to, which transfers control to the appropriate section of the program. One of the arguments of the co-routine is the switch parameter. Thus, either the initializing section, the pretrial section, the response-analysis section, or the terminal clean-up section receives control.

While interdependent, the individual program sections are written as if they were in fact four separate programs. The initialization section is the most obvious example of an independent organization. When this section is called, the experiment has not yet started and in fact the subject may not be ready to begin. The experimenter types in the identifying information and subject data (for example, weight and bird number). The program assures that the experiment chamber is in the proper state. It would be possible to initiate testing of the chamber at this time but we feel it is better for the experimenter to run a short fake experiment where he acts out the appropriate responses in order to test out all of the features of the system before running the experiment. After the experiment is initialized and the experiment has indicated that the subject is ready, control is returned to the monitor system with a request that the pretrial section for this experiment be called.

Within the pretrial program section is lodged the logic for calculating the necessary decision parameters for the upcoming trial. In many cases, this section will do little more than zero out some counters or initiate some intermediate data output of a summarizing nature. In other instances, this section will convert the variable-interval or variable-ratio specifications into the corresponding fixed-interval or fixed-ratio decisions for the upcoming trial. This section will be responsible for deciding when the experiment is complete. If the experiment is considered complete, the response section will be changed so that when the inter-trial completion signal is analyzed, control will be sent to the terminal section by the monitor.

The response section contains the logic of the experiment as described in the previous section of the chapter. When control is given to this section, we know that a response or a timing alarm has occurred. We may use a second computed go-to statement here together with a second switch parameter provided by the monitor to determine which response or alarm has occurred. In some instances (*e.g.,* a response on the "wrong" key) the response made is to be ignored. In these cases, the computed go-to statement will simply return control to the monitor program. In other instances, the decision procedure would be carried out as outlined earlier. As in the simplest examples, the decision to change the experiment environment might be made so that the return to the monitor would request an update in the output signal to the experiment chamber. If that request is to end the present trial, an additional request would be sent to call the pretrial section of the program.

Control is returned to the monitor program after each such action by the experiment program in order that the several programs each have sufficient running time in their individual sections. They each appear to be in sole control of the computer. The same programming techniques are being used as for the case when only one program is running at a time, except that they have been reorganized around the single entry point and the monitor controlled computed go-to's.

By introducing the timing constraints that a response analysis take less than 1 msec and that the pretrial calculations take much less time than the actual intertrial time, we have simplified the activities of the controlling monitor program so that it may in fact be simply coded using FORTRAN. Whenever a response is made, a special hardware interrupt servicing program takes control and determines which experiment is involved. This datum is stored and the routine checks that the experiment is not in the midst of pretrial calculations. If it is not, the response section is called by calling the experiment-control program with the two switch arguments properly set. The response analysis section returns control to this special interrupt routine. The only time that a response could cause difficulty is when the experiment program is already active and for this reason the check was made before relinquishing control. We found empirically that responses would run into the reinforcement period of a trial under several conditions. First, during long intervals or ratios, a pigeon would typically emit an additional response or two after the command to operate the feeder solenoid had been given. Second, if the feed hopper was clogged or not operating, the subject would respond throughout the entire period. Thus, by keeping track of these responses that are usually ignored, we not only had additional data of possible value, but also had a built-in check for feeder malfunction.

The remainder of the system could be coded in FORTRAN as one or more programs designed to keep lists of requests and provide successive requests according to the lists. We have simulated the system in FORTRAN but we ran into hardware difficulties when we attempted to expand the number of controlled chambers. This problem was due entirely to our trying to use a business-oriented computer for process-control work. In a more modern computer, the time needed to decide which experiment was concerned with the response would not be as prohibitive and this general approach would prove successful.

CONCLUSION

We have seen in detail the techniques needed for the five basic response-dependent forms of decision making, as well as the response-independent timing control. We showed how these techniques lent themselves easily to the implementation of a multiprogramming environment where several experiments were running simultaneously. The difficulties of controlling several simultaneous experiments are reduced if all real-time decisions are initiated in relation to some event that can serve to interrupt the normal flow of computer activity. For this reason, the timing requirements that are independent of subjects' responses are converted, using the "taxi-dispatcher" technique, into a series of sequential timing alarms that are then treated in the same fashion as subjects' responses. Calculation of complicated decision functions and organization of programming for timing are then relegated to running as "background" while "responses" are not being serviced. This plan is the approach taken in most present day time-sharing research. As a result, we are able to consider using process-control computers that have working software for such operations as controlling steel mills and petroleum cracking plants.

On an individual basis we then considered those decisions which, while slightly more time-consuming, did not threaten the real-time response needs of the experiment and suggested simplicity of specification wherever possible. We checked by observation, rather than by instruction counts, to see that the integrity of the experiment was always maintained. Throughout our research and in all of the examples given in the paper we have stressed the ease of using the FORTRAN language. Our philosophy would be better summarized by stating that we wish to stress the ease of using the best available high-level language for the computer in question. By taking advantage of the bookkeeping capabilities available, a minimum of machine language coding is needed to get the experiments running. Once having achieved the primary goal of actually carrying on behavioral research, better techniques for control and specification can be simulated using the available language. As common calculations such as fixed-ratio decisions are encoded into library function subprograms, we still will have the full calculation power of the high-level language as new experimental designs demand new decision calculations. As experience is gained in the running of experiments, different notations more suitable to specifying experiments may be considered in the light of writing a translator from the problem-oriented language statement of control requirements into either the FORTRAN specification or a FORTRAN-compatible machine language subroutine.

Our approach has thus been the pragmatic one of running experiments for the twofold goal of conducting behavioral research and conducting computer science research. We feel that our allocation of computing resources into fast and slow decision-making packages is basic to the efficient running of experiments and that the next problem we must confront in this areas is that of relieving the experimenter of the burden of making the actual allocation without penalizing him by restricting the class of experiments he can consider. We have experimented with different organizations as each new experiment has been written or updated and the resulting structure is more suggestive of automation diagram organizations (using complicated transition requirements) than the two-dimensional flow diagrams devised by Mechner (1959). Consequently, some state representation of an experiment will probably most easily translate into our existing practice. The problem of translating a notation far removed from the actual internal representation is quite complex when running-time constraints are present, so that it will probably be some time before a workable user representation, translator, and running system is realized. In the interim, with our approach, there is always the possible escape into the high-level algebraic language whenever the developing system demands awkward specifications for any given experiment.

ON-LINE DATA ACQUISITION

A great deal of usable information can be obtained on-line. In addition to the graphic record obtained with cumulative recorders, the teletypewriter can be used to record data of interest.

An example is shown in Figure 8, which is a copy of the teletype record with explanatory comments added.

When the monitor calls the program for the experiment that is selected, it is good practice to have the program indicate the name of the program. Thus, on the first line the name of the experiment has been typed on the teletype. The program cannot proceed until all the preliminary tests have been completed and parameters have been specified, the results of which are shown in the top half of Figure 8 (line 2-24).

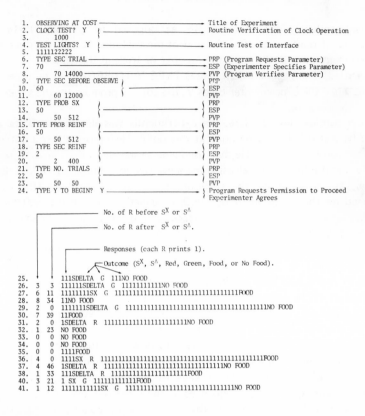

```
1.  OBSERVING AT COST ─────────────────────────► Title of Experiment
2.  CLOCK TEST?  Y  ⎱─────────────────────────► Routine Verification of Clock Operation
3.        1000       ⎰
4.  TEST LIGHTS?  Y  ⎱─────────────────────► Routine Test of Interface
5.  1111122222       ⎰
6.  TYPE SEC TRIAL ─────────────────────────► PRP (Program Requests Parameter)
7.  70 ─────────────────────────────────────► ESP (Experimenter Specifies Parameter)
8.        70 14000 ─────────────────────────► PVP (Program Verifies Parameter)
9.  TYPE SEC BEFORE OBSERVE ⎫                 ⎧ PRP
10. 60                       ⎬───────────────► ⎨ ESP
11.       60 12000           ⎭                 ⎩ PVP
12. TYPE PROB SX            ⎫                 ⎧ PRP
13. 50                       ⎬───────────────► ⎨ ESP
14.       50  512            ⎭                 ⎩ PVP
15. TYPE PROB REINF         ⎫                 ⎧ PRP
16. 50                       ⎬───────────────► ⎨ ESP
17.       50  512            ⎭                 ⎩ PVP
18. TYPE SEC REINF          ⎫                 ⎧ PRP
19. 2                        ⎬───────────────► ⎨ ESP
20.        2    400          ⎭                 ⎩ PVP
21. TYPE NO. TRIALS         ⎫                 ⎧ PRP
22. 50                       ⎬───────────────► ⎨ ESP
23.        50   50           ⎭                 ⎩ PVP
24. TYPE Y TO BEGIN?  Y ─────────────────────► ⎰ Program Requests Permission to Proceed
                                               ⎱ Experimenter Agrees
```

```
          ┌──────── No. of R before S^X or S^Δ
        ┌─│──────── No. of R after  S^X or S^Δ.
      ┌─│─│──────── Responses (each R prints 1).
    ┌─│─│─│──────── Outcome (S^X, S^Δ, Red, Green, Food, or No Food).
25. │ │ │ │  111SDELTA  G  111NO FOOD
26. 3   3    111111SDELTA  G  11111111111NO FOOD
27. 6  11    11111111SX  G  111111111111111111111111111111111111FOOD
28. 8  34    11NO FOOD
29. 2   0    1111111SDELTA  G  11111111111111111111111111111111111111111NO FOOD
30. 7  39    11FOOD
31. 2   0    1SDELTA  R  11111111111111111111111NO FOOD
32. 1  23    NO FOOD
33. 0   0    NO FOOD
34. 0   0    NO FOOD
35. 0   0    1111FOOD
36. 4   0    1111SX  R  1111111111111111111111111111111111111111111111FOOD
37. 4  46    1SDELTA  R  111111111111111111111111111111111NO FOOD
38. 1  33    111SDELTA  R  111111111111111111111FOOD
40. 3  21    1 SX  G  111111111111FOOD
41. 1  12    11111111111SX  G  111111111111111111111111111111111NO FOOD
```

Figure 8. Portion of on-line teletype record of an experiment on observing behavior. Lines 1-24 are a record of two test procedures and the selection of six parameters. Lines 25-41 were printed during the first 16 trials of the session, and show the sequence of all events in the trials (responses, exteroceptive stimuli, food, no food). See text.

After the name of the experiment, the teletype records the fact that two tests have been completed (line 2-5). We describe these below after describing the simpler process of specifying parameters.

Under program control, the teletype types an instruction to the experimenter, to which he must respond. The first instruction in this example is TYPE SEC TRIAL (line 6). The experimenter chooses the duration by typing "70". The experimenter then initiates the next part of the program by typing a control character. This causes the computer to type back line 8 and 9. The first number in line 8 indicates the number received by the computer as a check on errors of transmission. The second number is the first number in the units used by the program. Thus, since times are measured in units of 1/200 sec, 70 is represented as 14,000. Line 9 requests specification of another parameter, and the process continues until the duration of a trial (line 6-8) the period in a trial before an observing response has an effect (line 9-11), the probability of an observing response producing the stimulus S^X as opposed to S^Δ (line 12-14), the probability of reinforcement at the end of the trial (line 15-17), the duration of reinforcement (line 18-20), and the number of trials in the session (line 21-23) are specified. The program then causes TYPE Y TO BEGIN? to be typed (line 24) and when the experimenter types Y, the control program for the experiment is put into operation.

Now consider line 2. Here, the experimenter was alerted that if the clock was to be tested it had to be done at this point. He indicated that a test was to be performed by typing Y. He then used a sense switch on the computer console to time a real interval. On releasing the sense switch the program caused the real interval, as measured by the real-time clock, to be printed. This number happened on this occasion to be 1000, or exactly 5 sec. In the next test, the experimenter verified that the interface and devices in the chamber were functioning properly, by pressing the response keys. This part of the program caused the stimulus lights to be lit in sequence as the response keys (first one, then the other) were operated. When operating the keys the experimenter looked to make sure that all lights, and (not shown) the feeder, operated. He then looked at the teletype output and verified that the responses were being properly received, as shown by the typing of "1" for every response he had made on the left key, and "2" for every response he had made on the right key.

The operating program can be made to record on the teletype, during the course of the session, any desired information. We routinely have "1" and "2" typed for responses on left and right keys. In this experiment we chose to record on-line, responses, all the consequences of the responses, and the total number of responses (1's) before and after the response produced a change in key color. The last 16 lines of Figure 8 show the on-line record.

The fact that it has taken many words to describe Figure 8 indicates that it contains a great deal of information. The standard format is nevertheless easy to read, once it is explained. The advantages of having such a record are difficult to overstate.

The main advantages are: (1.) It indicates, as far as possible, that the experimenter's intentions regarding parameters have actually been carried out. (2.) It indicates whether the peripheral equipment (interface and chamber) was tested just before the experiment. (3.) It shows the sequence of every important event in the experiment, as the events occur. (4.) It provides a permanent, hard-copy record of the experiment that can be referred to without further use of a computer.

Important information that is more difficult and less useful to record on-line in this way is the time of occurrence of events. It is more difficult because typing numbers interferes with responding to subject's responses; it is less useful because it would produce a lot of paper covered with numbers and the problem of reducing these data would remain. These considerations make it desirable to use an additional system for purposes of data-analysis. We record data on magnetic tape, as described in the next section.

OFF-LINE DATA ANALYSIS

Once a magnetic tape system to record behavioral data has been established, it is virtually no additional trouble to record *all* the data generated by the operant conditioning experiments. The data of interest are rates of a discrete event (a "response") under various conditions. The only practical way to store information on the rate of responding is to record every response and its time of occurrence. If one has to do this for any event with almost any digital computer, it is no more trouble to do it for every event of interest. We record every event (responses and onset and termination of stimuli, including reinforcement) and its time of occurrence in units of 0.005 sec.

Figure 9 shows the tape organization. The first entry is a *header*, which identifies the source of the data, followed by coded times, read from the clock, and the events that occurred at each time. The end of the experimental session has a unique code. The sequential entry of coded times and coded events is not a peculiarity of our method, but is a characteristic feature of mechanized digital storage media.

In our original procedures for data analysis, no attempt was made to generalize the programs; each problem was treated as unique. We expected to build up a library of programs that could be used again. Thus, we expected that as our library grew larger the probability of having to write a new analysis program would gradually decline. We soon discovered that even problems that appeared very similar were sufficiently different so that little saving was achieved in modifying the "old" program, rather than writing a new program. This experience persuaded us to introduce a generality into our analysis programs. However, the more general programs were much more difficult to write. We reduced this difficulty by using subprograms to achieve the manipulations of data that commonly occurred. Each subprogram was completely general; its operations were completely specified, but the data on which the operations were carried out were variables that had to be specified by the experimenter. The outcome was that the programmer had available a relatively small set of familiar general-purpose "building blocks" from which he could fashion an unlimited number of data-analysis structures.

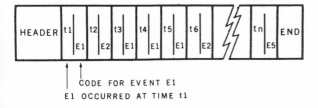

CODE FOR EVENT E1
E1 OCCURRED AT TIME t1

Figure 9. Organization of data on magnetic tape.

The mental bookkeeping required of the programmer is significantly reduced if the program building blocks are, not FORTRAN subroutines, but FORTRAN *Functions*. All the operations that can be performed by a subroutine can be performed by a Function, but, in addition, the Function values can be chosen to do at least two useful jobs. One job is error-checking: the value of the Function can be made to indicate a condition that should not exist or data that should not be used. For example, it can be used to prevent one from using the animal's recorded weight as performance data. Another job is what may be called *scouting*: the value of the Function is a number that either needs to be known for a subsequent manipulation or simplifies that manipulation. For example, the value might be the number of events of a particular kind, which would relieve the programmer from making special provisions for counting the events and storing the count.

SEEK SUBPROGRAMS AND BUILD SUBPROGRAMS

We distinguish these two types of Functions by what they do.

SEEK subprograms are used to scan the tape to extract entries that conform to some criterion. There are six SEEK subprograms; four of these used on arrays representing times. These are:

FUNCTION MORETHANA	(scan forward)
FUNCTION MORETHANB	(scan backwards)
FUNCTION LESSTHANA	(scan forward)
FUNCTION LESSTHANB	(scan backwards)

The arguments of these Functions specify the portion of tape (or core locations) to be scanned, and the criterion. The value of the Function is arranged to be zero if no entry satisfies the criterion and otherwise the ordinal number in the array of the first entry satifying the criterion.

The other two SEEK subprograms are used for arrays representing events. These are:

FUNCTION MACHFOR	(scans forward)
FUNCTION MACHB	(scans backwards)

The arguments of these Functions specify locations to be scanned and the event that is being sought. The value of the Function is zero if no event of the kind specified is found, or the ordinal number in the array of the first entry found to "match" the specification.

The SEEK Functions enable us to select from tape or core data that we are interested in for the current analysis, such as responses on the left key, inter-reinforcement times longer than 10 sec, and so on. We also have to *build*, using BUILD subprograms, arrays that contain data collected in categories

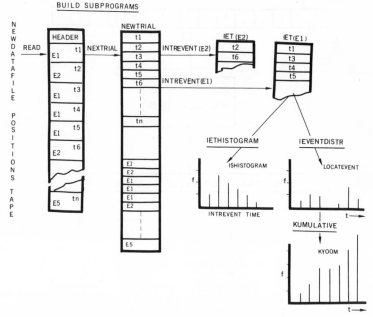

Figure 10. The manipulations of the taped data accomplished by the BUILD subprograms: NEWDATAFILE, NEXTRIAL, INTREVENT, IETHISTOGRAM, IEVENT-DISTR and KUMULATIVE. The subprograms produce arrays called NEW-TRIAL, IET, ISHISTOGRAM, LOCATEVENT, and KYOOM. See text.

meaningful to the experimenter, perhaps using the elements found by the SEEK Function. The order in which one *builds* and *seeks* is for some problems arbitrary. In other cases, when the experiment is simple and one needs to distinguish only responses and reinforcements, SEEK Functions might not be used. Indeed, one can always refrain from using them; one uses them only because they save time and effort.

The BUILD subprograms are:

> FUNCTION NEWDATA FILE
> FUNCTION NEXTRIAL
> FUNCTION INTREVENT
> FUNCTION IEVENTDISTR
> FUNCTION IETHISTOGRAM
> SUBROUTINE KUMULATIVE

The *NEWDATAFILE* Function performs all the necessary tape-handling preliminaries before the program proper is ready to run.

Figure 10 represents the reorganizations of data prepared by the basic BUILD subprograms.

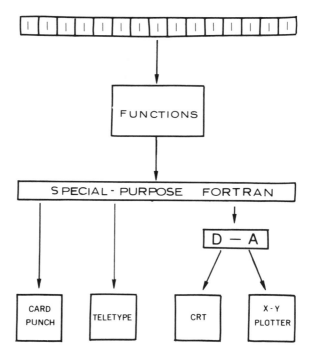

Figure 11. Organization of data-analysis procedures showing the output devices available to the experimenter and the position of program building blocks (functions).

NEXTRIAL creates the new array, NEWTRIAL, in which time and events are collected separately. Thus a list in the form:

$$1, 2, 3, 4, 5, 6 \cdots n$$

is transformed into the lists

$$1, 3, 5 \cdots n-(\text{times}) \text{ and } 2, 4, 6 \cdots n \text{ (events)}$$

A "trial" is a convenient chunk of data. We have found it most convenient to define a "trial" as all the data between successive reinforcements, but we can change this definition easily, since it must be specified in the argument of NEXTRIAL. One good reason for taking the data off tape in small segments by NEXTRIAL is that it allows a conservative use of core locations. The space used by the intermediate array NEWTRIAL can be reassigned as soon as the array IET is obtained. In most cases, all the data to be analyzed in a single run would overflow core.

INTREVENT creates the new array, IET, which lists the times that a particular, specified event occurred. In Figure 10, two IET arrays are shown, one for E1 and one for E2.

Table 1

BUILD SUBPROGRAMS

SUBPROGRAMS	DATA FROM	DATA TO	INFORMATION GIVEN BY VALUE OF FUNCTION	
			ERROR-CHECK	SCOUTING
FUNCTION NEW DATA FILE	TAPE (HEADER)	TELETYPE	RIGHT/WRONG TAPE POSITION	NO. CARD IM. BEFORE DATA
FUNCTION NEXTRIAL	TAPE (DATA)	NEWTRIAL	1. NO END OF TRIAL 2. END OF SESSION	NO. OF EVENTS
FUNCTION INTREVENT	NEW TRIAL	IET		NO. OF IETS
FUNCTION IETHISTOGRAM	IET	ISHISTOGRAM		MAXIMUM FREQUENCY
FUNCTION IETDISTR	IET	LOCATEVENTS	BUFFER OVERFLOW	NO. OF IETS USED
SUBROUTINE KUMULATIVE	LOCATEVENTS	KYOOM		

IETHISTOGRAM creates the new array, ISHISTOGRAM, which is a frequency distribution of inter-event times from IET.

IEVENTDISTR creates the new array, LOCATEVENTS. It represents the frequency of the event in successive time intervals. The subroutine KUMULA-TIVE cumulates the entries in LOCATEVENTS to produce a cumulative record in the array KYOOM.

A table of the BUILD Functions is given, (Table 1) with the self-descriptive names of the arrays that they use and the information provided by the Function value.

We can display the contents of any array by means of any output device. Our strategy can be illustrated by reference to Figure 11. Generally, we have tried to maximize the role of the Functions and minimize the use of special-purpose FORTRAN. Most problems require a minimum of non-standard FORTRAN "connectives" to relate the Functions. Those familiar with FOR-TRAN and the GE225 need only a few hours of instruction before they are able to retrieve data and perform complex analyses.

To illustrate the data analysis system, we shall describe its use in the context of an actual research program. In a series of experiments on the reinforcing value of information, pigeons were exposed to a procedure in which, on the food key,

M U L T   F R   20   F R   100

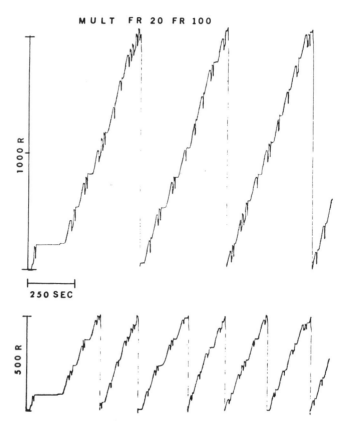

Figure 12. Computer simulation of a cumulative recorder using data retrieved from
magnetic tape. The output device was an X-Y plotter (Varian Associates,
Model F 80). The schedule was randomly either FR 20 or FR 100 (*mix* FR 20
FR 100) but associated cues could be obtained, until the next reinforcement, by
observing responses on another key (not shown); thus, observing response
converted the mixed schedule to the corresponding multiple schedule (*mult*
FR 20 FR 100). With the pen deflected downwards, the mixed schedule was in
effect; with the pen up, the multiple schedule was in effect. The scale factors of
the X-Y plotter were matched to the output voltages of the computer's D-A
converter to permit the display of the performance of an entire session in one
plot. Two plots are shown, illustrating how different scale factors may be chosen
for convenience in viewing or reproduction.

two fixed-ratio (FR 20 and FR 80 or FR 100) schedules of reinforcement
alternated unpredictably. Responses on a second key ("observing responses") lit
both keys with one of two colors (red, green), depending upon which ratio was
in effect. The light stayed on until reinforcement occurred. Thus, the lights had
an informative function and observing responses were secondarily reinforced by
the information they produced. Observing responses transformed the mixed-
ratio schedules into the corresponding multiple-ratio schedule. The procedure was
similar to that of Kendall (1965 *a, b*).

MIX   OR   MULT   FR 20   FR 100

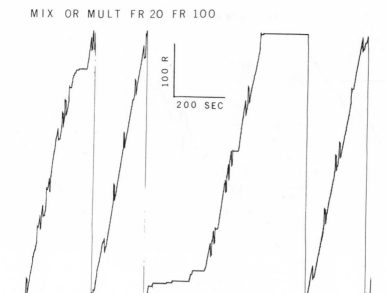

Figure 13. Cumulative response record when the informative cues signifying FR 20 or FR 100 were presented randomly by the experimenter. The pen was deflected upwards when a cue was on. If the pen was down, reinforcement was also marked with an upward deflection.

When few observing responses were required, the result typically obtained is shown in Figure 12. Figure 12 shows the contents of KYOOM, with two standard modifications: *a*. the cells of the array are modulo 1000 (upper trace) or 500 (lower trace) causing a reset to baseline at these points; *b*. a constant number was added to every cell when the informative lights were on. The lights were always off immediately after reinforcement. Therefore, after reinforcement the trace is displaced downwards. The fact that it remains offset for only a short time shows that observing behavior occurred promptly after reinforcement. Thus, if observing behavior always occurred promptly after reinforcement, the record, as in Figure 12, resembles a conventional cumulative record, with downward pips at (immediately after, in Figure 12) reinforcement.

We noted that when birds did not turn on the informative cues they occasionally paused near the middle of the long ratio. We speculated that in these cases the birds' behavior was acting as an effective cue, providing the information that the long ratio was in effect and thus generating a pause. Therefore, we continued the experiment with random, response-independent presentation of the appropriate cue. We could examine results by displaying KYOOM with any desired expansion of the X or Y axis.

Figure 13 shows the contents of KYOOM with the expansion of the X or Y axes chosen to approximate the resolution that would normally be obtained with a conventional cumulative recorder (100 responses=25 mm; 150 sec =25 mm). Figure 14 shows another record in which no cues were presented. A

FR 20 vs FR 80   (NO CUES)

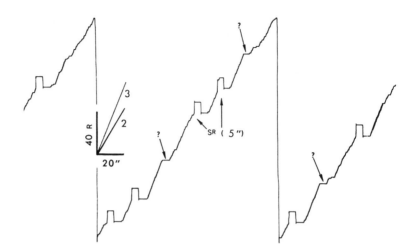

Figure 14. High-resolution cumulative response record showing intermediate pauses (marked "?") in the FR 80 component of *mix* FR 20 FR 80. Five-sec and reinforcements (S^R) are marked by upward displacements of the trace.

distinct, abrupt pause (indicated by "?" in Figure 14) often occurred after 30 to 40 responses in MIX FR 20 FR 80. The rate was generally higher before the pause and lower afterwards. These relations would be very difficult to detect with the usual methods of recording, unassisted by a computer or with normal resolutions as in Figures 12 and 13. The pause often lasted only a few seconds and the rate difference before and after the pause differed by fraction of a response per second.

The resolution is much greater in Figure 14 than in Figure 12 and 13. Our practice was to examine large samples of data as in Figures 12 and 13, then select smaller samples for detailed inspection as in Figure 14. Such a process is typical of experimentation in general. In our judgement the computer-based system has brought us considerable benefit in terms of speed and flexibility in the process of examining relatively "raw" experimental results, without even considering the advantages of speed and power in transforming data.

To compare a session's performance with and without informative cues, we established appropriate IET arrays, classified the entries according to ordinal position, made the necessary manipulations to determine means and standard deviations, and plotted these numbers. A typical result is shown in Figure 15.

It is immediately apparent from Figure 15 that performance in cued FR 80 (top right) differs from performance in uncued FR 80 (bottom right). In cued FR 80, pauses occur after about 15 to 25 responses and in uncued FR 80, pauses occur after about 25 to 40 responses. We chose to examine IRT durations because occasional long pauses would strongly affect their means and variances.

A somewhat different picture was given by plots of response speed, using the reciprocals of the IRT durations. An example is given in Figure 16. The average speed is uncued FR 20 (bottom left), is about 3.2 R/sec, with little trend. In uncued FR 80 (bottom right), the average speed is initially about the same, then dips to about 2.5 R/sec at 30 to 40 responses and finally rises somewhat to about 3.0 R/sec. In cued FR 80 (top right), response rate is more uniform at about 1.8-2.5 R/sec.

There is no simple statistical test that would demonstrate the character of the differences between cued and uncued FR 80. However, once in possession of the striking visual record shown in Figures 15 and 16, it is a simple and probably unnecessary exercise to verify, formally, the existence of those differences in which one is interested. It is probably true that the amount of computation required for Figure 15 and 16 would have deterred an experimenter from obtaining these results without the aid of a computer-based system for collection and analysis of data. Moreover, once the program for this analysis had been loaded, the results of any one of hundreds of sessions could be similarly analyzed and displayed in a matter of minutes. Also, the data selected for analysis could be quickly changed by changing the arguments of seek functions.

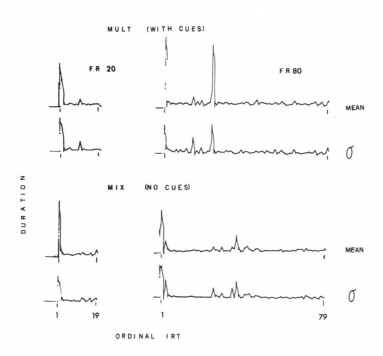

Figure 15. Means and standard deviations of durations of ordinally classified interresponse times in FR 20 and FR 80 with and without associated cues. These plots were obtained to assess differences in performance rather than to obtain absolute values; consequently the (linear) scale of the ordinate is not shown.

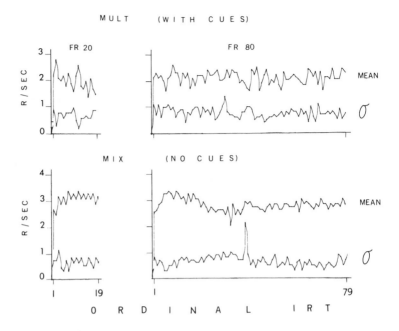

Figure 16. Means and standard deviations of ordinally classified response rates (reciprocal of interresponse times) in FR 20 and FR 80 with and without associated cues. The figure shows that absolute response rate depends upon the stimulus conditions as well as the contingencies of reinforcement. Other aspects of the nature of this dependence are illustrated in Figure 14 and 15.

The flexibility and speed of data analysis encouraged us to explore the data in depth, selecting, comparing, and altering analyses on the basis of what we discovered as we went along. Data analysis came to have the exciting intellectual flavor of empirical research, and ceased to be simply the final chore of a project.

The data presented above are experimental results, but they have the distinction of having been obtained without any prior intention to publish them. They are used here to illustrate the value of a computer-based system in solving day-to-day problems in the analysis of behavior.

The standardization of our data-analysis procedures follows from our general aim of making it as easy as possible to conduct experiments. FORTRAN represents a minimum deterrent for prospective experimenters, including students, in our laboratory. After learning to specify experiments in FORTRAN it is not difficult to learn to analyze the taped record of results. A particular routine statistical analysis of a session can usually be obtained within an hour after the session has ended. Simple descriptive statistics are provided on-line.

The structure of our system for data analysis has turned out, by unconscious design, as it were, to be admirably suited to the process of discovery of the implications of the data. It helps the experimenter to refine his "hunches" and formulate his tentative conclusions precisely. Most results that we obtain could be obtained more simply by writing an appropriate program for that purpose alone, but this presupposes that the experimenter knows at the outset what result he is interested in obtaining. These *a priori* judgments certainly exist, but in our experience they are usually false or too imprecise to specify in detail the writing of an analysis program.

ESTABLISHING A COMPUTER-BASED LABORATORY

We have described the creation of a FORTRAN-based control and analysis system on a business-oriented computer having minimal hardware modifications for our purposes. As we considered some of the improvements we envisioned for future developments, we made note of the fact that many of the hardware features we would find desirable were standard equipment on many small process-control computers. In addition, the arithmetic operations of these newer, less-expensive machines are not very different from those of the GE225 in capability and organization.

Most people considering the inclusion of a computer in their laboratory will confront the problem of implementing a new system that probably does not exist as a standard offering of any manufacturer. Our experience, we think, may be of value to these people, and, in concluding this chapter, we offer some general observations on choices they will have to make.

HARD AND SOFT FUNCTIONS

Choices in creating a computer-based laboratory are clarified if we separate two sets of functions: those to do with controlling experiments and recording data and those to do with man/machine interaction, as in data-retrieval and analysis, and development of new programs. We may call these respectively "hard" functions and "soft" functions. The hard functions are those carried out by the machine without any current human decision-making; with the soft functions the experimenter is "in the loop", and his decisions affect what the machine does. The hard/soft dimension for a typical laboratory is illustrated in Figure 17.

Generally speaking, any digital computer can be made to perform the hard functions. The ability to perform the soft functions is really what should guide the choices in designing a computer-based laboratory. This is difficult for experimenters to grasp if they have had little first-hand experience with computers. It seems obviously true that the essential functions of the computer are the hard functions; ability to perform soft functions is therefore seen as a kind of luxury or bonus. This is certainly not the case. It may happen that an experimenter will not be able to tell what happened in an experiment because he has failed to anticipate precisely the information he required from the data. In that case the results may be lost altogether, or an unwieldly inflexible man/machine system may delay the delivery of results for weeks or months.

The distinction between hard and soft functions, however, seems to be honored in the marketplace. "Small" machines generally are capable of performing only the hard functions. To perform the soft functions one needs a "medium-sized" (expensive) or a "large" (very expensive) machine. There is a conflict that results from this correlation of function and price. From the point of view of scientific capability, a large machine is usually better than a small machine. From the point of view of budget, a small machine seems to be better than a large machine.

There is a set of important variables correlated with price and capacity of computers, namely, organizational size and complexity. Here is a list of titles and functions, which is not entirely fanciful, of people in an organization that exists to do research in a laboratory based on a medium-sized computer.

Title	Function
Experimenter	Deciding what experiments to do and reporting experiments completed.
Programmer	Translating English descriptions of experiments, *etc.*, into the computer language.
Operator	Running the machine.
Research Assistant	Performing the experiments.
Senior Engineer	Diagnosing faults, optimizing use, implementing system changes.
Maintenance Engineer	Maintaining the equipment (preventive maintenance).
Cleaner	Keeping laboratory clean.
Clerk	Logging time, billing, ordering supplies, paperwork.
Secretary	Secretarying.
Manager	Worrying about the budget.

Such an organization is vulnerable because of the large numbers of people involved and the large number of distinct functions they perform. What happens if the operator falls sick?

We suspect that in most large laboratories the experimenter, having a history of self-sufficiency through his academic training, tries to perform all these functions himself, or to be able to perform them in an emergency. This may increase rather than reduce his productivity. Nevertheless, increased organizational size and complexity must be regarded as disadvantages of large computer systems.

If the soft functions available for a particular computing system serve as one of the important factors in making a selection, much of the complexity of the

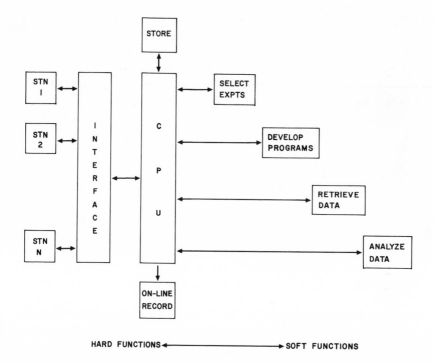

Figure 17. Representation of a computer-based laboratory showing the main functions. The usual relative position of these functions in the hard/soft dimension corresponds to left/right position in the figure.

organization will be reduced. While it is unlikely (but not really impossible!) for the computer to take on the chore of cleaning cages, designing experiments, or worrying about the budget, all of these chores can be easier with the assistance of the machine. There are two primary methods of improving the soft function of a given computing system. The first, and probably superior, method is to institute an effective computer communication link with the local computing behemoth. This generally huge, number-crushing, expensive property of the researcher's parent organization should be much better equipped to perform many of the routine analyses, charting, and even bookkeeping of the laboratory. The second alternative is to restrict the total number of experiments controlled in order to allow the laboratory computer and personnel to spend more time on soft functions.

The creation of a computer-centered laboratory is complicated by the incredible number of approaches to the simple-appearing decisions that have to be made. In these circumstances, it is prudent to contact the people in the computer science department or its equivalent. While these people may initially appear to be less understanding than the salesman as you describe what is desirable, they have probably solved the same problems in a different guise and can find the kind of technical people essential to the successful creation of any system.

We have tried to bring to light the guidelines we have found effective in considering new acquisitions. We offer them as some of the important considerations before the amount of available money and the laboratory workload have been decided.

EXPANDABILITY

The computer in a behavioral laboratory can be expected to be retained for several years. Over several years, one expects the work demands of a laboratory to increase in a normal growth pattern. In a non-computerized laboratory, such growth need not be especially planned for; a few more pieces of equipment and a few more people can be accommodated in the same space. The situation is completely different with a computerized laboratory. Growth must be planned for, and a poor choice of initial computer installation can inhibit growth. A particular installation may not be capable of being added to, only replaced at prohibitive cost in terms of hardware and start-up cost. The researcher who is considering a computer should ask not "What do I need now?" but "What will I need in 2 to 3 years?" He should consider what peripheral equipment he will wish to add, such as line printer, magnetic tape, plotter, A-D converter, card reader, visual displays. How difficult will it be to interface these devices with the CPU? How much software development will these additions require? How much additional core memory will they require? Is the core memory sufficiently expandable to handle the additional peripherals? Will it be possible to connect his computer with a larger computer in his organization? Will it be possible to have data collected on his computer processed on a more powerful computer?

The initial installation should emphasize the soft functions as much as is economically possible. Watching a teletype print out or load a program for an hour or so can destory an experimenter's ardor for computers. Very possibly your new-found friends in computer science can direct you to a local model of your proposed machine, complete with high-speed printer and card reader. The first computer in a laboratory will be used primarily for writing the programs that later will assist in the research process. Plan to ease that chore while being assured that the machine can be easily expanded to accept the increased workload that develops as the initial experiment programs begin running.

LANGUAGE

A higher-level language with subroutine or co-routine definition capabilities is essential. This is a basic point of this article. An established laboratory with a good deal of computer experience and established sources of technically trained computer people can afford to consider a new machine with virtually no software. If a computer appears outstanding in all respects other than this particularly important area, consider not only the cost of the hardware, but, in addition, seek out qualified software firms and get bids for writing a high-level language for the machine. The end result will in all likelihood be superior to the all-things-for-all people compiler a manufacturer would provide.

In any case, find out exactly what the manufacturer's attitude toward providing such software will be. Due to recent changes in marketing strategies by the large computer manufacturers, software and hardware may eventually be sold as separate items. While this complicates decision making, it may in fact mean greater value for a given investment as software houses become competitive. Under no circumstances should the newcomer to computer-controlled experimentation feel that he will be able to write his own compiler while simultaneously getting some experiments running. It would also pay to ignore largely the assurances of your new-found friends (from the computer center) that they will be able to whip together something for you.

Finally, as the specialty market in small computer systems grows, several companies will offer new systems consisting of complete software and hardware packages for the use of specific kinds of research. These packages should be evaluated as total systems rather than as separate components. They will appear expensive but only because both software and hardware costs are being realistically combined. The earliest systems have been designed for rather specific markets and if your lab fits within that particular market, the pricing will be competitive. However, your lab may not fit, so that a less-expensive system providing adequate software support for the soft functions will be a better selection.

MULTIPROGRAMMING AND SERVICING CAPACITY

In many fields, including experimental psychology, an experimenter's efficiency is determined, not by how much analytic power he can bring to bear on a single experiment, but how many experiments he can conduct simultaneously. Outstandingly productive laboratories are those where many different facets of a problem are being investigated concurrently in different experiments.

In the analysis of behavior, a single session lasts 1 to 2 hr per subject. Let us assume a standard duration of 2 hr including all the incidental activity of preparation. This means that four subjects can be tested in a working day. This is close to the minimum number of subjects for a single experiment. Therefore, using a computer with no time-sharing or multiprogramming capacity, the most sophisticated computer can handle about one psychological experiment per shift. However, besides computer control and data-acquisition there must be program development and data analysis. Program development and data analysis normally go on continuously, constantly competing for CPU time. With a machine that lacks time-sharing or multiprogramming one has a choice: either conduct an experiment, analyze data, or test a new program. Each of these vital activities constantly interferes with the others.

A time-sharing or multiprogramming environment will allow data analysis, program development, control of experiments, and data-acquisition to proceed at the same time, with no mutual interference. The number of simultaneous experiments that can be conducted will be limited essentially by the intellectual resources of the experimenter, rather than the characteristics of available hardware or the experimenter's effectiveness in competing for computer time with other experimenters.

If the straightforward approaches presented in this article are adopted, all multiprogramming chores are of a similar nature, so that a computer that is not being used for the soft functions of the laboratory may be used to control additional experiments. The computer systems should include the hardware capability of controlling at least 10 to 12 experimental stations. While some ingenuity will simplify the handling of individual stations so that computer time per experiment is minimized, the ability to switch quickly from one experimental station to another is a distinct advantage. Thus, the overall efficiency of the laboratory will be increased, if only by eliminating the set-up time between experiments.

Finally, from a hardware point of view, a computer with a multiple-level interrupt capability will prove superior to one with only one such interrupt. By minimizing the computer work involved in identifying which particular experimental chamber is demanding attention, more such chambers may be controlled. If some simple preprocessing of control and sensing signals is carried out external to the computer, the computing load will be further reduced. If, for example, slowly varying analog signals are being read by an analog to digital converter, the addition of equipment to interrupt the computer only when the analog voltage has changed will reduce demands on the computer without reducing the accuracy of the data.

It would be risky to indicate the desired number of simultaneous experiments that must be run when picking a computer because that number is a complicated function of the sophistication of control required. However, to go out on a digital limb, we feel that a minimum of four pilot studies or about 10 "production" studies is a good bench mark. While a good number might be obtained by simple economics—a comparison with dollar value of conventional equipment for similar experiments—such a comparison does not usually take into account the value of the non-existing soft functions or imprecise data-taking associated with traditional methods of control. Therefore, when we are put on the spot we usually say "seven", since that is a prime number, while secretly admitting complete bliss if we can run two at a time all night to get in 24 subject runs of 1-hr duration each day.

WORD LENGTH

Pick a medium-sized power of two. We think that 16 bits is an acceptable minimum for several reasons. In the first place, the longer the word length, the more complete the instruction set. The GE225 has 32 major instructions and the DEC PDP-8 has only eight. Several of these instructions do input-output or bit-chasing routines so that there are actually more than the indicated number of operations. As a second obvious advantage, when larger words are used to hold data and control information, more information is conveniently manipulated than when smaller word sizes force the experimenter to use several locations for a single piece of data. While simple fixed ratios will easily fit, (eight bits allows FR 256) medium length interval counts will easily overflow most small word length machine capacities. Several manufacturers will offer eight-bit machines that perform multiple-precision arithmetic. From a programming point of view, the potential will exist to handle the appropriate word length. However, each additional reference to the computer memory will add to the execution time of the control program, thereby reducing the effective running speed of the computer. The same situation exists when shorter word length computers attempt to execute instructions referring to data not in the immediate "vicinity" of the instruction. Additional memory references are required for the information to complete the operation.

Thus, a simple criterion for adequate word length does not exist. Our recommendation of 16-bits is based on an examination of existing offerings and an understanding of the complexities involved in producing an appropriate compromise between expensive core memory and overall processing efficiency. If for no other reason than the ease with which computer faults can be hidden while still presenting impressive statements of memory speed and word length manipulation power, the examination of the computer complete with software is the preferable selection strategy. If an eight-bit computer has a high-level language suitable for the class of experiments envisioned, and a 24-bit machine has no software, the hardware superiority of the 24-bit computer is eclipsed by the ease of programming the smaller computer.

SPEED

Speed of the machine is unlikely to be critical in behavioral applications. Reductions below a memory cycle of about 20 μsec are of no practical significance for the work the computer will do. Increasing speed has been one of the major goals of the computer industry because major customers needed "number-crushers" for business and scientific calculations calling for millions of computations. Accordingly, speed is often stressed in advertisements and the blandishments of manufacturers' representatives. However, in many cases, and certainly in behavioral applications, the limiting speed is set by the peripheral devices. For example, the microsecond differences between a fast and slow computer in initiating a feeder-operate command are negligible compared with the time lag due to the electrical and mechanical properties of the feeder itself. Even if 10 feeder-operate commands became "due" at the same time, so that they had to be serviced sequentially, a 20-μsec machine could still issue all the commands in some tens of milliseconds, still a practically negligible delay.

Talking about speed presents an additional opportunity to stress the desirability of evaluating a computer complete with running software. In presenting our system design for the GE225, we gave the times for and execution of instructions. Modern computers have operating speeds at least 10 times faster. In predicting the number of experiments we could handle, we referred to the service times of our FORTRAN-coded subroutines, rather than the computer speed directly. In much the same fashion as the 225 is faster than a smaller word size computer with the same memory reference time, so will a modern large word length machine with its potential for better software usually outperform the same speed small word length computer. A 1.5-μsec computer, which must use two cycles to retrieve most instructions, is actually a 3.0-μsec computer, and so on. It is difficult today to find a computer with a basic memory cycle time of less than 5 μsec. The basic question is not, "how fast?" but "what can it do at that speed?"

MEMORY SIZE

The three promotional factors, word size, speed, and (directly addressable) core memory size are closely related. In general, the more core memory that can be put into a computer, the better off you are. On the other hand, our experience with the GE225 tends to indicate that the memory is not required for actual program storage so much as for intermediate data storage, input-output, and a large buffer area for data manipulation. Calculation of needed core locations is complicated by the kind and quantity of input/output equipment and mass storage available on the computer.

Let us again emphasize the importance of having the software to utilize effectively the features built into the computer. What good is an additional 16,000 memory locations if the compiler cannot produce code to utilize it?

MASS STORAGE

It is possible to use a small computer to control experiments and make no attempt to use the computer for recording and storing the data. The possibility of storing the experimental data raises the questions: "What form of storage is most suitable—paper-tape, magnetic tape, drum, disc. *etc.*?" "What capacity of storage is required?"

We think that a mass storage device, such as a disk, is indispensible for the everyday running of experiments, data analysis, and intermediate data storage for very long-running experiments. Within the context of doing experiments in which long-term data storage is required, one of the new cartridge or minimum configuration digital magnetic tapes should be considered. A cartridge used for program storage must be of far higher quality than one designed for data storage, since the two types of information would be required with far different frequency. For example, the majority of high-quality audio cartridges can be read only 200 times. This is a lot of times when listening to music or even analyzing data: it is less than a week or two when reading popular programs.

Finally, we should not reject high-quality perforated tape or punched cards. The decision on the storage medium will have to be an individual one based on the read/write equipment of the computer and the frequency with which data are to be referenced. Paper tape costs about a dollar a roll. Mylar-backed aluminum perforated tape costs about fifteen dollars a roll. Intermediate qualities lie between these price extremes. Data use will dictate which investments should be made.

INPUT/OUTPUT

Finally, if we cannot get at the stored information, it is of no use. Fortunately, what is required in specifying the input/output equipment for most small computers is a function of the imagination rather than the availability of components. If the high-level language compiler is capable of communicating easily with machine-coded subroutines, the communication power of the computer is potentially unlimited. About the only expensive equipment required today is a good computer card punch. Everything else imaginable is readily available for less than $10,000. and in most cases less than $6000. New ink-squirting printers are as fast as many slow chain printers and yet cost about $5000. The same is true for medium-speed card readers, plotters and oscilloscope displays. While this equipment may seem expensive, until recently all computer-oriented equipment (other than the hardy but slow teletype) cost much more than $10,000.

All small and most medium sized machines are designed to permit easy connection of special purpose equipment such as will be needed for the running of experiments. The questions that must be raised are how much does it cost to add equipment and how hard it is to write the simple-minded programs needed to run the new devices?

CONCLUSION

We have advocated the acquisition of a 16-bit, 3-μsec, 8192-word computer with multiple interrupt levels, several hardware registers (including some index registers), a disk, card input/output, an ink-squirting printer, cartridge magnetic tape, and high-speed paper tape equipment. If we gave it a price tag it would appear that we had just copied it out of one brochure. In fact, the computer we desire does not exist and may never appear. We have to be content with using only what is available. We therefore continue to emphasize the importance of the soft functions and software rather than hardware.

REFERENCES

Kendall, S. B. Competing behavior and observing responses. *Psychonomic Science*, 1965, *3*, 279–280. (*a*)

Kendall, S. B. An observing response analysis of fixed-ratio discrimination. *Psychonomic Science*, 1965, *3*, 281–282. (*b*)

Mechner, F. A notation system for the description of behavioral procedures. *Journal of the Experimental Analysis of Behavior*, 1959, *2*, 133–150.

CHAPTER FIVE

APPLICATION
OF A DIGITAL COMPUTER
FOR RESEARCH
IN PSYCHOPHARMACOLOGY

V. B. CIOFALO, [1] R. H. TEDFORD,

D. L. DODGE,[2] and M. E. GOLDBERG[3]

Department of Pharmacology, Union Carbide Corporation, Sterling
Forest Research Center, Tuxedo, New York

[1] Now at Schering Corporation, Bloomfield, New Jersey.
[2] Digital Equipment Corporation, Maynard, Massachusetts.
[3] Now at Warner-Lambert Research Institute, Morris Plains, New Jersey.

INTRODUCTION

A variety of automated equipment has been used to investigate pharmaco-logical effects on the behavior of animals. Perhaps the most widely used is the conventional electromechanical relay system consisting of switching and timing circuits, cumulative recorders, and electrical impulse counters that control programming and recording of the experiment. In spite of the impressive performance of this equipment, there was a need to ease the burden of data acquisition, analysis, and storage for the investigator.

To keep abreast of this need in recent years, most manufacturers of behavioral equipment have begun to supply lines with solid-state systems that can be made compatible with conventional products. These aggregates were used to facilitate complex programming control as well as data acquisition to a degree. The assets of such a system provided the investigator with: (a) faster operation, due to transistors and ingenious circuit techniques, (b) reduction of high-level electrical artifacts, allowing use in areas with low-level, high-impedance circuits, and (c) smaller, quieter components and relatively trouble-free opera-tion. In addition, these units were designed so that they could be used in conjunction with a central programming system capable of utilizing a number of pre-stored complex programs interchangeably. The programs that have been assembled and debugged can be connected and used in a matter of minutes, thus adding to the attractiveness of the overall system. Perhaps this is the next best thing to a digital computer.

What about digital computers? The programming logic as well as the technological know-how that went into the solid-state circuit design is similar to contemporary digital computers. As an example, the programmed data proc-essor/PDP-8[4] makes available a compact, inexpensive, high-speed, magnetic-core memory system with compatible interface for use in behavioral research. The advantages of this system are: (a) a choice of doing on-line statistical analysis concomitant with control, or ability to devote the entire memory to control and perform off-line statistical analysis, (b) minor limitation in the number of different schedules that can be run concurrently, (c) less likelihood of down time, and (d) maximum statistical output without time-consuming data analysis by the investigator.

Perhaps we should elaborate on the laboratory context in which our computer is used. In this respect, we would like to relate our reasons for selecting a computer (specifically, a PDP-8), cost advantages, and specific features that led to the adaptation of a computer solution to our problems. In order to do this, we must reminisce for a moment to the early days of Union Carbide's entrance into pharmaceuticals in late 1965. At this time, our newly formed department was composed of a limited number of scientists, (computer-

[4] Programmed Data Processor—8/PDP-8. Digital Equipment Corp., Maynard, Mass.

naive) trained in various disciplines, and experienced in development of potential pharmaceuticals. The first task confronted was to establish goals that were compatible with training, experience, and market potential; after this, came the arduous task of implementation. Realizing the overwhelming burden of mass screening, it was decided to devote time to technological advancements commensurate with development of a well-balanced primary screen, and secondary evaluation program. Strides in electronic implementation were undertaken in each laboratory according to that laboratory's particular requirements. When it came time to consider a psychopharmacology laboratory, the thought of combining the control of behavioral schedules concomitant with data analyses appeared to provide significant challenge to the pharmacologists. The idea was discussed with the corporation's professional programming staff to obtain their reactions. To our satisfaction, the consensus was that such a system was feasible and programming service was available. The second step was to choose a reliable computer manufacturer offering the type of advantages previously described. About this time, members of our group were invited to attend a seminar given by Digital Equipment Corporation (DEC) representatives at Schering Laboratories, Bloomfield, New Jersey. To our delight, the computer sought had been described, along with a discussion on state logic concepts. This started the ball rolling, our computer was ordered and delivered in May of 1966, and in June we were headed for Maynard, Massachusetts to attend a one-week introductory computer course. Returning with overloaded memory, and a rapidly induced inferiority complex, we proceeded naively to design and fabricate the interface under the guidance of a DEC engineer. This entailed approximately 800 to 1000 man-hours of work. In September, a full-time programmer was temporarily assigned to our group. Previously we had been given the services of a part-time individual. It is recommended that a full-time programmer be on hand from inception. After a brief indoctrination involving interface, and behavioral psychology, programs to implement training schedules were written, and partial operation began in January, 1967. By May, 1967, baseline studies were initiated.

The time to develop software, including indoctrination, programming, compiling, testing, and documentation required approximately 1000 man-hours of work. The symbolic editor provided by the manufacturer was helpful in the preparation of program tapes. The write-ups of manuals provided by the manufacturer were considered well written, provided the reader has some background. Tapes generated from the numeric code in preference to the symbolic code saved considerable time in compiling, since one pass is required; use of the symbolic codes requires three passes before generation of a binary tape. We found this method to be quite satisfactory and it did result in significant time saving. A commentary on DEC software in addition to that which appears throughout the chapter, and perhaps an acceptable mention of the diagnostic tapes, would be difficult because our experience is rather limited.

The first two years represented 100 continuous hours of operation weekly. Major computer down-time occurred on two occasions. The first was attributed to the power supply, and the second to a number of internal problems. In addition, we experienced several minor maintenance problems amounting from one to two days down-time.

Cost advantages of the entire system must be equated against our ability to evaluate compounds in large numbers. For example, to outline briefly the day-to-day tasks of our laboratory may lend an appreciation to our decision. Utilization of this system afforded us the following capabilities:

(1) scheduling 212 runs (bimonthly)

(2) administration of 30 separate agents with a N of 6 (bimonthly), and

(3) under optimal conditions, the capability of determining ED_{50}'s[5] for 30 separate agents on various schedules in a six-week period.

Many advantages are inherent in this type of system, and hopefully this chapter and book will amplify on them and serve to overcome the skepticism of those who doubt its value. The ensuing pages provide a detailed description of our operation. It is intended to answer some basic questions concerning computer application and hopefully will prove helpful to future users.

SYSTEM CONCEPTS

The decision to develop an on-line behavioral control system requires a sequence of design phases, the order of which is necessitated through trial and error. These phases may be summarized as follows: (a) system design and specification, and (b) interface and program design (concurrently performed). The purpose of the system design phase is to attempt to construct an overall view of the requirements of the process being controlled, giving attention to the available hardware and the required programming effort. From this overall view, a set of system specifications emerges determining the direction of the phases that ensue.

During system design, the tasks to be performed must be exhaustively examined. Special consideration should be given to input rate (responses) and input-output transfer functions (*i.e.*, required computer manipulations of an input excitation before an output response). The importance of such input-output requirements cannot be over-stressed. All real-time computers respond to stimuli. It is the speed of response to a stimulus that allows the computer to distinguish successive stimuli. Therefore, the case of maximum theoretical response rate determines the specifications of the required system. As an example, if the operant response rate on a lever by an animal is assumed to be 10 per second, and if 10 rats are pressing randomly with respect to each other, the

---

[5] That dose which produces an effect in 50% of the treated group. This dose is based on calculations utilizing a range of three or more separate dosage treatments. Figures 3 through 5 were reprinted by courtesy of the Editor of *Behavioral Science*.

worst case possible is 10 x 10 responses per second, or one response every 10 msec. If one allows the occasional occurrence of a few responses in which instantaneous rate by one subject is appreciably higher, *i.e.*, 20 to 50 msec between two successive responses, the instantaneous input rate can approach 500 per second or one every 2 msec. It is during this 2-msec period that the processing of input-output transfer function must be completed. The exact nature of such input-output transfer can be defined as that function of the system that deals with:

(1) recognition that a response has occurred and source identification,
(2) recording of response occurrence,
(3) initiation of required action as a function of the number of responses, *i.e.*, reinforcement after 10 lever presses,
(4) alteration of the schedule state as a function of the number of responses (and/or time); permission to perform certain statistical procedures that require less priority than monitoring experimental control.

An important part of the system design and specification phase is the selection of the necessary computer hardware. Consideration should be given to computer ability to connect to and communicate with interface, external devices such as levers, shock scamblers, and feeder solenoids. Provision must be made for the computer to address each device and to sense discrete states or to initiate changes in state. Furthermore, the computer must be able to suspend or interrupt low-rate low-priority (background) processing upon demand (by a lever reponse or real-time clock tick) and rapidly process the input-output transfer function. In addition, a wide range of interface modules must be available to permit optimum interface design.

Since a computer processes input-output transfer functions by means of an orderly sequence of instructions called a program, the efficiency of the order code should be carefully considered. It is advantageous to prepare a flow diagram of a typical input-output transfer function and to ascertain the response time (execution) of the selected input-output transfer function when processed by the computer. In many instances, the manufacturer can supply an input handler or program to identify lever-press interrupts and initiate the processing of the required input-output transfer function.

After consideration of the above, together with a set of system specifications, the arduous task of computer selection is greatly simplified.

From the system design standpoint, the PDP-8 is well suited for the task of on-line behavioral control. An examination of the flowchart of a typical control schedule (exclusive of statistical analysis) is shown in Figure 1. In this case, a differential-reinforcement-of-low-rate (DRL) schedule with a limited hold is presented. The resultant sequence of instructions given in Figure 2 focuses attention on a few salient points:

(1) A compact and versatile instruction set, as utilized in the PDP-8, may be arranged to perform a variety of tasks.
(2) A few selected instructions can be used repeatedly.

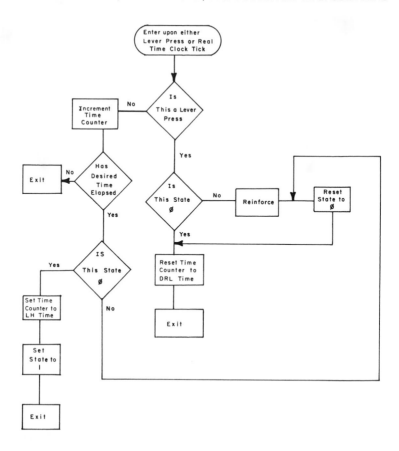

Figure I.   DRL WITH LIMITED HOLD PROGRAM FLOW
CHART FOR SCHEDULE CONTROL ONLY

(3) A 12-bit word is of sufficient length for on-line behavioral data
recording.

(4) A simple but flexible means of communicating with external devices is
essential.

Consideration of these points permits an economical selection of computer
hardware, yet provides the programmer with an easily learned and easily utilized
instruction set.

THE INTERFACE DESIGN

The choice of an interface configuration was dictated by the necessary
compromise between interface dollar economy and program economy. In this

```
DRL,        Ø               /Start of DRL routine; contains exit address

            TAD ITFLAG      /Get Interrupt type flag

            SZA CLA         /Skip if lever interrupt

            JMP TIME        /Not lever interrupt, service clock

            TAD STATE       /Get state flag

            SZA CLA         /Skip if state zero

            JMP S1          /Not state zero, must be state 1

SØ,         TAD DTIME       /Get DRL time

            DCA TCLOCK      /Initialize clock to DRL time

            JMP I DRL       /Exit

S1,         IOT             /Reinforce

            DCA STATE       /Reset state to zero

            JMP SØ          /Continue

TIME,       ISZ TCLOCK      /Increment time clock and skip if zero

            JMP I DRL       /Exit

            TAD STATE       /Get state flag

            SZA CLA         /Skip if zero state

            JMP S1+1        /Not zero state must be state 1

            TAD LHTIME      /Get limited hold time

            DCA TCLOCK      /Initialize clock to LH time

            ISZ STATE       /Set state to 1

            JMP I DRL       /Exit
```

FIGURE 2. PDP-8 PROGRAM FOR DRL WITH LIMITED HOLD TO IMPLEMENT FIGURE 1.

respect, both program length and running time were considered. This compromise resulted in two separate distinct interfaces: one to handle in-bound data in the form of lever responses, and a second to handle out-bound command signals to the accessory equipment.

One of eight basic computer instructions, the input-output transfer instruction, was used to communicate with and control 64 external devices. In addition, this instruction provided three programmable pulses, called input-output pulses, which were sent to the external device(s). The external device was responsible for detection, when its number was presented on the input-output lines, and for gating the input-output pulses to perform required functions. The logic device that performed both of these functions is called a Device Selector. In addition, the arithmetic register (or accumulator) inputs and outputs were presented to external devices on the PDP-8 input-output bus, permitting these devices to read the contents and to write data into the accumulator. The collection of external logic to perform the above functions was handled by the interface.

As mentioned previously, the ability to interrupt a program in progress and rapidly process the input-output transfer function was an important computer asset. The PDP-8 provided a single level interrupt bus by which external devices can request service. If one or more devices brought this bus to ground (0 v), the instruction or program pointer (often called the program counter) was stored in the first location in memory (Location 0), the instruction pointer was set to point to Location 1 and the interrupt disabled. The program was then sequentially executed starting from Location 1.

The interrupt program commencing in Location 1 was responsible for identification of the device that caused the interrupt. This removed or dismissed the interrupt condition and returned the program to its original position. To provide identification of interrupt source, an input to the computer called the skip bus was provided. If this bus was brought to ground by only one device, then that device could be uniquely identified. This was accomplished by execution of an input-output transfer instruction and by use of a device selector gated input-output pulse, which sensed the state of the device and brought the skip bus to ground if the device was in the ready state. If the device was ready, the next instruction was skipped and the one following it executed. The instruction to be executed was usually a directive to go to another program to service that device (*i.e.*, turn stimulus light on, turn shock off, *etc.*).

Once the program to service a device was in progress, the ready/not ready indicator (device flag) was reset by using a second device selector gated input-output pulse.

To permit successive interrupts, the interrupt must eventually be enabled. This was usually done upon completion of all current device service and was facilitated by the use of two special input-output transfer instructions, which initiated internal changes in the processor. These instructions were the *ION* instruction, which turned the *I*nterrupt *ON*, and the *IOF* instruction which turned the *I*nterrupt *OFF*.

INPUT

The lever input interface was chosen so that each 12-bit word could be used maximally. Each lever was buffered by a Schmitt Trigger to remove contact bounce and was used to set a Flip-Flop that served as a one-bit memory, as shown in Figure 3. Since only 12 bits were read from the external device(s) into

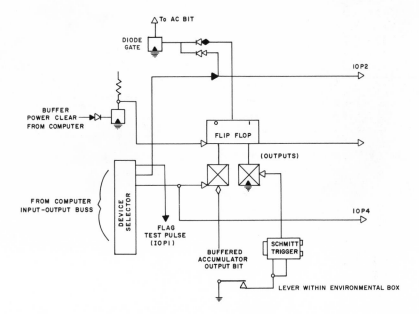

Figure 3.   INPUT INTERFACE

the accumulator at any one time, the levers were sampled in groups of 12. Whenever one or more levers caused their corresponding bit to be set, a signal called an interrupt was sent to the computer, which signified that a device required service. This is illustrated in Figure 4. The computer was set to respond to interrupts and the devices were tested sequentially, employing one of the input-output pulses, IOP 1, to determine whether the lever interface was the device that originated the interrupt. If such were the case, the program read the contents of each group of 12 bits using a second input-output pulse, IOP 2. Since lever presses were random with respect to each other, it was possible that when reading one or more responses into the accumulator, one or more levers were in the process of simultaneously setting their respective bits. The third input-output pulse, IOP 4, was used unconditionally to clear a group of 12 bits in order to receive the next successive response, which made it possible to lose responses. To eliminate this possibility, the only reset or clear inputs that were activated for clearing by the third input-output pulse were those one-bit memories that were actually read into the accumulator. This was done by conditioning the clear input with the corresponding buffered accumulator output bit.

Since most behavioral schedules are time-dependent, a 0.1-sec clock was provided in the input interface signifying that the computer was interrupted every 0.1 sec by the clock. Elapsed time was accumulated by counting successive

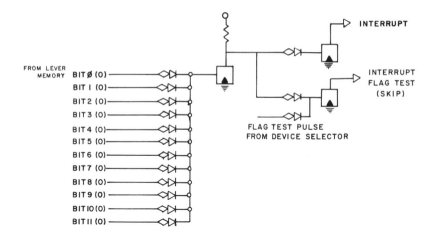

Figure 4.   INTERRUPT

clock pulses. When the accumulated counts were equal to the desired clock counts, the clock pulse counter was reset to zero and other operations were initiated, such as turning on a shock unit or providing a reinforcement.

OUTPUT

The output interface requirements were dictated by the needs of the environmental boxes and shock units. Since these operated at higher voltages than the interface logic components, solenoid drivers (which were capable of supplying 600 mA to ground from a load return to as high as −70 v) and relay drivers (capable of supplying 100 mA to ground from a load return as high as −15 v) were used as buffers between the interface logic outputs and the environmental boxes and shock units. Since the shockers, speakers, stimulus lamps, and houselights were required to be on for varying lengths of time, flip-flops were set (either on or off until cleared), using IOP 2 (Figure 5), according to the state of their respective accumulator bits as presented on the input-output bus. This output word was then stored in the computer memory where it was revised as dictated by the program. After each revision of the bit pattern in the output word, the output interface flip-flops were first cleared using IOP 1 (Figure 5), and then set as previously mentioned. The solid and liquid reinforcement mechanisms were typical devices that are pulsed. For this reason, adjustable one-shots, triggered by IOP 2 according to the state of their respective accumulator bits, were used to turn the solenoid reinforcement drivers on for the required length of time.

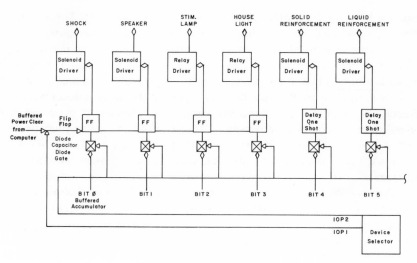

Figure 5.   OUTPUT   INTERFACE

PROGRAMMING CONCEPTS AND DESIGN

A computer program, which is a detailed set of instructions and data, causes the computer to perform a predetermined course of action. Preparation or coding of these instructions and data in a form suitable to the computer is called programming. Coding, however, is only a fraction of the overall task in problem-solving using a digital computer. Specifically, there are four basic steps in problem solving: (a) definition, (b) analysis and solution, (c) implementation, and (d) documentation.

The definition is a complete narrative or outline containing all relevant information. The analysis and solution of a problem requires examination of the information in the problem statement and development of a set of procedures. The program flowchart is a major step used in implementing a data processing problem. Other useful procedures are layouts of the input-output formats, a rough storage map, and decision tables. At this point, it is essential that the persons requesting the program and the programmer communicate closely and review preliminary work. This will give both sides an opportunity to review the definition, ensuring that analysis and solution is proceeding in the right direction.

It is now possible to implement the desired problem, which is accomplished by translating flowcharts and diagrams into a language that is understood by the computer. Manufacturers usually supply one or more machine languages for this purpose. Knowledge of machine language and binary arithmetic are mandatory in testing and debugging the program. The initial translation of the procedural steps is called the source program. The coded statements are converted into machine language by another program known as an assembler. The assembled program is the object program that will be operated on by the computer.

The second stage of implementing a program is testing and debugging, in which test data and results are evaluated. A detailed flowchart is helpful in trying to isolate a bug in the program logic. Sample problems should present all important alternatives. Perhaps the most important step of all is documentation. Frequently, programs are discarded because of changes in personnel and unavailability of complete information. Adequate documentation must be filed with each new program before it is accepted for use. As a minimum, documentation should include: abstract, sample output, system flowchart, and operational instructions. Detailed flowcharts and program listing, though desirable, are optional for the master file. Included in the abstract are the purpose, special features, important equations, input-output types, machine requirements, relation to other programs, and the average run time. Operational instructions should cover the machine set-up, run instructions, data formats, preparation of input data, scheduled and unscheduled (if possible) program halts, and the expected run time.

A discussion of our real-time program used for the control of behavioral research is given below.

SYSTEM MONITOR

The program is divided into two parts; the system monitor (or supervisor) and the behavioral chamber schedules. The system monitor contains the routines necessary for servicing interrupts, constants, temporary buffer registers, print-out, calculations, and multiplication subroutines. These routines occupy approximately 60% of available core storage. The program actually operates through a series of interrupts.

The behavioral schedules, in addition to responding to interrupts from the real-time clock, also respond to interrupts generated by lever presses, the teletype keyboard (ASR-33), and the teleprinter (ASR-33). The programming routines used to identify these interrupts are located in Page One[6] of computer memory. In order of priority they are: clock, lever, keyboard, and print-out (Figure 6). The clock and lever interrupts can occur during print-out operations. However, clock and lever service routines are not interruptable. When an interrupt occurs, the program tests the interrupt flags to determine which type has occurred. The program must then identify which box or boxes must be serviced at that time. For clock, lever, and print service routines, bits are turned on (set to one) or turned off (reset to zero) for each box. A word has been assigned to each of these interrupts and bits 0 through 9 represent behavioral chambers A through J respectively (10 boxes are used currently). Bits 10 and 11 are not used presently. Boxes that require servicing will have their bit turned on.

---

[6] The PDP-8's 4096-word memory is divided into 32 blocks of 128 words each. These blocks are called Pages and are numbered from 0 to 37 in base 8 notation.

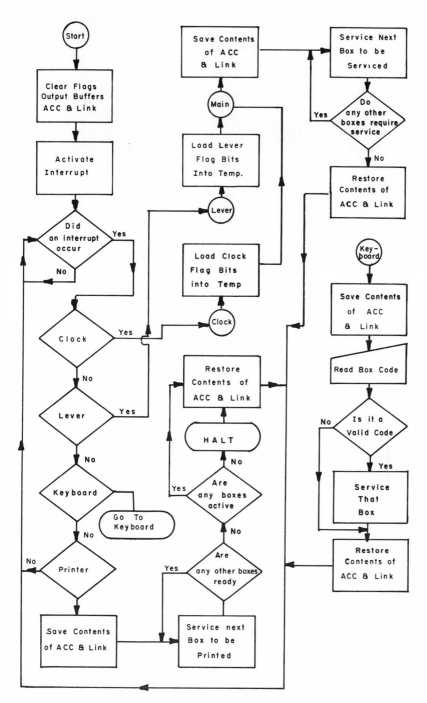

Figure 6.   INTERRUPT SERVICE ROUTINES

Page	Contents[c]
0	Temporary buffer registers, short sub-routines, constants and statistic dump area
1	Interrupt service routines
2	FR system
3-14	Box schedules
15	FR system
16	Data storage for boxes H, I, and J
17	Data storage for boxes A, B, and C
20	NDA and DRL systems
21	Data storage for boxes D, E, F, and G
22	NDA system
23	NDA and DRL systems
24	FR system
25	PD system
26	PD system
27	PD system
30	PD system
31	FR system
32	FR system
33	Print-out and calculations sub-routines
34	Print sub-routines
35	Multiplication sub-routines
36	Print-out and calculations sub-routines
37	Binary and rim loaders

FIGURE 7. CORE MEMORY MAP

[c]These are the primary contents of each Page. There may be some small subroutines on any given Page that are used by other systems. The chamber schedules and Pages 16, 17, and 21 of the core memory will vary depending upon which systems are currently in use.

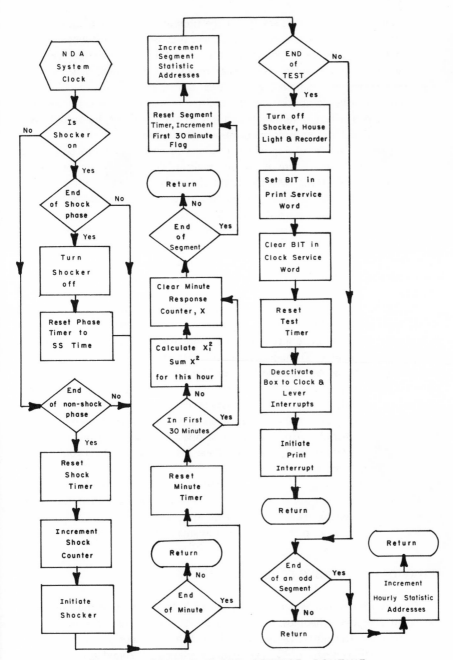

Figure 8. SAMPLE CLOCK SERVICE ROUTINE

For clock interrupts, bits are set by the program after manual initiation by the experimenter from a remote source. These bits are turned off when the test duration has elapsed. Lever interrupt bits are set by the interface hardware circuitry in the lever buffer register as previously described. When a lever interrupt occurs, the contents of the lever buffer register are read into the accumulator of the computer and the register is cleared to zero by the read operation. When a test is terminated in any of the chambers, its output bit is turned on. This bit is reset after the print-out is complete.

The method of identifying which chamber or chambers are to be serviced for these interrupts make use of the link register. This one-bit register may be rotated right or left along with the 12-bit accumulator in a few microseconds. Under program control, the link is reset to zero and the accumulator is loaded with the interrupt's service word. Then, by successive shifting of the accumulator word into the link, and counting the number of shifts, the chamber to be serviced is identified. If the link contains a zero after shifting, the chamber is bypassed. This process continues until all chambers requiring service have been identified and serviced. The maximum time for this operation is approximately 250 μsec.

Keyboard interrupts are handled by a different routine. As mentioned above, each behavioral chamber has been identified with a letter from A through J. The octal code for these letters is loaded into the accumulator when a key is struck by the operator. Through a series of subtractions, the program is able to determine which chamber is being addressed by the operator. After the letter has been correctly keyed into the computer, one to four additional characters are needed to identify the particular schedule desired for that chamber. The remainder of the system monitor is made up of the specific routines required by the behavioral schedules. Routines to type one character, read one character, and an exclusive OR were written into Page Zero. The statistical routines are found in Page 33. Print service routines such as carriage return, line feed, and binary to decimal converters are located in Page 34. A double precision multiplication routine and a special routine for squaring two numbers are contained in Page 35. Page 36 contains special routines for printing the nomenclature, responses per segment, reinforcements per segment, *etc.*

BEHAVIORAL CHAMBER SCHEDULES

The system monitor is permanently stored in the memory of the computer. Individual chamber schedules, however, may be altered by the experimenter when necessary. Currently, we are using four different experimental schedules: Punishment Discrimination/PD (1), Non-Discriminated Avoidance/NDA (2), Continuous Fixed Ratio/FR (3), and Differential Reinforcement of Low Rates/DRL (4). Figures 7 to 10 illustrate a typical core memory map, flow-charts of a NDA schedule (clock, lever, and keyboard service routines) and a listing of chamber schedule summaries.

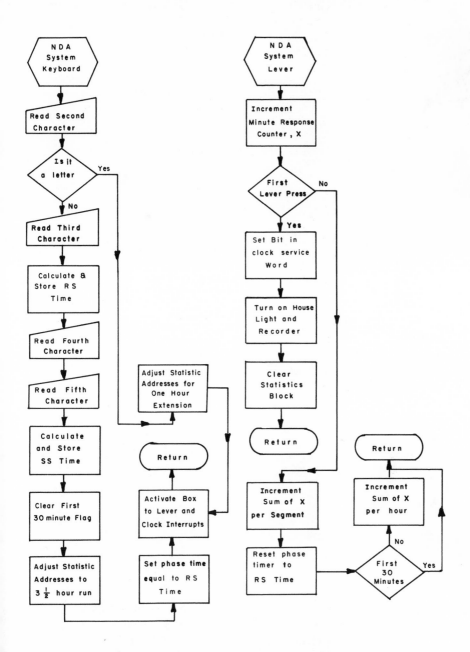

Figure 9. SAMPLE KEYBOARD and LEVER SERVICE ROUTINES

PD SYSTEM

Schedule	Call	Duration	Variables
FR1	/	1 hour	None
VI2	∅	1 hour	None
VI2 + FR1 w/T	1	1 1/2 hours	None
VI2 + FR1 w/T + S	2	1 1/2 hours	None

NDA SYSTEM

Schedule	Call	Duration	Variables
RS 4∅/ SS 2∅	4∅2∅	3 1/2 hours	RS & SS Times
Extension	X	1 hour	None

FR SYSTEM

Schedule	Call	Duration	Variables
FR15	15	1 hour	Fixed Ratio

DRL SYSTEM

Schedule	Call	Duration	Variables
DRL 2∅/LH2	2∅∅2	2 hours	DRL, LH
DRL 2∅/NLH	2∅∅∅	2 hours	DRL

All Calls shown would be preceded by the Chamber Letter

FIGURE 10.   CHAMBER SCHEDULE SUMMARY

The first three chambers (A, B, and C) utilize the PD schedule. Actually, there are four possible variations available under this system; any of these may be called for by any or all of the chambers. The criterion schedule consists of six 15-min segments. Each segment of the multiple schedule contains a 12-min VI 2 component (one reinforcement on the average of every 2 min) (3) and a 3-min FR 1 component (one reinforcement for each response) (3). A constant tone is introduced during the FR 1 component in which each lever press is simultaneously reinforced (liquid reinforcement) and punished (shock). The shock

Call: A/

FR1, BOX A

SG	1	2	3	4	5	6
RT	125	132	47	23		
SR	125	132	47	23		

327   327

Call: AØ

VI2, BOX A

SG	1	2	3	4	5	6
RT	253	264	219	188		
SR	7	8	7	7		

924   29

Call: A1

VI2+FR1+T BOX A

SG	1	2	3	4	5	6
VI/RT	165	156	172	147	161	152
VI/SR	6	5	7	6	7	5
FR/RT	23	25	9	15	11	8

953   36   91

Call: A2

VI2+FR1+T, S BOX A

SG	1	2	3	4	5	6
VI/RT	149	126	135	142	156	175
VI/SR	6	5	6	7	5	6
FR/RT	4	2	1	3	2	2

883   35   14

The numbers under each box summary are the totals of the
first, second, and third rows in that order.

FIGURE 11.   PD SYSTEM SAMPLE PRINT-OUTS

duration is fixed at 0.4 sec and the current intensity is varied manually for each
animal. Three schedules are used for training the animals. The first level of
training is a continuous reinforcement (CRF) schedule in which each lever press
is reinforced (3). The subject is then exposed to a variable-interval schedule, in
which one reinforcement occurs on the average of each 2 min (VI 2).
Reinforcement occurs only after an elapsed interval of time and when a response

Call: D4Ø2Ø

NDA   4Ø/2Ø   BOX D

SG	1	2	3	4	5	6	7
RT	3Ø	4Ø	4Ø	4Ø	4Ø	4Ø	74
SR	75	75	75	76	76	76	68

CUM DATA	FREQ.	D SQ	S SQ
Ø3Ø-Ø9Ø	1.333	393.339	6.66Ø
Ø9Ø-15Ø	1.333	393.339	6.66Ø
15Ø-21Ø	1.699	651.41Ø	14.423

Call: DD (one hour extension of previous run)

NDA   4Ø/2Ø   BOX D

SG	1	2	3	4	5	6	7
RT						4Ø	4Ø
SR						78	78

CUM DATA	FREQ.	D SQ	S SQ
Ø3Ø-Ø9Ø	.ØØØ	.ØØØ	.ØØØ
Ø9Ø-15Ø	.ØØØ	.ØØØ	.ØØØ
15Ø-21Ø	1.333	693.339	11.745

Calculations exclude the first 30 minute segment. The times under the CUM DATA heading refer to the inclusive times of the session in minutes.

Call: H15

FR   15, BOX H

SG	1	2	3	4
RT	25	25	25	25
SR	1	2	2	1

CUM DATA	FREQ.	D SQ	S SQ
ØØØ-Ø3Ø	1.666	166.674	5.723
Ø3Ø-Ø6Ø	1.666	166.674	5.723

FIGURE 12.   NDA AND FR SYSTEM SAMPLE PRINT-OUTS

was made in the last 0.5 sec of the interval. If the subject does not respond, the interval is suspended. The final training stage is the same schedule as the criterion schedule mentioned above without the introduction of shock during the FR1 component.

The basic NDA system comprises boxes D, E, F, and G. Alternate binary tapes are available that will extend this system to all boxes. The schedule used in this system has several components: (a) the response-shock interval (RS), (b) the

Call: H2002

DRL   20 /LH   2, BOX H

SG	1	2	3	4	5	6	7
14	18	9	2	1	2	3	5
28	4	8	10	[15]	15	9	2
42	2	1	2	0	0	0	0

RT   108
SR   15

Call: I2010

DRL   20 /LH   10, BOX I

SG	1	2	3	4	5	6	7
14	29	3	3	2	2	5	4
28	10	10	9	8	7	3	3
42	[2]	1	2	2	1	1	1

RT   108
SR   23

Call: J2000

DRL   20 /LH   , BOX J

SG	1	2	3	4	5	6	7
14	10	1	1	2	2	3	4
28	6	10	10	12	11	7	4
42	3	5	4	4	3	2	4

RT   108
SR   59

Blocked in areas represent the pay-off regions.

14 - This row contains the number of responses made at intervals of 0 to 14 seconds.

28 - This row contains the number of responses made at intervals of 14 to 28 seconds.

42 - This row contains the number of responses made at intervals greater than 28 seconds. The first six segments represent the intervals from 28 to 40 seconds and the last segment is for all response intervals over 40 seconds.

FIGURE 13.   DRL SYSTEM SAMPLE PRINT-OUTS

shock-shock interval (SS), and (c) the shock component. The latter is fixed at 0.5-sec duration, and it commences at the termination of the RS or SS interval. During shock, no lever presses are serviced. In our program, the RS interval may be varied from 1 to 99 sec. This component is entered at the start of the test and after each lever press is serviced. The SS interval may also be varied from 1 to 99 sec. This component is entered at the termination of shock. If a response occurs in the RS or SS interval, the schedule reverts to the start of an RS interval. As in the PD program, the shock intensity may be varied for each animal.

Boxes H, I, and J are primarily assigned to the FR schedule. As before, an alternate tape is available to extend this schedule to include boxes D, E, F, and G. In this schedule, a response is reinforced after a fixed number of lever presses. The fixed ratio may be varied from 1 to 99 for each test run.

The DRL schedule utilizes chambers H, I, and J, when they are not assigned to another schedule. In this schedule, a response is reinforced when the interval between responses satisfies the test criteria. From the input, upper and lower limits are established for the proper response interval. The lower limit may be varied from 10 to 30 sec in 2-sec steps. The upper limit can be set from 2 sec above the lower limit to infinity (NO LIMITED HOLD). When a limited hold is specified, the upper limit does not exceed 40 sec.

With the systems available we can operate any of the above schedules in the following 12 combinations:

Chamber	1	2	3	4	5	6	7	8	9	10	11	12
A	PD	PD	PD	PD	PD	PD	NDA	NDA	NDA	NDA	NDA	NDA
B	PD	PD	PD	PD	PD	PD	NDA	NDA	NDA	NDA	NDA	NDA
C	PD	PD	PD	PD	PD	PD	NDA	NDA	NDA	NDA	NDA	NDA
D	NDA	NDA	NDA	FR	FR	FR	NDA	NDA	NDA	FR	FR	FR
E	NDA	NDA	NDA	FR	FR	FR	NDA	NDA	NDA	FR	FR	FR
F	NDA	NDA	NDA	FR	FR	FR	NDA	NDA	NDA	FR	FR	FR
G	NDA	NDA	NDA	FR	FR	FR	NDA	NDA	NDA	FR	FR	FR
H	FR	NDA	DRL	FR	NDA	DRL	FR	NDA	DRL	FR	NDA	DRL
I	FR	NDA	DRL	FR	NDA	DRL	FR	NDA	DRL	FR	NDA	DRL
J	FR	NDA	DRL	FR	NDA	DRL	FR	NDA	DRL	FR	NDA	DRL

The discussion above describes the procedures that we have used in the control of various behavioral experiments. In addition to experimental control, certain statistical analyses are accumulated during the tests for print-out at the end of each run. When a print-out is initiated, the data are dumped in a reserved area on Page Zero (a section of memory which may be addressed directly from any other memory location). The print-out proceeds with interruptions by clock and levers from other boxes taking priority over the print-out. Examples of the print-outs for each schedule are shown in Figures 10 to 13. A brief description of the nomenclature follows:

DRL: Reinforcement that depends upon the immediately preceding rate of responding.

DSQ: The statistic, $\Sigma\, d^2$, derived by the formula:
$$DSQ = \Sigma\, (X^2) - \overline{X}(\Sigma\, X)$$
where X is the number of responses per minute and $\overline{X}$ is the average number of responses per minute.

FR: Number of responses for each reinforcement in a fixed-ratio schedule.

FREQ: Average number of responses per minute.

LH: Limited hold in seconds above the minimum time. If blank, no limited hold used.

NDA: The numbers following this symbol, signifying a nondiscriminated avoidance schedule, represent the time (in seconds) for the RS and SS components.

RT: Number of responses made during each segment of time.

SG: Segment Number; in the PD and FR schedules each segment of time lasts for 15 min, in the NDA system each segment lasts 30 min, and in the DRL system, each segment represents a 2-sec interval on the time axis.

SR: Number of reinforcements (positive or negative) received during each segment.

SSQ: The variance (standard deviation squared, s^2) around the FREQ, derived by the formula:
$$SSQ = \frac{DSQ}{N-1}$$
where DSQ (previously defined) and N is the number of observations.

S: In the PD schedule description, indicates that each response made in the presence of tone is simultaneously punished and reinforced.

T: In the PD schedule description, indicates that a constant tone is introduced to the chamber during the FR 1 phase.

No entry in a given printout heading indicates that the animal failed to respond.

RECOMMENDATIONS

HARDWARE

1. Use of a 12-bit word is recommended strongly; thus providing for multiple contingencies, and if desired, cumulative-event and response-pen control, which is not provided for in our system.
2. 600-mA drivers are necessary to provide adequate reserve power.
3. All relays and solenoids should be suppressed with good quality diodes, not neon lamps or RC networks.
4. Isolation of shock outputs from all control lines, logic, and power supplies cannot be overemphasized.
5. All outputs should be distributed by an easily programmable patch panel.
6. The interface should be designed and wired to include as much flexibility as possible. This flexibility, however, need not be implemented initially (e.g., logic modules may be purchased at a later date and plugged in).
7. Solid-state shock scramblers (if available) are strongly recommended, otherwise follow through on the third recommendation.

8. House current of 3 amps (115 vac) is imperative.
9. Consideration to lead dress, and a good surplus supply of spare modules during interface debugging is needed.
10. Consideration should be given to the purchase of a spare ASR-33 teletype and preventive maintenance checks on the computer, which tends to keep the investigator on-line longer, and with relatively trouble-free operation.

SOFTWARE

1. Before attempting to write a computer program of this nature, the programmer should be thoroughly versed in the following areas:
   (a) The behavioral schedules that *may* be desired by the experimenters.
   (b) The programming languages that are available, especially assembly language.
   (c) The programming requirements of the interface and associated peripheral equipment.
2. Now select one schedule and carry it through to completion. Once you are on-line it will instill confidence so that the overall job can be done.
3. Of course, to implement any one schedule, you will need to have the supervisor completed for that schedule's service routines.
4. After you have the first schedule operational, proceed with the remaining schedules, one at a time, until the system is completely written, tested, and debugged. During debugging, you may want to disengage the internal clock.
5. During each phase of the total program, make full use of the familiar programmer's tools: flowcharts (mandatory), decision tables, comments in your program statements, and provide for some kind of memory dump.

Finally, don't be afraid to make changes. We had to revise the interface configuration and supervisory program many times during the time it took to get the entire system on-line. Naturally, we learned from our mistakes, and the next psycho-computernik will benefit.

SUMMARY

An on-line system utilizing a small digital computer for control of various behavioral schedules in animals has been described, in which data generated by several experimental subjects at high and variable rates can be analyzed concomitant with experimental control of the subjects.

Schematics with reference to interface design, and flowcharts of a typical control schedule, as well as real-time programs have been provided and discussed.

REFERENCES

Geller, I. Use of approach-avoidance behavior (conflict) for evaluating depressant drugs. In J. H. Nodine and J. H. Moyer (Eds.), *First Hahnemann symposium on psychosomatic medicine*. Philadelphia: Lea and Febinger, 1962. Pp: 267–274.
Sidman, M. Avoidance conditioning with brief shock and no exteroceptive warning signal. *Science*, 1953, *118*, 157–158.
Ferster, C. B. and Skinner, B. F. *Schedules of reinforcement*. New York: Appleton-Century-Crofts, 1957.
Skinner, B. F. *The behavior of organisms*. New York: Appleton-Century-Crofts, 1938.

CHAPTER SIX

REAL-TIME, ON-LINE COMPUTER APPLICATIONS IN THE PSYCHOPHYSICAL LABORATORY

WILLIAM R. UTTAL

The University of Michigan

[1] The research reported in this chapter was supported by several NSF and NIH grants over the last few years. However, at a more personal level, I would like to acknowledge the contributions of several people who have contributed directly to these studies. Section III of this chapter was originally published as a separate article in a somewhat modified form in collaboration with Miss Pamela Smith. Her contributions in running the experiment and analyzing the data are gratefully acknowledged. The late Peter Headly had contributed his enormous programming skills to the construction of the control and data analysis program in that same experiment. Miss Anne Byrnes' editorial skills are as ever, magnificent and continually appreciated. I would also like to express my appreciation to Mr. Jon Baron and to the members of the faculty psychophysics seminar at the University of Michigan whose conversations contributed to many of the ideas expressed in Section IV of this chapter.

215

INTRODUCTION—REAL-TIME COMPUTERS—
THE UNMECHANICAL$_2$ MACHINES

The word mechanical can be defined in several ways. Two definitions are of particular interest in this chapter. The first definition (mechanical$_1$) pertains to the device itself. The second definition (mechanical$_2$) is related to such terms as pre-designated, automatic, and deterministic, as well as connoting a process free of will and adaptability and, therefore, to some, also free of interesting complexity. The first definition refers to a concrete object; the other to a style——a modus operandi. Sadly, these two meanings have been confused throughout history, almost to the point of a pun, with the object often taking the blame for the manner in which it is fitted into social structures and functions. Mainly for this reason there has usually been opposition to each new technological innovation. The Copernican system, the microscope, and vaccination, among almost all other really novel ideas, received a shower of this sort of criticism.

At present, the clamor is aimed at the computer, the most threatening machine of all, for it alone among all other mechanical$_1$ innovations of the past centuries, is able to substitute its own abilities for some of the intellectual activities many writers have previously attributed usually to man, infrequently to animals, and even less often to machines. Opposition has arisen to the "depersonalizing" way census information or the income tax is collected, to the "mechanization" of education, to the intrusion into our previously random sex lives by the match-making or dating services, and to the frightening spectre of a society in which complete records are kept of the medical, financial, and political history of each of its members. Wise old (and some very elderly young) men have counseled caution, urging us to consider the social implications of the inventions our laboratories and research centers are spawning forth, before implementing what they feel may be monsters that will ultimately deny us freedom of action, of thought, and even the freedom to commit those crimes of omission that allow, encourage, or impel others to crimes of commission. Their cry is: "Beware of the possible (if not the improbable) electronic peril of mechanization of human values."

The computer, indeed, seems subject to extraordinary amounts of this conservatism, because it is so extraordinarily interesting and so obviously socially influential. The significant thing to consider is that the present day computer is the prototype of the nonmechanical$_2$ machines. The fact overlooked by many critics is that in many instances, the rigidity and inevitabilty of our usual mechanical$_2$ way of doing things has been set aside by this new mechanical$_1$ artifact, because of this machine's ability to adapt to the environment. As a cogent example, what could be more mechanical$_2$ than the lecture in a conventional college classroom, and what could be less mechanical$_2$ than some of the excellent tutorial dialogues with a mechanical$_1$ computer? (See my other chapter in this volume for a detailed discussion of just how unmechanical$_2$ a computer tutor can be.)

How is it possible for this to be the case? What is a computer? The answer to these questions can best be approached by considering that computers perform their extraordinary functions as a result of certain unique and basic features that distinguish them among the artifacts of human culture. To understand the computer's impact on society, we must look to these underlying features for an explanation of how this particular mechanism can operate in a nonmechanical$_2$ manner. The essential feature that most uniquely distinguishes the computer may be expressed in two different ways, each of which is a corollary of the other. The first expression is based upon the computer's ability to store instructions in a form indistinguishable from data. (Burks, Goldstine, and von Neumann formally spelled out this notion for the first time in their classic 1946 paper.) Thus, arithmetic and logical operations can be performed on instructions (including the address of the appropriate operands) as well as on data. From this simple notion flow all other features of the computer, including the most involved and complicated interactive real-time natural language manipulations so far conceived.

The other starting point that can also be used to express the essential nature of the computer is not a structural characteristic as is the one just described, but is its functional equivalent. In this case, we would identify the essential feature of the computer as its ability to make sequencing decisions *contingent* upon the value of some internal or external state. In other words, what will happen after step A may be either B, C, or D, depending upon various tests of the current status of either the internal or external environment.

These primitives, common to all modern computers, define a number of more molar features, just as the features of the single nerve cell act as the primitive of molar organismic behavior. We can now consider what some of these more significant molar features of computer operations are, that have come to be appreciated as being especially significant in defining the realm of applicability of computers to man's problems in general and psychophysical research in particular.

ADAPTIVE INTERACTION

The most general feature of computers' molar performance is their adaptive interaction with their environment. This may be very clearly exemplified by the real-time control of a contingent psychophysical experiment in which sequential stimuli are dependent upon previous responses made by the subject. The essential idea is the dynamic nature of the response of the subject to a stimulating environment in which the sequence of stimuli might not be fixed, but contingent, and if properly programmed, adaptive.

REAL-TIME RESPONSIVENESS

The high-speed characteristics of a computer are really irrelevant to the important organizational features stressed above. However, the sheer speed of a computer, when coupled with its ability to respond to its environment, introduces a new innovation—real-time responsiveness, a notion of considerable importance in today's psychophysical laboratory. Computers are now capable of interacting with experimental subjects in such a way that they do not delay the self pacing of trials by the subject. In other fields of endeavor, there has been an enormous engineering effort to develop such well-known techniques as time sharing, multiple-user operations, or on-line electrical connection of computers to the entities of the environment. However, it must be emphasized that all of these techniques are but technical means of achieving real-time responsiveness and are of secondary interest to a user such as a psychophysicist. In fact, he often profits more by the full commitment of a small computer to his experiment, than he would from the shared usage of a vastly more powerful computer.

LIMITED ANTICIPATION: THE BARRIER TO UNIVERSAL COMPUTER APPLICATION

The essential nature of a computer as well as defining its strength, also defines its limits. It is realistic to acknowledge that computers are not universally applicable to all problems in a practical sense, even though mathematicians have shown that all concepts (for example, sentences) can be expressed in an equivalent string of binary code. The great technological limitation can be summed up in a single notion—the principle of limited anticipation. This notion implies that a contingent and adaptive machine capable of proceeding to a subsequent step B, C, or D, must have steps B, C, or D to proceed to, or at least an algorithm for their generation. Throughout all applications of computers, programmers constantly encounter the unanticipated, the ill-defined, or the overly generalized output that is not structured enough to be handled. Computers are incapable of accepting unanticipated generalized verbal strings in a way that allows significant and meaningful manipulation to occur. In all instances of successful linguistic manipulation by computers, the feat has been accomplished by restricting the verbal input to a very specific pre-programmed vocabulary, or by intentionally programming routines to detour around the unanalyzable.

The process of anticipation is being formalized and the meta-languages—compilers and assemblers—can be considered to be a form of cultural memory that helps us to avoid the necessity for complete anticipation by each user each time he turns to the computer. Specific applications, however, still require constraints on accepable input. Meta-languages are getting progessively more sophisticated and capable of anticipating more and more. Recently, there has been a surge in the development of procedure-oriented languages that call up complicated and complete procedures (such as a total matrix multiplication), rather than single operations, with a single command.

It has often been said that it takes 50 years for a new idea to reach the general public awareness. In this era of rapid communications, it may be somewhat less for the public, and considerably less for the practicing scholar or scientist. Many psychologists, however, still don't seem to appreciate the theoretical and experimental impact that the computer will have on psychophysical experimentation.

The remaining sections of this chapter attempt, through various examples, to make the point that computers are changing our theories (as all instruments do) by exposing us to new observations. Experiments that could not have been performed in the past are now being executed daily in many different laboratories. New statistical techniques are being forced into existence by banks of data from experiments in which the stimulus sequence follows the subject's responses. New experimental control and termination procedures such as the PEST techniques of Taylor and Creelman (1967), which require computer control for their implementation, are becoming standard in psychophysical laboratories. Certainly, before the real-time, on-line computer, the more complex decision-making psychophysical procedures (see Green and Swets, 1966) were extremely difficult to implement. Keith Smith (1967) summed up this notion when he pointed out that modern experimental psychology is now for the first time, under the influence of the laboratory computer, developing a statistical methodology better suited to its needs than those of the agricultural heritage out of which the latin square and other similar procedures evolved.

To present and support this thesis, the rest of this chapter is devoted to the technique and substance of some psychophysical experiments in which we have been interested. First, a standard package of interface components is considered that can be attached to any small computer and thus make that computer able to communicate with almost any psychophysical experiment one could imagine. Then, the rationale and details of two psychophysical experiments are examined. One concerns the ability of the somatosensory system to decode nerve impulse patterns with irregular intervals and the other deals with the ability of the human eye to detect and recognize characters in a peculiar sort of random visual noise.

The reader of this volume might conceivably be distressed with the depth of the details of the psychological substance, but there is an important point to be made by this seeming overemphasis. That point is that the methods and the problems considered by each generation of researchers are intimately tied to the available technology. Therefore, the depth of our understanding and the nature of our theories also must be based in large part, on this same technological context. These experiments, I believe, constitute new thrusts into problem areas that had been only vaguely defined up until now. As such, they illustrate specifically how new technologies can open the door to new theoretical issues. I hope that the significance of the problems themselves will be effective in demonstrating the importance of a constant awareness of the availability and power of new technologies to influence our more theoretical perspectives.

A GENERAL PURPOSE INTERFACE PACKAGE
FOR PSYCHOPHYSICAL EXPERIMENTS[2]

The purpose of this section is to present the technical details of what has developed in our laboratory as a standard psychophysical interface package. This package of interface components represents a basic set that allows almost any kind of psychological or psychophysiological experiment to be run under the control of an appropriate computer program.

An interface package is that group of devices that collects information from and transmits information to the external environment. The external environment for the computer in the case of a psychological experiment, of course, is the subject or animal preparation itself. Interface devices are required to transform the patterns of signals from the computer into a pattern usable by the subject and *vice versa*. The representation of a given pattern within a computer may be in a form that is not usable by a subject simply because of power levels. But more fundamentally, this incompatibility may be due to a difference in the languages used by the computer and the subject. In addition, the time scales of the two patterns of information may be so disparate that it is necessary to synchronize the one to the other by slowing down or speeding up the flow of information. In general, therefore, the interface acts as a communication link that not only allows information to flow but also translates codes or languages, amplifies or reduces power levels, and alters the basic time units of the subject and the computer to accommodate the real-time base of the other.

No claim to originality of design or configuration is implied. Many other researchers have utilized similar devices and the design of these devices is what the patent office calls a simple engineering extension of the state of the art. The general nature of the group of devices added to our computer, however, may suggest, to some, novel ways to run their experiments which they had not previously considered.

LOGICAL SYMBOLS

Before discussing specific interface devices, it is necessary to present a brief nomenclature for the logical symbols used in the drawings. It is not well

[2] This section of this chapter appeared in a somewhat modified form under the title "Basic Black" in Computer Interfaces for Psychological Research. *Behavioral Research Methods & Instruction*, 1968, *1*, 35—40.

appreciated by the novice when he first looks at the superficial complexity of a digital computer that computers are, in fact, simple concatenations of a very small number of different components. It is well known to mathematical logicians and computer logical designers that it is possible to build a computer out of a set of components consisting of no more than two different devices. It is further realized that several different sets of these pairs of components will do the job. In the practical case, however, it is usually a fact that a wider variety of components are used for secondary reasons of economy and convenience, but even then the number of different units in the set of logical elements is typically quite small. Four basic units are used in most computer design. The first of these units is the inverter which is capable of multiplying a signal by minus one, *i.e.*, inverting negative voltage to positive voltage and *vice versa*. The second unit, the basic storage element, is variously called a flip-flop, trigger, or bistable multivibrator. This device has two stable states, either of which can be set by activating one of two inputs. Usually, the flip-flop also has two outputs, one of which is activated when the flip-flop is in the "1" state and the other when the flip-flop is in the "0" state. The third and fourth devices are actually different utilizations of a single physical unit. This single unit, usually called a gate, can be implemented in a number of different ways with transistors alone, transistors in combinations with diodes, or special multiple base transistors. In any case, however, a gate is characterized by multiple inputs that must be activated or asserted in a particular way to produce an active output. The two functions to which it can be applied are logical "and-ing" and logical "or-ing". The "and" operation is defined such that the output signal of a gate will be asserted only when all of the inputs to the diode gate are themselves asserted simultaneously. The "or" operation is defined such that the assertions of any single input will result in the assertion of the output. Figure 1 shows the standard symbols for the four basic functional units.

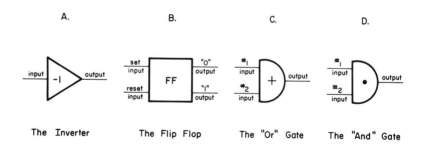

Figure 1. Symbols for the four basic components used in computer logical design.

There are a number of other complications about the design of logical circuits that are more or less special to each particular commercial line of components. Voltage levels, in particular, must be of the appropriate polarity as defined by the electronics of the logical unit. For the purposes of this chapter, I have ignored these special details and concentrated only on the functional utilization. Assume that an activated input will result in an activated output without reference to what the signal characteristics (rise time, voltage level, or polarity) would have to be. There are also a number of specially designed units that are required for special functions at one point or another in the circuits. These are described as they are encountered.

It is generally the case that small computers are connected to the interface equipment, which is described in two ways. There is usually a parallel set of signal lines coming from some buffer register that conveys an entire memory word of coded information to the external equipment. These are referred to as data signals. There are also, usually, a series of pulse lines that can be used to select or initiate a given operation. These pulse lines are activated by the execution of a specific input-output instruction by the computer and are otherwise dormant. The data signals, on the other hand, may be present continuously. The data signals are usually, therefore gated by "and-ing" them with a control pulse into a secondary storage buffer when needed. In addition, signals entering the computer from the outside world are also able to indicate their need for service by means of an interrupt signal. Each of the various computers has its own special means of generating these input and output pulses and this brief chapter also ignores these details.

I turn now to the specific interface devices themselves and discuss their use, special requirements, and present a simple logical diagram showing how they can be constructed from the standard set of logical components.

STIMULATOR TRIGGERS

Purpose. In many psychological experiments, some special peripheral instrumentation is necessary to create the desired stimulus condition. This stimulus might be a flash of light, an acoustic click, or a cutaneous constant current stimulus pulse. The critical function of the computer in this case is not to produce the stimulus itself but to emit a trigger pulse at the correct time to activate the external equipment.

Special Requirements. The brief control pulses emitted by a computer will, in general, not be suitable in either duration, polarity, or amplitude for the triggering of external equipment. It is, therefore, necessary to extend them in time and amplify them in voltage to meet the input needs of the external equipment. The elongation of the pulses is accomplished by means of a device called a single shot or monostable multivibrator. This device, when triggered, emits a pulse, the duration of which, like the all-or-none response of a neuron is independent of the characteristics of the triggering signal. The duration of this pulse is usually adjustable over wide ranges. The output of this single shot is then amplified, typically by means of a special voltage amplifying inverter, to meet the input criteria of the peripheral equipment. Figure 2 shows a schematic block

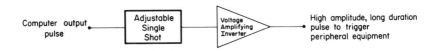

Figure 2. A simple pulse stretcher and voltage amplifier that can be used to trigger peripheral equipment.

diagram of a convenient stimulator trigger. At least a pair of these are always needed and in some cases, four to six have been used simultaneously.

RESPONSE SWITCHES

Purpose. One of the most often used forms of response in psychological experiments is a simple key press. If the number of switches that might be depressed is large, some standard coded keyboard would be most appropriate. If, on the other hand, the number of switches is small, or if there is some other special requirement, it is usually convenient to construct a special set of switches. These devices may be mounted at great distances from the computer.

The meaning assigned to the depression of a given switch is, of course, a function of how the computer is programmed, so a single set of switches can serve many different purposes.

Special Requirements. Electromechanical switches produce a jagged and noisy output signal, when they are depressed, that is so slow that a single key depression could cause multiple operations by the very high-speed computer. Most switches are therefore buffered with a switch filter, a passive resistor-capacitor circuit, that integrates the jagged response from the switch into a monotonically rising one. The rise is still slow, however, and this is usually compensated for by the use of a device that has a sharp amplitude threshold for its transition between two binary states. Such a threshold controlled flip-flop is called a Schmitt Trigger, after its designer. The high-speed transition of its output is usually used as the signal that a key has been pressed, rather than the slow rise of the switch filter. A conventional flip-flop is necessary to remember that this transition has occurred until such time as the computer is able to service the action stimulated by the switch closure. The output of the flip-flop may be used also as an indicator of which switch was depressed. It may also be combined through an "or" circuit to activate the interrupt input to signal the computer that something has happened. Figure 3 is a schematic diagram of a usable set of response switch inputs.

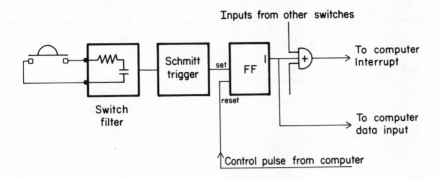

Figure 3. The logical design of an interface device capable of handling switch activations as response inputs from the subject to the computer.

A MILLISECOND REAL-TIME CLOCK

Purpose. Very few psychological experiments do not in one way or another involve the measurement of time. A number of techniques exist whereby a real-time computer can measure time. These techniques include program loops and complete external hardware clocks that actually contain a complete statement of real-time in units varying from milliseconds to days. In many psychophysical and human performance experiments, however, it is possible to use a simple piece of hardware that emits only a periodic interrupt signal to the computer in place of those previously mentioned more complicated, time-consuming procedures. A simple regulatable oscillator can be connected to the computer in such a way that every time it emits one of its periodic pulses, the computer stops whatever it had been doing and increments one of its regular core memory registers. When this register counts up to a certain value, that value multiplied by the basic period of the oscillator is a precise measure of elapsed time. Setting the oscillator to 1 kHz (1 msec between pulses) has been found to be a most useful value for measuring a wide variety of psychological and neurophysiological times.

Special Requirements. Other than the fact that a special oscillator to serve as the clock itself is necessary, the most important functional requirement for the millisecond real-time clock is that it is possible to turn it off when it is not being used. This is easily accomplished by gating the signal from the clock through an "and" circuit conditioned by a flip-flop that can be either turned off or on by control pulses from the computer. Figure 4 depicts the general organization of this controllable millisecond real-time clock.

DUAL DIGITAL TO ANALOG CONVERTERS

Purpose. Interfacing a computer to a psychological experiment often requires patterns of information quite different than the bit structure of an

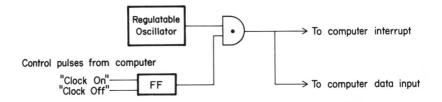

Figure 4. A simple controlled real-time clock capable of interrupting a computer at precisely defined intervals.

internally stored digital word. Psychologists are likely to require signals that are spatial patterns for visual experiments, temporal patterns for acoustic experiments, or amplitude modulated analog information of other kinds. The device that can convert the digital information as it is encoded within the computer into equivalent analog values is called a digital to analog (D-A) converter. D-A converters can now be purchased as completely packaged units or constructed from the logical units already described. In general, they operate by adding a series of voltages proportional to the significance of the bit combination representing the signal level desired.

Two independent channels are necessary to drive a two-dimensional display, such as a cathode ray tube or any one of the various kinds of plotters. Once connected, these devices can then be used to represent almost any geometrical pattern, including rows of alphabetic figures or even cartoon-like motion pictures. One channel of D-A conversion is sufficient to drive an audio system, although both could be used to generate stereo effects. We have presented to subjects speech sounds that were stored in the computer in this manner with a relatively high degree of fidelity, even though the speech sounds had undergone an A-D conversion, a D-A conversion, and the resulting approximations of digital storage.

Special Requirements. The output voltages of D-A converters are usually standardized in magnitude and level by the particular equipment utilized. It is often necessary, therefore, to amplify these signals further. This can be easily accomplished with any one of the many operational amplifiers now manufactured by several different companies. The output of the D-A converter is fed into the input of the amplifier. The amplifier is then adjusted for the required gain and level and its output sent to the peripheral device being driven. Figure 5 indicates the signal flow but not the complete details of the dual D-A converter. Also indicated in Figure 5 is an additional pulse stretcher and amplifier that can be used to produce a signal capable of modulating the intensity of the dot of light on the face of a cathode ray oscilloscope. By intensifying the beam only after the beam has been positioned on the face of the scope, those ghost images created during beam movement can be suppressed. This third dimension is usually called a Z-axis control.

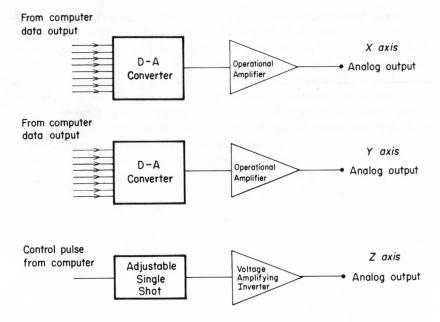

Figure 5. The dual D-A converter that can be used in many different ways to convert digital signals to analog signals. The z-axis circuit can be used for CRT trace intensification.

ANALOG TO DIGITAL CONVERTER

Purpose. While the D-A converter was required to convert the digitally coded information within the computer into signals that could be utilized by subjects, the analog to digital (A-D) converter is necessary to convert analog signals generated by subjects into the digitally coded information required by the computer. Analog signals of several different kinds typically require this service. The voice messages mentioned above were originally entered into the computer by this means. However, the largest class of signals that require A-D conversion are the bioelectric signals developed by physiological mechanisms. A wide variety of analytical methods have been developed to process bioelectric signals. These methods are spelled out in great detail in another source (Uttal, 1968) and are not germane to the purpose of this chapter. Nevertheless, all digital computer processing techniques for bioelectric signals require A-D conversion as the initial step. A-D converters can be very fast, so much so that it is not usually appreciated how quickly one can flood the available memory resources of a small computer. Another related problem concerns the amount of computer processing required to perform some apparently relatively simple process, such as a cross correlation. Anyone interested in applying this and related analytical tools might do well at least to consider the use of some analog computation facility instead.

Special Requirements. A number of different devices are usually appended to all but the simplest A-D converter. One often-used special facility is an input multiplexer that can switch any one of a number of different inputs into the A-D computer in almost any order directed by the computer. The multiplexer is particularly useful in reducing the number of separate A-D converters required by a single system. However, a surprising thing has been happening. The price of A-D converters has been dropping rapidly, along with their size and complexity. It is now, for example, possible to purchase a complete analog to digital converter manufactured on a single integrated circuit chip. Multiplexer prices are such that in some cases it would be more economical to have a large number of A-D converters rather than a single A-D converter and an input multiplexer.

Another important auxiliary device used with A-D converters is the "sample and hold circuit". There is an inevitable error introduced into all A-D conversions due to the change in the level of the signal that occurs during the conversion period. It is, therefore, usually helpful to have the signal sampled during a short temporal "window" and that instantaneous voltage remembered by being stored on a capacitor for what may be a much longer conversion period. Sampling "windows" as short as a few hundred nanoseconds have been achieved, even though conversion periods of several tens of microseconds are still typical.

Finally, a note about the construction of A-D converters. Figure 6 is a block diagram of the A-D system discussed. But there are many different ways to

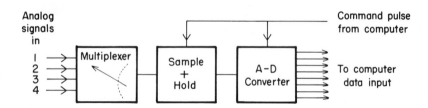

Figure 6. The A-D converter showing the input multiplexer and the sample-and-hold accessories.

accomplish A-D conversion. Most of the newer ways, however, do depend upon a prior D-A conversion and then a comparison of the voltage so generated with the input analog signal. The variety of ways in which this comparison is effected is so large that no purpose would be served by more detailed logical diagrams of our particular circuit.

MULTIPLE POWER LEVEL BIT CODED DISPLAY CONTROLLERS

Purpose. Along with the development of computer sciences, there has also been in the last two decades an actively developing interest concerning the problem of how humans process binary coded information. This has been expressed in the laboratory in a host of studies in which the stimulus materials are binary coded displays. In some instances, the number of these discrete stimuli is small enough so that they may be activated by binary signals from the computer without any preliminary decoding. Thus, the output signal lines from the computer, which I have mentioned as inputs to the digital to analog converter, for example, might themselves be used directly to light small lamps in some sort of stimulus matrix. The problems remaining, once decoding has been eliminated, are simply those of time and voltage matching. This can usually be accomplished by constructing a buffer flip-flop register into which the pattern of bits is loaded directly from the computer.

Special Requirements. This buffer register stores the state of the various bits for a period defined by the computer program. The outputs of the register are amplified to a level sufficient to activate the binary stimuli. This output amplification may be accomplished by a simple transistor with a power output sufficient to drive a small incandescent light. However, some applications may require high power levels (such as the activation of a solenoid operating some mechanical device) and special high-current relay and solenoid drivers may be required. The output of these latter units is sufficient to activate an electro-mechanical relay whose contacts themselves may be able to carry even higher currents. Some alphanumeric character displays, for example, require this sort of power buffering. It has been suggested that a general purpose binary output device can be constructed for multiple uses such that its output may either be a low-power or a high-power signal as required. A single buffer register, shown in Figure 7, is loaded by the coincidence of a control signal "load register

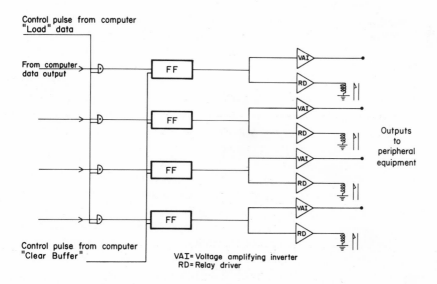

Figure 7. A typical multiple power level output interface device for binary coded displays from the computer to the subject.

pulse" and the information bits themselves. This register has a dual output. One of the outputs is a simple voltage amplifying inverter providing a signal of the appropriate level to light a small lamp or provide the input to some other similar low-power device. The other output is a high-current capacity driver connected to a set of relay coils. Either (or both) of the two devices may be used as necessitated by the peripheral equipment that is to be connected to the appropriate output. The advantage of such a dual output is that a single set of computer instructions and buffer circuitry can be used in any of a number of different experiments at different times with but the simplest switching operation required between experiments. The single buffer register may also be used as the signal inputs to other devices, such as the D-A converter, which also requires an equivalent function as part of its circuitry. Depending upon the work load on the computer, the amount of simultaneous time sharing by different users and the number of bits of information required, this dual output resistor may result in a substantial savings in equipment costs because identical functions that might never occur simultaneously are all served by this single device.

A NOTE ON THE COMPUTER-CONTROLLED TYPEWRITER

Perhaps one of the most often used—and most often underestimated—devices for human interaction with a computer is the electric typewriter standard on most computers. A computer-controlled electric typewriter is capable of both transmitting information from the subject to the computer and displaying information from the computer to him. Many experimenters have used typewriters successfully and have demonstrated their wide applicability for communicating alphanumeric information. For the low data rates encountered in alphanumeric interaction between a human and a computer, the typewriter is eminently suitable, not imposing undue restrictions on the computer, as do some more powerful all-electronic displays. Many of the alternatives to such a keyboard-driven device also deprive the user of the opportunity to construct alphabetic responses fully. As shown in the second of the two experiments described below, the character set to be recognized was so large (24 characters) that the full keyboard of a teletypewriter-like device was the only way to enter repsonse information into the computer.

Some recent innovations are compromises betweeen the typewriter and the cathode ray tube. These new electronic typewriters have typewriter-like keyboards with simple CRT (cathode ray tube) displays replacing the platen of the typewriter. The special CRTs are often limited in scope in order to maintain simplicity and can only display alphanumeric characters. Electronic typewriters have the advantage of electronic reliability and silence but functionally are indistinguishable from a typewriter. They should, however, be distinguished from the full-capability CRTs, which allow full geometric display.

ON THE PSYCHOPHYSICAL DISCRIMINABILITY OF SOMATOSENSORY NERVE ACTION POTENTIAL PATTERNS WITH IRREGULAR INTERVALS[3]

In recent years, there has been a considerable amount of research reported in the neurophysiological literature concerning the detailed measurement of the variability of interpulse intervals in the train of nerve action potentials resulting from sensory stimulation. (For an excellent review of the general problem, see Moore, Perkel, and Segundo, 1966.) This work has generally been characterized by an experimental paradigm in which a natural stimulus impinging upon the usual transducer elicits a train of neural activity. This activity is detected by electrodes capable of transducing the activity of single cells. The temporal pattern of the nerve action potentials is then analyzed to show long-term statistical trends, as well as microchanges in the timing. It has been shown, for example, that the variability of interpulse interval is, like the mean frequency, functionally related to the stimulus amplitude (Buller, Nicholls, and Strom, 1953; Werner and Mountcastle, 1963). Werner and Mountcastle have suggested on the basis of these results that the variability of interpulse interval itself may be an information-carrying code for sensory information; *i.e.*, they suggest the existence of a hypothetical variability detector at some higher level of the nervous system.

This neurophysiological experimental paradigm, however, is not adequate to demonstrate the sufficiency of the hypothesis that interpulse interval is truly an information-carrying code for one or another stimulus dimension. Werner and Mountcastle carefully indicate their agreement with this notion by describing their observed results merely as a possible neural code. A complete proof of sufficiency of the hypothesis that interval variability is conveying information in a biologically significant way requires tests whose results show that the information encoded by the variability, as such, is not lost at some higher level of the nervous system. If the information is lost, the variation of interpulse interval can, at best, be considered a sign of some utility to the neurophysiologist but psychophysically insignificant. (See Uttal, 1967, for a detailed discussion of the significance of the terms *signs* and *codes* and some possible associated conceptual artifacts.) From one point of view, the usual neurophysiological experimental paradigm, as important and as powerful as it has been, also is capable of forcing our thinking toward the commission of a misconception about the coding process. Unless we are willing to concede, *a priori*, an extremely high degree of economy in the nervous system, such that most, if not all, observable neurophysiological patterns are actually used as codes in one way or another, we must consider the likelihood that many of the observed patterns

[3] This part of this chapter appeared in a somewhat modified form in *Perception and Psychophysics,* 1967, *2*, 341–348.

of response are going to be irrelevant. They may be reflections of some underlying metabolic variable or effects of the complicated electrochemistry of cell membranes (Calvin and Stevens, 1967) without being truly involved in those processes that ultimately will be identified with behavioral states.

Reports of tests in which measurements are made of the effectiveness of a given temporal pattern on some subsequent response, are infrequent for several reasons. First, natural stimuli cannot appropriately be used because they produce patterns of nervous activity that are essentially uncontrolled in regard to interval variability. Thus, when a stimulus acts on a transducer it is the transducer properties, rather than the temporal properties of the stimulus, that in large part determine the microtemporal patterns. Furthermore, there is no guarantee with natural stimuli applied to the normal transducers that the information is not being encoded redundantly by several different parameters of nervous activity.

For these reasons, it is necessary to force the desired nerve action potential pattern with electrical pulse stimuli—the only stimulus energy capable of defining a temporal pattern in neurons free of the above-mentioned difficulties.

The second difficulty limiting our knowledge of this important problem revolves around the fact that the distinction between a sign and a true code requires not only that information carried by some suggested coding dimension be transferred across a single synapse, but also that the pattern of information be maintained up to the level at which some neural activity actually becomes identifiable with some behavioral response. The great powers of the electrophysiological technique unfortunately do not include the ability to track a neural response through the several synaptic relays.

In this context, it becomes clear that the only way in which we can distinguish between a true information-carrying code and a sign is a behavioral test. The specific question we ask: is it possible for the organism to distinguish between two patterns that differ only in terms of the variability of the interpulse interval? The specific test we use: a test of psychophysical discriminability.

In the electrophysiological literature, there is but one report of which we are aware that observes differences in response as a function of a forced temporal pattern of nerve impulses. Segundo, Moore, Stensass, and Bullock (1963) observed differences in postsynaptic responsiveness (as measured by the amplitude of the postsynaptic potential) in aplysia. They did find that the temporal pattern of the presynaptic spike action potentials did produce changes in the amplitude of graded postsynaptic potentials and in the number of spike responses in the postsynaptic neurons independent of mean frequency. Earlier, I (Uttal, 1960) reported that triplets of spike action potentials in peripheral nerves were also differentially effective as measured with psychophysical tests of subjective amplitude. However, in that case, the differential sensitivity could be completely accounted for in terms of the summed amplitude of the compound action potentials as modified by sequential refractory periods.

The purpose of this study is to determine the limits and characteristics of psychophysical discriminability of nerve action potential patterns with irregular intervals. The nerve action potentials are patterns forced by direct electrical stimulation of peripheral somesthetic nerves by electrical pulses.

It should be noted that for all practical purposes, it is generally not possible to carry out this type of psychophysical experiment on any other than the somesthetic system. The deeply buried acoustic and visual nerves are inaccessible to direct electrical stimuli unless surgically exposed. In this context, our experiments can be seen to speak directly to the problem of the discriminability of nerve action potential patterns while other similarly designed experiments, such as the elegant work of Pollack (1967), and the studies of Cardozo, Ritsma, Domburg, and Neelen (1966), in audition describe the information processing capabilities of the entire system, pooling the transduction, transmission, and decoding processes into a single information measure. Our experiments specifically concern the transmission codes in peripheral nerves. The nerve action potential patterns resulting from peripheral electrical stimulation are designated only at the level of the first neuron in the ascending somatosensory pathway. Beyond that, we do not know whether the specific pattern we have created is maintained. It is, however, not germane; for we are more concerned with the maintenance of the information contained in the variability than the variability itself. If the pattern is discriminable with a psychophysical test, then we do know that the information is maintained regardless of what subsequent encodings it may have been subjected to and that the variability at the level of the first-order neuron is a true information-carrying code.

I should also point out in this introduction that the experimental procedure used in the present experiment is also beset by certain limitations. First, although electrical pulses are used to drive the nerve-action potential pattern, the evoked responses are not trains of spikes in a single nerve fiber but the simultaneous responses of large groups of fibers. The complications that this compound response might introduce are not known but must be considered as a possible source of artifact. The work of Casby, Siminoff, and Houseknecht (1963) suggests that it may not be too significant, however. Second, the behavioral response used is a psychophysical judgment made immediately after the stimulus presentation. Ours is, therefore, an experimental situation that falls under the general rubric of sensory studies. It is not at all clear, however, that other longer-term effects of nerve-action potential pattern might be manifested but not observable by the present methods. One could criticize our work on the basis of some long-term memory effect that we cannot observe but that does differentially affect behavior.

In spite of these limitations, this experimental approach does offer an additional and, I believe, powerful means of evaluating the significance of various temporal patterns as possible neural codes, which is not possible in the conventional neurophysiological or psychophysical experiment.

METHOD

Subjects. Six undergraduate students, five male and one female, participated in this experiment. All were paid hourly wages and had either participated in similar experiments earlier or were pretrained on a related task before formal data collection began. The data of only five subjects are used in some of the experiments because of attendance problems not related to experimental procedures.

Apparatus. Uttal and Krissoff (1966) described the nature of the electrical pulse stimuli used in the present experiment. The individual pulses were constant current regulated and lasted for 0.5 msec. Throughout the experiments reported here, the amplitude of the pulses was kept constant at 4 mA. The particular pattern required for each experimental trial was generated under the control of a small digital computer that automatically controlled all experimental operations. Stimulus patterns were timed, responses acquired, and statistical evaluation of the data compiled on line by the computer. Final shaping of the pulses was accomplished by a series of pulse formers external to the computer. The electrical pulse stimuli were conveyed to the subject through two test tubes containing body normal saline solutions. The subject inserted the index and middle fingers of his left hand into the test tubes up to the first joint. He responded by pushing a switch with his right hand to one of two momentary contact positions. The subject was seated in a small (3 by 3 ft.) acoustical cubicle in subdued lighting.

Procedure. The general purpose was to determine how well the human somatosensory system is able to deal with irregularities in the intervals of a train of nerve impulses. Since it is well established (see for example Uttal, 1960) that electrical pulse stimuli produce compound nerve responses in peripheral somatosensory nerves on a one-for-one basis, it is safe to assume that proper timing of the stimulus train forces the nerve-action potential pattern to follow exactly the same temporal pattern. Three experiments were carried out in this initial attempt to explore the parameters of human discriminability of nerve action potential patterns with irregular intervals.

Experiment I. The subject was required to select which one of two sequential bursts of 10 electrical pulses was irregular or rough. The two stimulus bursts separated by 1.75 sec were generated by the computer, which also randomly selected whether the first or second of the two bursts actually contained the irregular intervals. The nature of the irregularity in this experiment was that an otherwise constant interpulse interval (termed the basic interpulse interval) was "jittered" in a quasi-random fashion by adding to each interval some proportion of a correction factor or perturbation index called R. For each proportion of an R that was added to one of the intervals in a train, an equivalent proportion was subtracted from some other interval so that the total length of the train when jittered remained the same as that of the unjittered reference train.

The only exception to this occurred when the subtraction of some proportional part of R would result in an interval shorter than 8 msec. An interval this short is well below the temporal acuity threshold. Subjective magnitude increases could therefore occur in this time region, which could bias the results of this experiment. By limiting the minimum interpulse interval to a minimum value of 8 msec, some differences are occasionally unfortunately introduced into the durations of the two stimulus bursts. Typically, however, the thresholds for irregularity were higher for the trials in which this duration difference existed and it therefore appears that for these trials other effects swamped out any cues the subject might have obtained from duration differences.

The proportions of the basic perturbation R that were used included: $+R$, $+3/4\,R$, $+1/2\,R$, $+1/4\,R$, $0\,R$, $-1/4\,R$, $-1/2\,R$, $-3/4\,R$, and $-R$. These nine perturbation values were added to the basic interpulse interval in random order to form a table of jittered intervals. The table was then used to define the characteristics of the jittered burst emitted by the computer.

The intervals of the jittered burst can, therefore, seem to be randomly selected in a constrained fashion such that each interval occurs only once. When R is very small, the degree of irregularity is very small, since even the largest perturbations added to the basic interpulse results in an interval only slightly different than the unperturbed one. When R is large, then the difference between the largest and smallest interval can be considerable. Figure 8 is a drawing of a standard stimulus burst with equal interpulse intervals and a jittered stimulus burst showing the type of irregularity generated by these rules.

As mentioned previously, the independent variable in this experiment is the basic interpulse interval of the unjittered burst. The values of the basic interpulse intervals used in this experiment were 10, 12, 14, 16, 18, 20, 25, 30, and 40 msec. The dependent variable was the mean threshold size of R for a just-noticeable irregularity. An initial value for R of 3 msec was chosen at the beginning of each daily session with each subject, but in subsequent blocks during that session, R was automatically set to the mean value of R for the previous block.

The psychophysical method used was a contingently designed two alternative forced-choice procedure (Green and Swets, 1966) in which a correct answer (subject selected the jittered burst) reduced the size of R by ΔR and an incorrect response (subject selected the regular burst) increased R by 3 ΔR. No direct feedback of the correctness or incorrectness of his answer was given to the subject. ΔR itself was also set to an initial value of 1 msec for each daily session but in each subsequent block was automatically set to a value equal to one-tenth of the range of R on the previous block.

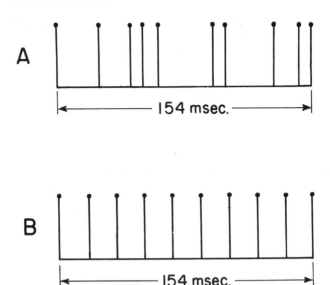

Figure 8. A plot of two different stimulus bursts. *A* is an irregular burst with jittered interpulse intervals. *B* is a regular burst with a constant interval between serial pulses. These figures have been redrawn from oscillographic photographs.

Within each block, the contingent stimulus procedure precluded the pre-specification of a detailed protocol; however, the computer was programmed to type out the value of the dependent variable and the subject's answer upon each response. Within each trial, the randomization procedure placed the longest interval (IPI + R) and the smallest interval (IPI − R) in unpredictable locations in sequential trials.

Each of the experimental conditions was presented once each day so that each daily session included nine blocks. The experiment was run for nine days with each day's blocks being presented in a different constrained random order. Each block consisted of 59 trials of which only the last 50 were used in the computations of the various statistical measures evaluated by the computer to avoid the effects of the initial hunting of transients from one condition to the next. Each point on the curve plotted in Figure 9 represents the mean of 2250 estimates by these subjects.

Experiment II. One of the main possible sources of artifact in a design such as that used in Experiment I is that the subject might not be using all of the information presented to him by the jittered intervals. It may be that, for example, he is simply using the largest interval as a cue, rather than the overall statistical structure of the stimulus burst. A number of studies have been reported in which the parameters influencing the detection of a single gap in otherwise regular stimulus burst were explored. (See Uttal and Krissoff, 1966, 1967.) To guard against the possibility of this sort of artifact, it was therefore necessary to compare the results for Experiment I with an equivalent set of data for the gap test. The previous data, however, had been collected using an up-and-down method of limits as the psychophysical procedure with a yes-no answer. It is well known that the data resulting from such a method will, in general, give higher thresholds than those obtained from a forced-choice technique. We therefore replicated the study in which the effect of the size of the interpulse interval of a regular burst on the gap threshold was determined using a forced-choice technique. This experiment also used nine different interpulse intervals, but the interpulse intervals were all of the same size (except for the middle interval—the gap) in the burst of 10 pulses. Intervals of 10, 12, 14, 16, 18, 20, 25, 30, and 40 msec were used. Nine daily sessions for each subject were run with each of the nine conditions being randomly presented (with the same constraint of no repetition as in Experiment I) each day. Fifty responses by the subject were used to determine the statistics of each block. The dependent variable in this case was simply the additional time that the S on the average added to the basic interpulse interval for a threshold response. Each point on the curve plotted in Figure 9, displaying the results of this experiment also, therefore represents the average of 2250 estimates by these subjects.

Experiment III. The third experiment considered a related problem. If the statistical sensitivity is observable, it should also be expected that there would be some effect of the number of pulses in the train on the threshold for the detection of the irregularity in the jittered pulse train. This would be expected on the basis of the larger sample of interpulse intervals with which the subject could deal. The third experiment therefore varied the number of impulses in the jittered train but held the basic interpulse interval constant at 16 msec. Bursts containing 3, 4, 5, 6, 8, 10, 12, 15, and 20 pulses were used. Each block contained only one such number and nine blocks were presented in constrained random order each day for nine days. The same forced-choice psychophysical procedure described in Experiment I was used and the subject was instructed in this case also to respond by indicating which burst was irregular or rough. Each point on the curve drawn in Figure 10 represents the mean 2700 estimates by these subjects.

RESULTS

The results of Experiments I and II are plotted on the same graph in Figure 2 so that the two sets of data can be directly compared.

The results of Experiment I, in which the subjects were asked to make a choice of which of the two bursts was "rough," are plotted with circles. The resulting functional relationship between the basic frequency and the just-detectable amount of jitter appears to be made up of two segments. Below a basic

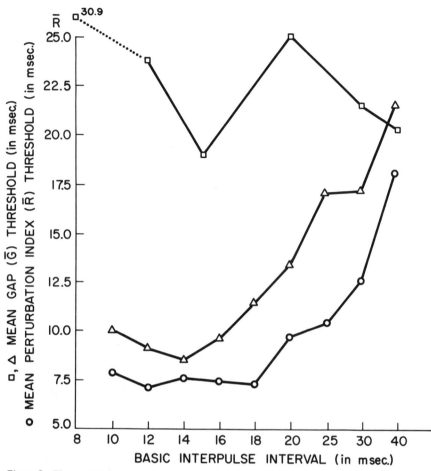

Figure 9. The results of Experiments I and II and some older data for gap detection. The points plotted with circles are the results of the roughness detection experiment with a forced-choice technique. The points plotted with triangles are the results of the gap-detection experiment obtained with a forced-choice technique. The points plotted with squares are the results of a gap-detection experiment measured with a yes-no procedure. Data for five subjects in each case. Data for the gap thresholds are given in terms of additional time required above the basic interpulse interval for a just-detectable gap.

interpulse interval (20 msec), the subject displayed a sensitivity to a constant amount of jitter, independent of the basic interpulse interval. For intervals above 20 msec, however, the subjects required increases in the amount of jitter for detectability as the interpulse interval increased.

The data for Experiment II (the replication of our earlier experiment, in which the subject was required to detect a gap) are shown by the points plotted with triangles on Figure 9. This curve also displays one effect obtained in the earlier experiment wherein it was shown that there was an elevation of the

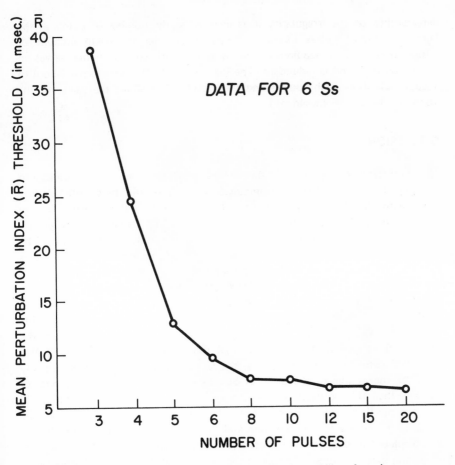

Figure 10. The effect of number of pulses on the detectability of roughness.

threshold at the shortest intervals. The minimum detectable gap for this experiment was found at 14 msec, rather than at the 10-msec basic interpulse interval. However, comparison of this data with the results (points plotted with squares) of the earlier experiment, which used the yes-no psychophysical procedures, does show an important difference in the results. The yes-no technique resulted in just-detectable gap sizes that were essentially constant (except for the shortest interval) over the entire range of the values of the basic interpulse interval used. There is general agreement between the methods for the largest values used. But, for the smaller values, there is a substantial difference between the two sets of data. The forced-choice technique leads to substantially smaller thresholds in this region.

The results of Experiment III, in which the number of pulses in the train was varied, are shown in Figure 10. It can be seen from these data that the detectability of the irregularity does increase as the number of pulses in the burst of stimuli pulses increases. Apparently, after a certain amount of information has been acquired by the subject, additional information serves no further purpose and is redundant. The increase in effect is seen to persist out to a count of about eight pulses and then level off at about the value for the 16-msec interval in Experiment I.

DISCUSSION

The basic question asked in this study is whether or not subjects are able to discriminate between bursts of impulses with regular interpulse intervals and those with slightly irregular intervals. The corollary to this question is: can subjects integrate, over time, a series of irregularities to give a more precise answer than that obtainable from a single interval of maximum divergence? The data answering these questions appear in both Figures 9 and 10. Figure 9 shows that the threshold for an irregularly intervaled burst is lower than any value of the single gap test. The closest approach between the two curves is found at an interpulse interval of 14 msec. There is, however, an additional source of bias that suggests that the difference might be even larger under completely equitable conditions. The computer program generating the series of intervals in the irregular burst places the largest interval (basic interpulse interval + R) at a random location in the burst. Thus, the largest interval could appear equally often at the middle of the burst or at either end. Uttal and Krissoff (1966) showed that the position of the gap in the gap-test paradigm significantly affected the threshold for its detection. The lowest threshold occurred when the gap was centrally placed in the train and thresholds were elevated when the gap was displaced to one side or the other of center. Assuming that the largest gap plays an especially important role in the detection of the statistical irregularity, then the random positioning of that particular interval throughout the pulse burst would be expected to lead to a general overestimate of the size of the threshold. Thus, the difference between the two curves may be somewhat underestimated in our data.

Experiment III (in which the number of pulses was varied) also shows a substantial decrease in the threshold for the detection of the irregularity as the number of pulses increases up to the limit of about eight pulses. This suggests that the subjects are able to make use of the additional information being made available to them in a statistical fashion but only up to a certain point. This should be contrasted against the negligible effect of the number of pulses on the gap-detection test reported by Uttal and Krissoff (1966). This newer result, however, is ambiguous in that it may define either an integration requiring a certain number of pulses or an integration period. Uttal and Smith (1968) established that it is indeed the number of intervals, rather than the elongated duration, that is primarily the cause of the increase in sensitivity in this psychophysical task.

Another piece of evidence supporting the notion that the subject is able to make use of the statistical information in a way quite different from the way he might if he were only responding to the single largest gap is that the threshold for irregularity (as indicated by the size of R) is independent of the basic interpulse interval up to 20 msec. This is in contrast to the data for the gap test, which show a more complicated functional relationship between the size of the gap and the basic interpulse interval.

Consider now the problem of the discrepancy between the data for the gap-detection experiment as measured with a yes-no test and as measured with a forced-choice technique. Psychophysical testing with different methods usually results in somewhat different results. The subject is, in effect, being trained to make his judgments on the basis of different criterion levels in each case. There is no *a priori* validity of one or the other set of results. In this experiment, however, the primary interest is in defining the information transmission limits of the nervous system. This adds a special criterion for the choice of a specific psychophysical technique, which does make one more "valid" than another. That criterion is that any technique used that genuinely lowers the threshold is considered superior. A finer discrimination, as evidenced by lower threshold, demonstrates an ability to distinguish between two stimuli that had been classified as indistinguishable. As such, it meaningfully alters the estimate of the information transmission capacity of the nervous system. If we had, on the other hand, been studying the nature of decision making, the difference in psychophysical methods could not be ordered along a continuum of validity, but rather would simply represent two different conditions of an independent variable that itself is of some intrinsic consequence. The results of Experiment II are now submitted as a more up-to-date estimate of the additional time that must be added to the gap at each basic interpulse interval for a just-detectable response. Uttal and Krissoff (1966) concluded that the additional time was a constant over a wide range. That notion can no longer be accepted in the context of these newer data.

Another significant feature of the curve relating the basic interpulse interval and the size of R required for detection of roughness is the existence of two separate segments. This feature is similar to one of the results reported by Mountcastle, Talbot, Darian-Smith, and Kornhuber (1967) for the detection of vibratory stimuli. They found that the curve was also made up of two segments, with the point of demarcation between the two occurring at about the same place on the frequency scale, as indicated on our chart. They concluded from their results that two different somatosensory systems were operating in the detection of vibratory activity. The first was sensitive to low frequencies and was mediated by receptors located in the skin. The second was sensitive to higher frequencies and was mediated by receptors buried deep in the tissues of the hand. The differences in the receptors that were activated, they suggested, were directly dependent upon the frequency of the mechanical vibration. It is similarly possible that the two-segment curve obtained in this experiment also was a function of two different sets of nerve fibers. However, considering the nature of our stimulus, there is no reason to assume that the pulses affect different fibers as their frequency of occurrence is increased. It is more likely that since our stimuli activate large numbers of the neurons in the nerve trunk, and even though almost all fibers are active, there is some segregation on the basis of the temporal processing capabilities of two groups of neurons. On the other hand, it is also possible that the two segments of the response curve do not represent two different groups of receptors or fibers but rather represent a dual characteristic curve for temporal processing in a uniform family of fibers.

As an alternative explanation of the two-segment curve reported by Mountcastle and co-workers and by our laboratory, I suggest the following hypothesis. Uttal (1960) had shown that subjects are relatively insensitive to the temporal properties of a short burst of three stimulus pulses, all occurring within 10 msec, if one corrected for amplitude changes due to refractory effects. This may be the explanation for the increase in the threshold as the basic interpulse interval decreases below 14 msec on the gap test and the slighter suggestion that the detectability of the jittered pulse train is also less sensitive at 10 msec.

On the basis of these data, we may speculate that there is a continuum of several regions of differing temporal processing capabilities as the frequency spectrum is scanned. Below 10 msec (100 Hz) there is a region of fusion in which there is generally a very low sensitivity to the temporal characteristics of the signal. In this time zone, the number of impulses is more important. Above 10 msec and below 20 msec a region exists in which there is an independent sensitivity to the second-order statistics—the irregularity—of the interpulse intervals. Above 20 msec, one crosses into a region in which the mean interpulse interval is so large that the integrative powers of the nervous system are no longer capable of taking advantage of such higher-order statistical data and judgments are made on the basis of mean interval or some independent measure of the size of local intervals.

MASKING OF ALPHABETIC CHARACTER RECOGNITION BY DYNAMIC VISUAL NOISE (DVN)[4]

A remarkably general experimental paradigm has appeared in recent years in many different experiments, each of which is presumably aimed at a different theoretical question. The paradigm typically involves the sequential presentation of two visual stimuli. Depending upon the interval between the two, a wide variety of different phenomena can be demonstrated.

This experimental paradigm has been used, for example, to study visual masking in a forward or backward direction. Such masking phenomena are

---

[4] This paper appeared in a somewhat modified form in *Perception and Psychophysics*, 1969.

characterized by interference with the recognition or detection of geometric forms by a preceding or following visual stimulus. The results of such experiments have typically shown that the masking effect can persist for elongated periods. In general, when two stimuli activate the same receptors, the masking occurs maximally at the shortest interstimulus intervals. Crawford's (1947) original studies of the backward masking phenomenon using flashes of light have been replicated many times. Generally, the interference effects last for well over 100 msec. Schiller (1966) showed further that the masking effect of letters on letters lasts longer than 200 msec, and that the effect is increased with an increase in the intensity of the masking stimulus. Schiller (1965), comparing monoptic and dichoptic masking, used a threshold test that apparently resulted in a less persistent masking effect, lasting only for about 40 msec. But it should be noted that his masking stimulus never drove the probability of detection of the masked form to chance levels. Raab (1963) reviewed a large selection of older studies on retroactive masking, a phenomenon that has captured much of the attention in this area.

When the two visual stimuli do not fall on the same retinal areas there is also some interference. However, the result is quite different. Typically, for the retroactive masking condition (metacontrast) a U-shaped function obtains. Alpern (1953) found maximum dimming of a test stimulus when the masking stimulus followed about 120 msec after the test stimulus. Weisstein and Haber (1965) found a similar effect but with the maximum retroactive effect at 30 msec. Kolers and Rosner (1960) actually found dichoptic metacontrast effects when the interstimulus interval was about 80 to 100 msec, and a decreasing effect as the interval increased. Kahneman (1967) pointed out the intimate relation between the experimental results concerning metacontrast and apparent motion and reported peak metacontrast effects at 80 msec.

It is not at all certain that the many different backward masking phenomena observed by the different investigators and the two different types of response distinguished here are due solely to the conditions of overlap of the stimuli. Kolers (1962) considered the problem in detail and also recognized the two different categories of response, which he named Type A and Type B respectively. He listed a large number of other conditions such as contrast and duration, which affect the type of response one will obtain in any given experiment. Most interestingly, he also assumed the type of response can be affected by the response demanded of the subject.

This same experimental paradigm has also been used to study the phenomena of short-term visual storage and the scanning processes used to inspect the stored image. Sperling (1963), following some of the older work of Baxt (1871), found that a static noise field completely obliterated the perception of an alphabetic character when the two were presented simultaneously. Furthermore, the noise terminated the scanning of a stored visual image when several characters were presented in the stimulus and the static noise appeared after the display. Interestingly enough, he found that all subjects required at least 20 msec to see anything after leading static noise, when the intensities of the two were comparable. More intense leading noise fields could mask for as long as 100 msec.

Another application of this same paradigm is in the context of temporal acuity or perceptual simultaneity, or as it has sometimes been called, the psychological moment. The general notion here is that since the visual image is stored someplace in the visual system for a substantial period, two stimuli that impinge upon the eye within a certain minimum period should appear to be present simultaneously. Thus, Piéron (1952) reported that the temporal resolution of the visual system is typically about 100 msec, although he does mention that under certain stimulus conditions it can be reduced to 20 msec. In any event, for most practical situations such as the cinema, no break is seen in the action when individual frames are projected at about 40-msec intervals. Fraisse (1966) reported that characters appear to be simultaneous whenever the total duration of the two characters and the interval between them is shorter than 80 to 120 msec. Lichtenstein (1961) obtained data showing an equivalent value of about 125 msec and further showed that this result was independent of the interval pattern between the individual elements of a diamond-shaped stimulus array. (This latter paper is also of considerable interest as a guide to some of the older literature on this subject.)

The idea to be emphasized, by pointing out the procedural similarities of these experiments, is that their differing results may represent different aspects of a more general perceptual process. Hopefully, some future psychologist will be able to rationalize all of these data in terms of some generalized ability of the visual system to deal with sequential stimuli.

It is, however, also probably true that several separate mechanisms are mixed together in all of these experiments. First, there is a simple signal-to-noise ratio consideration in which simultaneous stimulus and masking patterns interfere with each other to the degree that the stimuli are hidden or confused with visual noise of similar quality. This effect seems to be introduced by either monoptic or fused dichoptic viewing. Schiller's (1965) investigations showed that masking with patterns was dichoptic, while masking with flashes of light was purely monoptic. These results suggest that this type of pattern or "signal-to-noise" masking is a process occurring at nervous levels higher than the retina. Second, there are also interacting processes due to the inertia of the transduction processes involved in vision. This latter effect would presumably be mediated by mixing due to simple photochemical inertia in the peripheral receptor layers of the retina.

How can we separate the pattern or "signal-to-noise" type of masking from the retinal receptor effects? One way is to use Schiller's (1965) or Kolers and Rosner's (1960) dichoptic observation technique. Another is to make use, as was done in the present experiment, of a special type of masking stimulus that is generated by the serial presentation of small dots at random locations. I have called this type of stimulus Dynamic Visual Noise (DVN). Dynamic visual noise was introduced in a slightly different form as a psychological research medium by MacKay (1967). He used random patterns in which a large number of points was presented simultaneously on sequential frames of a motion picture film strip. Each frame contained many dots but the pattern of dots was different from one frame to the next. Each frame was projected at ordinary cinema speeds. In the present experiments, dots are plotted individually on the face of the oscilloscope with the interval following each dot individually controllable.

DVN of this sort has some important qualities. Since each retinal locus will be stimulated only infrequently on the average, therefore it is unlikely, for practical noise levels, that retinal locations stimulated by signal dots will be simultaneously stimulated by noise dots, even with monoptic stimulation. Thus, the retinal effects can be separated from the perceptual confusions of pattern or "signal-to-noise" effects. Masking with gross patterns or a bright flash of light delivered to the total retina, however, confounds masking due to signal and noise confusions and masking due to retinal lability and other complex interactive effects, such as lateral summation or inhibition.

By using test patterns (alphabetic characters) composed of dots and dynamic visual noise (DVN) composed of equivalent dots, but ones located randomly in time and space, photoreceptive effects can thus be minimized, even in the monoptic or binocular cases. Because of the persistence of the visual image, the characters, if plotted quickly enough, appear to be simultaneous displays of all constituent points. Similarly, the DVN appears to be composed of many dots at any given time, except for the lowest interdot intervals. We thus are in a position to explore the nature of "signal to noise" or pattern masking *per se*, as well as study the time course of the decay of this pattern masking in a way that is independent of peripheral photochemical effects.

The particular experimental paradigm with which I have recently been concerned is aimed at measuring the effects of DVN on the recognition of these characters. Obviously, if the dots of the DVN are frequent enough, the character will be obscured simply because the individual dots of the character cannot be separated from the individual dots of the DVN. The first experiment established the basic functional relationship between the DVN level and character recognizability when the DVN completely overlaps the character in time. The second and third experiments examined the effects of DVN on character recognition when the DVN precedes or follows presentation of the character. Specifically, the second experiment examined the effect on character recognition of leading noise separated from the character by a variable interval, while the third experiment examined a similar effect of trailing noise. An intuitive appreciation of the nature of this experiment can perhaps best be gained by consideration of Figure 11. Remember, however, that in the present experiment, all of the stars are of the same magnitude and are twinkling on and off in random order. Also remember that only one stimulus character is present and it appears for only a very brief instant.

"And the trouble is there's not a thing we can do about it."

Figure 11. Drawing by Smilby; © 1968, *The New Yorker Magazine,* Inc. (with permission).

METHOD

Subjects. Twenty undergraduate male and female subjects participated throughout the series of three experiments, although no more than eight were involved in any one experiment. Each data point in the graphs represents the averaged scores of six to eight subjects. While no subject was arbitrarily discarded, the exigencies of academic life did not permit a full complement of

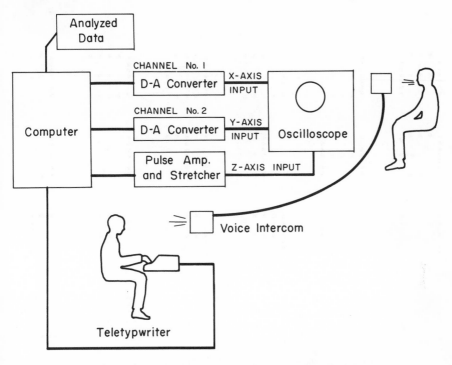

Figure 12. A block diagram of the experimental apparatus used in this study.

eight subjects for all cases or the same group of subjects throughout the entire course of each experiment. All subjects were given pretraining to familiarize themselves with the character set used in the experiments.

Apparatus. The subject was seated in a darkened and acoustically insulated cubicle. A cathode ray tube (CRT) was positioned 14 in. in front of his eyes, measured at the bridge of his nose. A metal frame bearing against the forehead regulated the appropriate head position.

The face of the CRT was masked off, exposing a window 2.25 by 1.5 inches. The DVN described below filled this entire window when it was being presented. The character presented was slightly smaller; each character being a maximum of 1 in. high and 0.75 in. wide. Thus, the visual angle subtended by the entire display was about $9.2°$ vertically and $6.13°$ horizontally, while the characters subtended a visual angle of about $4.08°$ by $3.03°$.

The CRT was driven directly by a digital to analog converter connected to the output of a medium-sized computer. The digital to analog converter used is a 10-bit, two-channel system. One channel was connected to the x-axis input of the CRT, and the other to the y-axis input. A third channel was connected to the intensity control and determined when a point would actually be plotted.

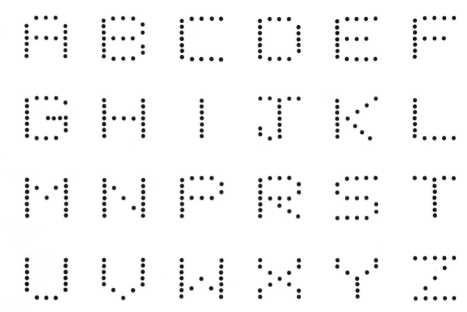

Figure 13. The character set used in this study as test stimuli.

This third channel intensified the electron beam for 10 μsec upon command. The system is thus acting as a point plotter. To form any pattern with such a point plotter, each and every point of that pattern must be individually calculated and plotted. Individual points could be plotted in about 20 μsec, but the minimum interpoint interval actually depended upon the algorithms for coordinate specification for each character. Figure 12 shows the equipment arrangement used to accomplish these functions.

The precise manipulation of the duration of the intensity control would serve no useful function if the light emitted by the CRT phosphor persisted for any appreciable length of time. For the present experiments, a special ultra-short persistence phosphor (P-15) was used. Its light output decays to 0.1% of its original intensity in 50 μsec. Thus, the duration of each dot was of this order of magnitude. An entire alphabetic character was plotted in less than 500 μsec. Therefore, all the dots of each character appeared to be plotted simultaneously. Figure 13 shows the family of alphabetic characters plotted by this method and

INTERDOT INTERVAL

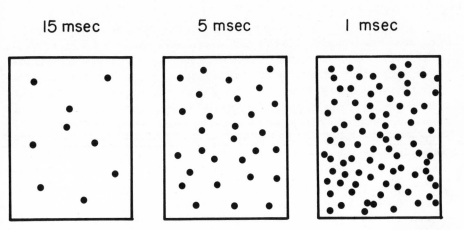

Figure 14. A visual impression of the dynamic visual noise (DVN) at the three interdot intervals indicated. These are not copies from photographs, but artist's impressions of the apparent dot densities. The characters, composed of dots of the same size and brightness, appear physically placed within the limits of this DVN.

used in the present experiment. 0 and Q were not used, leaving a 24-character stimulus set. The DVN was controlled by the specification of a single constant in the computer program. This constant regulated the duration of the interval between sequential noise dots. The position of each dot was randomly selected by a two-dimensional random number generator. Figure 14 shows the general appearance of the DVN at three of the different interdot intervals.

As mentioned, the visual system integrates, to a certain extent, dots presented within a given period so that the screen does appear to have many more than one dot present at all times, except at the lowest dot rates. Of course, the pattern appears to be constantly dancing from one configuration to another. However, as we shall see, the present results indicate that this integration is not complete and some separation of character dots and DVN dots is observed.

In addition to making the DVN field larger than the character field, we also attempted to control for pseudorecognition of characters in fixed positions by partial cues by jittering the position of the characters. Each character was presented in a location within the visual noise, which varied in the vertical direction from trial to trial.

General Procedure. The entire experimental procedure was under the control of the computer. During each session, the order of character presentation was randomized. However, the noise level remained constant during each 1-hr session. Two subjects ran together in each hour-long session. Each served as the observer subject for half an hour, and in the alternate half hour transcribed the responses of his partner (who reported his observations verbally over an intercommunication system) into a special keyboard that entered the data into the computer. Both the stimulus character and the observer subject's response were then displayed on a monitor television. The transcriber subject gave feedback to the observer subject by informing him of the correct character whenever an error was made. Subjects were given a 2-min break at the end of 10 and the end of 20 min in the experimental cubicle.

Data were collected in raw form on a digital magnetic tape. At the end of each session, two analysis programs, DAP 1 and DAP 2 were used to summarize all results. DAP 1 reduced the data for each subject to a summary table in which the number of presentations of each character, the number correctly identified, the percentage correctly identified, and the specific errors were tabulated. DAP 2 reduced these summary tables for each subject to a group summary, identical in format to the individual ones, except that specific errors were not recorded because of space limits. Six to eight subjects were run each day and there were approximately 2500 responses for each condition indicated by a point on our graph. This number varied from 2000 to 3000, primarily depending upon the difficulty of the task and the amount of feedback given by the transcriber subject.

In all instances, the CRT displayed some sort of a ready signal. In the experiments with the leading noise, the noise itself was initiated to indicate to the observer subject that the transcriber subject had entered his last response and the system was ready for his next trial. The observer subject held a pushbutton with which he controlled the emission of the stimulus, thus self-pacing the experimental sequence. In those situations without leading noise, a dim fixation point was plotted on the face of the CRT as a ready signal. It was extinguished when the button was pushed and after a short pause, the character was presented. The trailing noise followed the character at the delay specified for each given condition.

In the first experiment, the DVN completely overlapped the character in time and space. In other words, both leading and trailing noise was present. The duration of the DVN preceding the character was variable, dependent upon the time the observer subject took to release the character with the pushbutton.

However, this period could be no shorter than 1 sec, a minimum duration programmed to prevent the subject from shortening the duration of the leading noise to a brevity at which it might no longer be effective. The noise following the character lasted for a constant 1 sec. Since the display of the character could be accomplished by the computer in less than 0.5 msec, the noise at all interdot intervals appeared continuous, and the character appeared embedded in this continuous stream of dots. The noise levels used corresponded to interdot intervals of 13, 12, 11, 10, 9, 8, 7, 6, 5, 4, 3, 2, and 1 msec. Sampled data at longer interdot intervals showed no effect on character recognition scores. The maximum recognition score (group average) obtained under optimum conditions was about 95%. The 5% error margin was attributed to eye blinks, or transcription errors, and does not represent errors due to an inability to read the character through the DVN.

The observer subject was signalled that the previous response had been acquired and that a new stimulus was available by the reappearance of the DVN on the CRT. All subjects were instructed to respond with phonetic alphabet names (for example, "A as in ALPHA") to help reduce transcription errors.

In the second experiment, the noise following the character was deleted and the DVN preceded the character by a variable delay (the independent variable) that changed from day to day. The values of the DVN used in this experiment are indicated in Figure 15. While we originally started out collecting data at rather great densities, the stability of the data (a typical result in a computer-controlled experiment) led us to reduce progressively the number of data points collected in this and the third experiment. Data were obtained for two values of DVN interdot interval, 3.0 and 1.0 msec.

In the third experiment, the leading noise was deleted and DVN was presented only following the character. A variable delay, changed from day to day, was interposed between the character and the DVN. The values of the delay used for each of the two conditions of DVN used (3.0 and 1.0 msec.) are indicated in Figure 16.

RESULTS

In all three experiments, the percentage of the total number of characters presented that were correctly identified was the main dependent variable. Figure 15 presents the results of Experiment 1. The data are plotted with the interdot interval of the DVN on the abscissa and the percentage of correctly identified characters on the ordinate. There was a gradual but extremely regular decrease of the ability of subjects to identify the characters as the interdot interval decreased. It should be appreciated that it is not possible to use the DVN metric of interdot interval directly to specify the noise level, for there is another important variable confounding the actual noise level. The eye, because of inertia of the photochemical effects does integrate over time, and as shown in

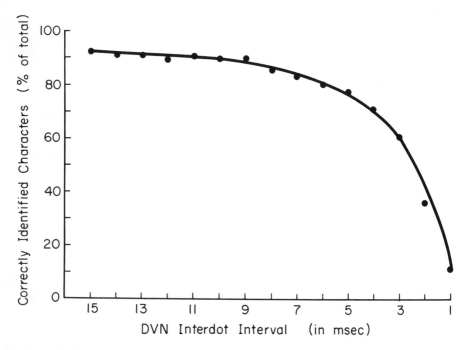

Figure 15. The results of Experiment I showing the decrease in character recognizability as the interdot interval of the DVN decreases.

Figure 14 there are apparently many more than a single dot present on the surface of the CRT at any given perceptual instant. In fact, the eye, as a first approximation, seems to be sliding an integrating temporal window along the time axis. The width of this temporal window is associated with the persistence of visual images among other factors. As will be seen, however, there is an enormous discrepancy between this simplistic notion of an integrating temporal window and the separability of the characters from the DVN in Experiments 2 and 3.

In Experiment 1, a sig ificant decrease in the recognizability of the characters begins at a DVN interdot interval of about 10 msec. The downward trend of the curve, as can be seen, gradually accelerates, decreasing to a level only slightly above chance (4.1% is the chance performance level for our 24-character alphabet) when the DVN interdot interval is 1 msec.

Table 1. The data for the 3-msec interdot interval condition of Experiment 1, showing the range of recognizability scores for the character set at this noise level. This table is one of those summaries of data from only six subjects and thus the total N is somewhat less than the 2500 typically obtained.

Symbol	N	NC	%C
A	74	42	56.7
B	66	36	54.5
C	74	44	59.4
D	72	46	63.8
E	73	55	75.3
F	65	49	75.3
G	80	53	66.2
H	66	37	56.0
I	81	71	87.6
J	73	46	63.0
K	67	53	79.1
L	61	46	75.4
M	75	29	38.6
N	72	30	41.6
P	86	42	48.8
R	71	23	32.3
S	67	40	59.7
T	64	40	62.5
U	68	53	77.9
V	59	32	54.2
W	70	28	40.0
X	75	52	69.3
Y	69	48	69.5
Z	94	67	71.2

(NT = 1722, NCT = 1062, %C = 61.6)

However, there are irregularities implicit in this smooth curve that are not immediately obvious. For example, the characters do not lose their ease of recognition equally. This is evidenced by the data summarized in Table 1 in which the data for all subjects for DVN with an interdot interval of 3 msec are tabulated. This table is the equivalent of the single data point for 3 msec in Figure 15. The recognizability of the characters at this DVN interdot interval varies from 87.6% for the character I, down to 32.3% for the character R. Two features of character recognizability emerge from an examination of this table and the related confusion matrix data. First, straight lines are seen with a great deal of ease compared to curved lines in the DVN. Second, some character groups like P, R, K, and F, and A, H, W, M, N, and U have large confusion scores. Why they should do so is obvious if one examines the font shown in

Table 2. Confusion matrices for all data of Experiment 1. Errors for about 37,500 trials are tabulated but only error scores greater than 10 have been entered to avoid cluttering up the table. Each error score greater than 50 has been underlined for emphasis.

RESPONSE CHARACTER

	A	B	C	D	E	F	G	H	I	J	K	L	M	N	P	R	S	T	U	V	W	X	Y	Z
A	×	10																				16		
B	15	×		23			20															14		
C	21	27	×	40		20	21															35		
D	20	40	13	×	11	17	71				11											17		
E	12	20	25	12	×	*54*	12	19	12		13											17		
F	21	12	12	15	12	×	12	14	18		12	34										32		
G	12	21	11	13	14	10	×	21	11		18	*63*		47								23		
H	11	11	13	13	10	*119*	17	×	18		44	13		13								17		
I		35	35		16	*67*		41	×	15	11	30		11								25		
J					11			*80*	*60*	×	15	15		10								18		
K								13	*75*	*81*	×	34	42	*80*		13						23		
L								34	27	*81*	34	×	14	27		22			11			23		
M									13	16	12	13	×	*219*	29	23			*97*		11	10		
N									11	11	12		*281*	×	42	15			15		14	23		
P									*131*		30		10	15	×	*81*			11	21	48	20		
R									13		*53*		20	30	*320*	×		24	10	10	46	*66*		
S									*67*		11		45	42		12	×	*120*	37	12	*246*	11		
T											36		46	*168*		12	15	×	29	16	11	17		
U														14			21	11	×	12	*62*	15	13	
V																		15	*72*	×	42	*73*	12	
W																		21	36	13	×	*70*	18	
X																			15	11	16	×	28	37
Y																			15				×	17
Z																			21					×

Figure 3. The distinction between each of the members of these two sets of characters depends primarily upon a small number of critical distinguishing dots that are extremely susceptible to DVN obscuration. Confusion data for the entire set of characters used in this experiment are shown in Table 2. In this table, all of the data for all of the different values of interdot interval have been pooled. Errors for approximately 37,000 trials are tabulated with the exception that no error scores less than 10 have been tabulated to avoid cluttering up the table. All error scores greater than 50 have been underlined for emphasis.

The results of Experiments 2 and 3 have been plotted together in Figure 16 to emphasize the symmetry of the obtained data. The data for the two DVN conditions for leading and trailing DVN can be seen to produce nearly equivalent results. There is but the most moderate decrease in the ability of the subject to recognize the character in the 3-msec DVN as the delay between the noise and the character decreases for both the leading and trailing noise. The lowest

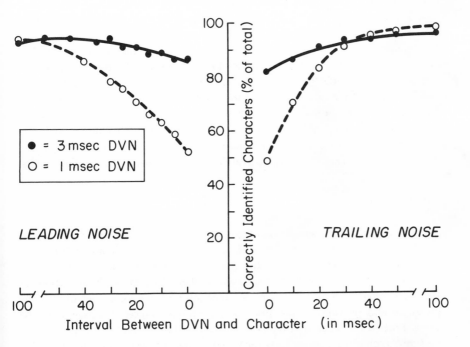

Figure 16. The results of Experiments II and II showing the effects of bringing the character closer to either leading or trailing DVN for two values of interdot interval.

recognition scores for the 3-msec noise (86.5% and 82.5%) occur when the noise immediately follows or precedes the character with no interposed delay. This, however, is a considerably higher recognizability score compared to the situation in which the characters are embedded in equivalent DVN levels as in Experiment 1. The comparable value for the embedded condition is 61.6%. Similarly, the decrease in recognizability when the leading or trailing noise is at the 1-msec level is considerably less than the masking produced by continuous noise with an interdot interval of 1 msec. The values in this case are 52.6% for leading noise immediately preceding the character, 49.1% for trailing noise immediately following the character, and 12.5% for continuous noise.

The important result here is that even though an initial consideration of the appearance of the DVN suggests the existence of a temporal integrating window, the differences reported above suggest that the subject is not limited by this integration when he has the task of separating the character signals from the DVN. He is, in this case, able to separate the characters and the DVN from each other even when the delay between the two is virtually nonexistent. The older notions of the psychological moment or of short-term visual storage that implied that any two stimuli that occurred within a brief interval were dealt with as if they were simultaneously present are strongly challenged by these results.

Figure 16 also shows that even the moderate decrease in recognizability occurs only with delays of about 30 to 40 msec, even under the most effective masking condition (DVN interdot interval of 1 msec). These results indicate a temporal discrimination capability of the eye for these viewing conditions that is considerably more acute than might have been predicted from the reports cited in the introduction. As discussed below, this is believed to be mainly due to the fact that we have separated retinal photoreceptive lability effects from pattern discrimination effects. The effects examined here fit mainly in this latter class.

DISCUSSION

The general experimental paradigm used in this experiment, characterized by the sequential presentation of a signal and DVN, has wide applicability. As mentioned in the introduction, the present findings are relevant to current interests in short-term visual storage, backward and forward masking, notions of the psychological moment, character recognition, and signal detection. The paradigm also provides insight into the neurophysiological foundations of the visual process by separating peripheral photoreceptor effects from the pattern discrimination effects presumably mediated by the central nervous system.

Nevertheless, the present experiment focused on two main issues. First is the recognizability of the dot characters in varying densities of DVN. Second is the measuring of the persistence of the masking effect when the character and the DVN are not simultaneous, thus considering the nature of the temporal window that is defined by these transient persistencies. The results in the latter case show that the present situation fits in the Type A response category (monotonically decreasing masking effects with increasing interstimulus interval) suggested by Kolers (1962). This is in spite of the fact that the contrast, luminance, and size of the individual dots are identical and the overall patterns are similar—conditions that Kolers suggests should lead to a Type B response (a U-shaped response curve with maximum masking at some intermediate interstimulus interval). However, the present task and stimulus conditions are so different than the ring and the disc type of stimulus used in many of the other studies that the two situations may not be truly comparable.

Experiment 1 was designed simply to measure recognition performance as a function of the DVN level. However, in the spatio-temporal universe of these visual experiments, the usual single dimensional measures of, say, an acoustic

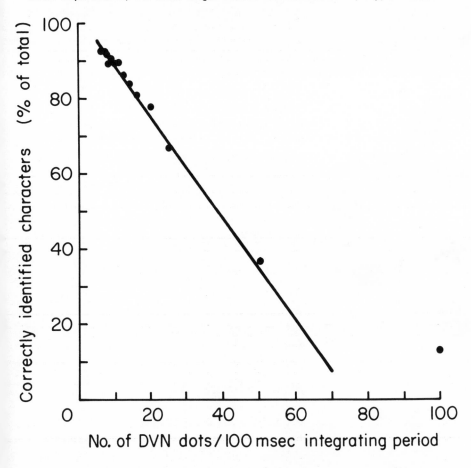

Figure 17. A replot of the data shown in Figure 15 assuming a 100-msec integration period. This graph shows the excellent fit by a straight line except for the one point at the point at the 1-msec interdot interval. This single deviant point is almost totally due to the continued high recognizability of the characters I, K, L, and X.

signal, cannot be directly used to specify the information content of either the test character or the noise. Some approximation to the information content of the character is possible because time has been essentially collapsed to a single instant by plotting the points so closely together. However, a similar notion of the information content of the DVN in terms of the number of noise dots that occur in a given interval is not immediately available. This is so both because of the random spatial distribution of the noise dots and because of the temporal integrating properties of the visual system.

However, the functional relationship between percentage character recognizability and the interdot interval of the DVN can be precisely specified on the basis of our experimental results. This function will serve the same purpose as a more conventional plot of signal to noise effects on recognizability, since the information content of the character set—the signal—whatever it is, is constant from one condition to the next.

Assume the integrating time window of the visual system to be of the order of 100 msec, for example, and therefore that the number of dots simultaneously perceived during any given 100-msec window is a direct function of the interdot interval (IDI). Therefore, the data of Figure 15 can be replotted with the new abscissa N, where N = 100/IDI. This has been done and the data of Experiment 1 are replotted in Figure 17. The straight line so generated intercepts the vertical axis at about 103%. This mathematical fiction reflects the facts that some of the data are outside the region within which the addition of DVN dots has any effect, and that 100 msec is not exactly correct as an estimate of the integrating period. We may assume that this value should be 100%. Therefore, the line has a slope of $-\frac{100}{76}=-1.31$ where 76 is the intercept on the abscissa. The equation of the straight line using the slope-intercept formula ($y = mx + b$; where m = the slope and b = the y intercept) is:

$$\%\text{Correct} = 1.31 \text{ (number of DVN dots)} + 100. \qquad \text{(Equation 1)}$$

Since the number of DVN dots is equal to $\frac{100 \text{ msec.}}{\text{IDI}}$ the analytical expression for the original unlinearized recognizability function is:

$$\%\text{Correct} = -1.31 \left(\frac{100}{\text{IDI}}\right) + 100 \qquad \text{(Equation 2)}$$

or

$$\%\text{Correct} = 100 - \frac{131}{\text{IDI} \text{ in msec.}} \qquad \text{(Equation 3)}$$

The only data point that deviates from the assumption of linearity is that one on Figure 15 that corresponds to an IDI of 1 msec. I believe that this deviance is almost entirely due to the continued recognizability of the characters

I, K, L, and (surprisingly) X. The data for X are thought to be artifactual, for several subjects reported that they gave an X response when they saw nothing, since X had been the first character to disappear as the DVN level increased. This disappearance is most probably due to the absence of any long straight-line segments in the particular X pattern used in the experiments.

With some trepidation, one can also point out that the intercept of the straight line on the abscissa is a rough estimate of the maximum information capacity of the visual system, for it is at this intercept (actually the intercept with the chance guessing value [4.04%] would be more appropriate) that theoretically no further information processing capacity is available for character recognition. The hesitancy to do so is primarily based upon the fact that certain characters are indeed still recognizable. Nevertheless, 76 dots in a 100-msec integrating period, or—converted to the original metric—a 1.31-msec interdot interval, can be considered a preliminary estimate of the information processing capacity of the total visual system in the current context. Though this value is somewhat higher than earlier estimates, it is for a situation that is somewhat more comparable to the real visual processing tasks of everyday life.

Now that a formal relation has been established for the effect of DVN on character recognizability, we can consider the results of Experiments 2 and 3. A major result of these experiments is the difference that obtains between the results for a character embedded (as in Experiment 1) in 1- or 3-msec DVN, and the equivalent points of Experiments 2 and 3. In general, we see that placing the character at either the beginning or the end of the DVN allows a much higher level of character recognizability. The most salient difference is for those points for which there is no delay between the character and the DVN. (These are the four points in Figure 6 that have abscissae of zero.)

The fact that characters can be separated from noise if they are at the beginning or the end of the noise is an extraordinary result. It indicates first of all, that the simplistic notion of a temporal window in which all stimuli are integrated must be modified. In other words, it raises the question: how can this separability occur if our perceptual world is made up of a string of psychological moments strung together in a fixed way like a string of sausages?

The initial interpretation of this result is that the integrating moments or windows are not arranged end to end like those metaphorical sausages, but are more closely approximated by a sliding temporal window that moves along the real temporal dimension. Thus, the leading characters can be seen and interpreted rather well because they occur in the last position of the sliding temporal window before the leading edge of that window enters the noise. The trailing characters can be seen because they also are present in a window that does not include the noise, *i.e.*, the window whose trailing edge is just emerging from the DVN as the character is emitted. The notion of a sliding temporal window and the resultant separability of DVN and character holds, of course, even if the masking due to trailing noise and the masking due to leading noise are, as is suggested by the present data, additive in either a linear or in some weighted fashion.

How then can we accommodate this notion to the tracking data of Stroud (1955), who has shown that stimulus information delivered within a 100-msec period cannot effectively produce a separate response? Similarly, how can we make this result compatible with the notion of perceptual simultaneity of stimuli occurring within 100 msec of each other? I would like to propose that the psychological moment of those experiments might indeed by a "receptor moment" or a "response moment," rather than a "central psychological moment". A receptor moment would result from those interactive phenomena that are due to the integrating properties of the retina. Such effects seem to have very long persistence and seem capable of overriding the otherwise more sensitive temporal discrimination abilities of the central nervous system. Thus, those experiments that involve sequential stimulation of the same retinal locations typically show an inertia greater than that produced by experiment that stimulate separate loci. (The one exception to this generality is the disc and annular ring typically used in the the metacontrast experiments. But that situation has several special features that suggest other mechanisms may be involved.)

Therefore, the results obtained by an experiment such as the present one, in which separate loci are stimulated, should provide more valid estimates of the temporal discriminatory powers of the higher levels of the nervous system, unconfounded by retinal effects and the resulting "receptor moment." In fact, from a certain point of view we can consider stimulation at the same retinal loci to be misleading in the same sense that we would be misled if we ignored the decay time of a particularly persistent CRT phosphor.

Stroud's data might possibly also be explained in terms of the physical inertia of the response mechanism or some other motor programming limitation. While in both cases the receptor and effector obviously do limit the total performance of the organism, they are in no sense indicative of a psychological moment, if by a psychological moment we are referring to that indivisibly small quantum of perceptual and decision-making time.

The nature and the shape of the visual integrating period and the psychological moment shall be considered in detail in a subsequent paper. For the present, let me simply mention several possible alternatives. In addition to the sausage-like string of psychological moments, I have already suggested the possibility of a sliding temporal window. There are many different "shapes" the temporal window might take in either case. The window could be heavily weighted to emphasize the information at its center. Thus, rather than being rectangular in its weighting and equally open throughout its course, it is possible that the window might symmetrically decrease its degree of "openness" the further a stimulus is from its center. The overall weighting distribution could be triangular, a normal distribution, or even some more complex shape. Some of the data in Figure 16 suggest that it is indeed non-symmetrical. This is suggested by the fact that the persistence of the effect of noise as the interval between the character and the noise is varied is not identical for both forward and backward masking. Leading noise appears to have some effect even when the interval is as great as 40 msec. Trailing noise on the other hand, seems to have an effect only when the interval is shorter than 20 msec. This suggests that the leading edge of the temporal window protrudes considerably further ahead in time than its trailing edge drags behind.

The important general conclusion to which we have come is that the many points of dissimilarity between data of this sort and the previous studies mentioned are due to the fact that we are dealing with only a portion of those processes that can produce persistent masking effects. The present experiments, because of the statistical properties of DVN, examined those processes that are specifically characteristic of the central pattern recognition processes and are therefore unconfounded estimates of visual temporal resolution or the psychological moment. While at some later time others may be able to subdivide the pattern effects we have dealt with to an even finer degree, I believe that these measures give more meaningful estimates of man's ability to process sequential visual signals than do the older studies. A strong cognitive component dependent upon the nature of the task is suggested. Thus, a host of new questions is opened up by this technique, each of which was not, in a certain sense, even conceptualizable before the technology became available that allows this sort of experiment to be performed. And that is indeed the explicit message of this chapter and this volume.

SOME PRACTICAL CONSIDERATIONS

So far in this chapter, we have spent a large amount of time and effort trying to demonstrate, by example, the key point of this entire volume—namely, that the type of experiment pursued and the type of theory evolved in any era are both critically dependent upon the type of instrumentation available in that era. But now that this point has been made and we have reflected on some of the changes that can occur in the laboratory as a result of the equipment, consider some of the more practical considerations concerning the use of computers in a psychophysical laboratory environment such as the one described.

The two computers used in these experiments are rather typical of a large number of small computers available in ever-increasing abundance from a large number of manufacturers. The somatosensory experiment was carried out on a PDP-5 and the visual experiment was carried out on a PDP-9. Both are manufactured by the Digital Equipment Corporation. The general family of small computers, of which these are but two examples, are transistorized machines with what, only a few years ago, would have been considered fantastically inexpensive purchase prices for the central processor, i.e., the computer itself. Some usable small machines are available for as little as $2850.

But, of course, this central and indispensable part of a total working system is but the head of the camel; and one had better be well prepared for the rest of the camel in his financial tent to make use of the full range of capabilities offered by the computer. A fully usable system for a typical laboratory like ours might be expected to cost between $15,000 and $30,000.

Unlike some other users who have proclaimed the large amount of hardware problems that they have found themselves involved in upon delivery of a new computer, our experience has been just the opposite. Currently, almost all of the computers that are delivered by almost all of the manufacturers today are capable of reliable and continuous performance over long periods of time after some negligible shakedown period. Of the two machines we now use, the older one (the PDP-5) has been routinely running experiments for over three years with no electronic failure. Other than the electromechanical teletypewriter used as the input control device and the paper-tape reader, the computer has been steadily working since our most recent failure in late 1966. Our newer and considerably larger machine has had but one electronic failure, actually a group of failures, that cost us only three lost work days in 18 months. As a matter of fact, this delightful dependability had led to another serious problem. We no longer see the manufacturer's service representative and he does not see this older machine. This, coupled with the usual turnover in that profession, means that there is really no one now trained to maintain the machine should some problem eventually develop. Hopefully, in the dim recesses of the manufacturer's plant there is a "little old computer technician" whom we can call upon if necessary.

As a general principle, however, electronic failures tend to become fewer and fewer as marginal components are weeded out of machines, a fact that is well known among electrical engineers. The argument for replacing an older machine with a newer one thus has to be extremely compelling before one should go to the effort of a changeover from our point of view. If one doubts the general acceptance of this concept of increasing dependability for the smaller aging machines, one has only to attempt to find a second-hand small computer. They simply do not exist at present, although many thousands of computers have been manufactured and sold over the last five years.

Thus, the maintenance problems on the central processors of small digital computers are well under control and one probably can be assured of increasing long-term reliability from any small computer hardware one might choose to buy. As mentioned above, the exception to this generalization almost exclusively lies in the realm of the electromechanical hardware. The input-output teletypewriters and magnetic or paper-tape handling devices often require service in their mechanical parts, even though their electronic circuitry works on and on.

Some of these devices are specifically designated as having a limited life span. For example, the popular Model 33 Teletypewriter used on so many small computers by various manufacturers has been designed to operate for only about

2500 hr. In this case it is appropriate to assure the reader that this design specification has been met! At about this number of hours of usage of a teletypewriter, the service calls increase to the point that the entire computer system may be unusable for large amounts of its otherwise usable time. The solution is to have the teletypewriter rebuilt, junk it, and buy a new one or, better still, replace it with what one should have purchased from the beginning, a Model 35 heavy duty teletypewriter with a designed life of 40,000 hr.

Nevertheless, in spite of the significant weaknesses of electromechanical devices, the general overall reliability of computer hardware has been excellent and is getting better each year as more and more highly reliable integrated circuitry is used in the construction of even these smaller machines.

Considering the software—the programs provided by the manufacturers—we must, however, tell a different story. Generally, most small machines come with a set of programs that help the user do his job. The basic ideas of what constitutes a basic assembler, editor, or even a program debugger have become fairly well standardized. Some manufacturers have now gone beyond the elementary level represented by this set of basic programs and have begun to offer more sophisticated programming systems. The Digital Equipment Corporation, for example, offers a keyboard-controlled version of these and related utility programs operating under the control of a monitor program, which is very good. It, however, was available at the time our PDP-9 was purchased. On the other hand, a more sophisticated version of this keyboard system that has some simple time-sharing capability has been promised for over two years (as of the date of this manuscript: November, 1969) and not yet delivered in an acceptable form. Furthermore, there is the suggestion that even their ultimately delivered system will not really do a successful job because of the extraordinarily large core memory requirements required by this kind of software. The moral of this typical story is simply: accept no promises for future delivery of software, in particular, if the particular part of the total system is critical to your operations. Be sure before one purchases the computer that what is available *now* will solve your minimum needs.

From the point of view of the psychophysicist, I believe that there is little to distinguish the various machines from one another on a purely technical basis. The general capability of almost any small computer exceeds the needs of all but the most esoteric psychological experiments and it is probably true that no one machine simply because it is larger or faster or more expensive will necessarily do some jobs better than any other.

The criteria for choosing a small computer then become ones that are secondary to factors such as the instruction set or cycle time. Generally, one would be better off choosing a computer that is accompanied by a suitable library of subroutines, which is easy to interface or, perhaps most important, which happens to have a local service office in our neighborhood; the latter consideration is a most important one to all save, perhaps, those who live in southern California, the nesting place of small computers in this decade.

The variety of languages on small computers is typically considerably less than that available with some of the large systems. Usually, only an assembly language and some abbreviated form of FORTRAN are provided. For the type of experimental control used in the research described in this paper, however, this is not a seriously abbreviated list of available programs. In fact, we use only the machine assembly language. The reason for this is obvious. Throughout all of our programs we are trying to control micro time to the ultimate possible precision. Absolute control, therefore, must be kept over the action of each and every instruction. Compiling and interpreting languages do not allow the user to do this. In other words, these higher level languages are not designed to optimize the machine language program. They are, rather, designed to make the programming simpler for the user who pays some compensatory price in terms of the efficiency to output code.

In our laboratory, much of the highly detailed control programming manipulating the stimuli and acquiring responses is done personally by the principal investigator. This procedure has a number of advantages in that the investigator's attention is directed—almost forced—to the specific details of the experiment. It is surprising how hard it is to communicate to a programming assistant exactly what is desired in many instances. Alternative possible ways of programming even the most clearly stated verbal statement of experimental design often leads to completely disastrous results. It is my personal opinion that each experimenter who uses a computer should be able to program at least the critical portions of his experiment at this detailed level of the assembly language. Considering that some of the assembly languages deal only with a couple of dozen different machine language instructions, this does not seem to be too much of a burden for the researcher.

Programming of data analysis programs is, however, something that is regularly turned over to a service programmer in our lab. The details of time and space are not so strict and unforgiving in this regard and a moderately good programmer can handle this sort of work easily. The DAP 1 and DAP 2 programs described earlier were actually written in assembly language and run on the same computer running the experiment when the daily sessions were ended. In later versions, the data analysis program, DAP 1 was actually integrated into the control program so that individual experimental results were printed out as soon as the subject's daily session was complete. These programs might well have been written in FORTRAN or some other higher-level programming language, of course, but it still would have been preferable to have these data analysis programs executed on the small laboratory computer. The reasons for this somewhat unusual bias are that, in spite of the fact that a small computer may have much less memory capacity and somewhat slower execution times in carrying out basic instructions, it is surprising to realize just how much computing power is available to the user if he allows the small machines to do their work at their own speed. A 4000-word memory, 2.0-msec memory cycle machine may execute a typical data analysis program in two or three times the time required by a larger faster system, but in total elapsed time it may actually be very much faster and more desirable to choose the small machine. The convenience and availability of the small machine may in the long run overcome the disadvantages of its own time limits.

An anecdote that illustrates this point most clearly concerns a new printer recently acquired for our laboratory. The printer operated at roughly half the speed of a much more expensive line printer available down the hall. We were interested in making a benchmark comparison of the two. The printer on our computer was set up and timed during the listing of a long program. We then took the same program and went to the higher-speed printer. If was not immediately available and, in fact, we waited for over a day before we could carry out the listing, only to find that indeed it was twice as fast—but twice as fast only if one considers the printing time alone. But that is not the only time to be considered. One must add also all of the logistical delays involved in the use of a remote system even if it is more capable in some operational sense. Which machine was really faster? Where does one begin to mark time in such a situation?

Questions such as those discussed in the preceding paragraph raise points that go far beyond a simple comparison of the particular technical details of the various available computers. Such questions also suggest the practical notion that not only does the choice of the computer depend very much upon second-order considerations such as logistical support, but the more basic issue of whether or not one should get involved with a computer at all also is to be answered on the basis of similar second-order considerations. These second-order considerations include the skills and interests of the investigator as well as a more objective evaluation of what doors the new experimental procedures might be expected to open. But, most important of all is whether or not the substantive issue under attack can profit from such a methodology. The most apt warning, though, is that the investigator who chooses not to try these techniques for some kinds of work, particularly the psychophysics of human information processing, is doing so at what may turn out to be a substantial career risk.

Admittedly, some new skills are required of the computer user and some investigators may not find these worth their personal effort. It is my belief that while one can always hire an electrical engineer or a programmer, it turns out that it is very easy to lose control of the experimental situation unless these relatively simple skills are added to one's own repertoire.

There are a host of other practical considerations that might have been discussed in this chapter. I have spoken of special techniques to produce random numbers or to plot dots on the face of CRTs. In each case, the particular way it was done was of relatively limited interest, special to the particular experiment or input-output equipment available. The single point to be made concerning these special issues is that they do, indeed, exist and that like all of the other special problems that arise do so in a context of "getting the job done" in the best possible way. The laboratory control computer represents for some of us the best possible way. The experiments described here are, patently, beyond the capability of conventional methodology and from this perspective, we can see that computers play their most important role in the way they influence the manner in which we examine the world around us. Tools are to be used and are significant only in the terms of their use. This is why I have emphasized the substance of the research performed even in this text on computer methodology.

REFERENCES

Alpern, M. Metacontrast. *Journal of the Optical Society of America*, 1953, *43*, 648—657.

Baxt, N. Ueber die Zeit welche nötig ist, damit ein Gesichtseindruck zum Bewusstsein kommt und über die Grösse (Extension) der bewussten Wahrnehmung bei einem Gesichtseindrucke von gegenbener Dauer. *Pflüger's Archiv für die gesamte Physiologie, des Menscher und der Tiere,* 1871, *4*, 325—336.

Buller, A. J., Nicholls, J. G., and Strom, G. Spontaneous fluctuations of excitability in the muscle spindle of the frog. *Journal of Physiology* (London), 1953, *122*, 409—418.

Burks, A. W., Goldstine, H. H., and von Neumann, J. *Preliminary discussion of the logical design of an electronic computing instrument.* Part I, Vol. I. Institute for Advanced Study, Princeton University.

Calvin, W. H. and Stevens, C. F. Synaptic noise as a source of variability in the interval between action potentials. *Science*, 1967, *155*, 842—844.

Cardozo, B. L, Ritsma, R. J., Domburg, G., and Neelen, J. J. M. Unipolar pulse trains with perturbed intervals; perceptibility of jitter. *IPO Annual Progress Report, No. 1* (Institute for Perception Research, Eindhoven, Holland), 1966, 17—27.

Casby, J. U., Siminoff, R., and Houseknecht, T. R. An analogue cross-correlator to study naturally induced activity in intact nerve trunks. *Journal of Neurophysiology*, 1963, *26*, 432—448.

Crawford, B. H. Visual adaptation in relation to brief conditioning stimuli. *Proceedings of the Royal Society of London*, 1947, *134B*, 283—302.

Fraisse, P. Visual perceptive simultaneity and masking of letters successively presented. *Perception and Psychophysics*, 1966, *1*, 285—287.

Green, D. M. and Swets, J. A. *Signal detection theory and psychophysics.* New York: John Wiley, 1966.

Kahneman, D. An onset-onset law for one case of apparent motion and metacontrast. *Perception and Psychophysics*, 1967, *2*, 577—584.

Kolers, P. A. Intensity and contour effects in visual masking. *Vision Research*, 1962, *2*, 277—294.

Kolers, P. A. and Rosner, B. S. On visual masking (metacontrast) dichoptic observation. *American Journal of Psychology*, 1960, *73*, 2—71.

Lichenstein, M. Phenomenal simultaneity with irregular timing of components of the visual stimulus. *Perceptual and Motor Skills*, 1961, *12*, 47—66.

MacKay, D. M. Ways of looking at perception. *In:* Weiant Wathen-Dunn, (Ed.) *Models for the Perception of Speech and Visual Form.* Cambridge: The M.I.T. Press, 1967. Pp. 25—43.

Moore, G. P., Perkel, D. H., and Segundo, J. P. Statistical analysis and functional interpretation of neuronal spike data. *Annual Review of Physiology*, 1966, *28*, 493—522.

Mountcastle, V. B., Talbot, W. H., Darian-Smith, I., and Kornhuber, H. H. Neural basis of the sense of flutter-vibration. *Science*, 1967, *155*, 597—600.

Piéron, H. *The sensations: their functions, processes and mechanisms.* New Haven: Yale University Press, 1952.

Pollack, I. *Personal communication*, 1967.

Raab, D. H. Backward masking. *Psychological Bulletin*, 1963, *60*, 118—129.

Schiller, P. H. Monoptic and dichoptic visual masking by patterns and flashes. *Journal of Experimental Psychology*, 1965, *69*, 193—199.

Schiller, P. H. Forward and backward masking as a function of relative overlap and intensity of test and masking stimuli. *Perception and Psychophysics*, 1966, *1*, 161—164.

Segundo, J. P., Moore, G. P., Stensaas, L. J., and Bullock, T. H. Sensitivity of neurones in *aplysia* to temporal pattern of arriving impulses. *Journal of Experimental Biology*, 1963, *40*, 643—667.

Smith, J. E. K. Dynamic stimulus selection and the effect of computer control on experimental design. *Mental Health Research Institute Preprint, #209* University of Michigan, Ann Arbor, May, 1967.

Sperling, G. A model for visual memory tasks. *Human Factors*, Feb., 1963, 19—31.

Stroud, J. The fine structure of psychological time. *In:* H. Quastler (Ed.) *Information theory in psychology*, New York: Free Press, 1955.

Taylor, M., M. and Creelman, C. D. PEST: Efficient estimates on probability functions. *Journal of the Acoustical Society of America*, 1967, *41*, 782—787.

Uttal, W. R. The three pulse problem: A further comparison of neural and psychophysical responses in the somatosensory system. *Journal of Comparative and Physiological Psychology*, 1960, *53*, 42—46.

Uttal, W. R. Evoked brain potentials: Signs or codes? *Perspectives in Biology and Medicine*, 1967, *10*, 627—639.

Uttal, W. R. *Real time computers: technique and applications in the psychological sciences.* New York: Harper and Row, 1968.

Uttal, W. R., and Krissoff, M. Effect of stimulus pattern on temporal acuity in the somatosensory system. *Journal of Experimental Psychology*, 1966, *71*, 878—883.

Uttal, W. R. and Krissoff, M. On the refractoriness of somesthetic temporal acuity. *Perception and Psychophysics*, 1967, *2*, 115—118.

Uttal, W. R., and Smith, P. Further studies on the psychophysics of irregular nerve action potential patterns. *Perception and Psychophysics*, 1968, *3*, 341—345.

Weisstein, N. and Haber, R. N. A U shaped backward masking function in vision. *Psychonomic Science*, 1965, *2*, 75—76.

Werner, G. and Mountcastle, V. B. The variability of central neural activity in a sensory system, and its implications for the central reflection of sensory events. *Journal of Neurphysiology*, 1963, *26*, 958—977.

CHAPTER SEVEN

USE OF A LABORATORY DIGITAL COMPUTER IN THE SINGLE-UNIT ANALYSIS OF SENSORY SYSTEMS

WILLIAM H. TALBOT

The Johns Hopkins University School of Medicine

INTRODUCTION

Laboratory digital computers can play a variety of roles in the experimental study of the nervous system. Quite simple computer systems are sufficient to take over many of the burdensome repetitive tasks involved in data collection and analysis; more complex systems may control complete experiments in which patterns of stimulus presentation are more or less continuously modified on the basis of immediate analysis of incoming data. The system described here is intermediate between these extremes. It is simple enough to have been installed, developed, and maintained by physiologists who have had little or no previous experience with computers, yet powerful enough to control a variety of quite complex experiments, to record large quantities of physiological data, and to apply to these data any of a number of simple analyses. Although in our laboratory we have access to a large general-purpose computer and for a number of years employed a full-time professional programmer to maintain a system of analysis programs for this machine, we now rely almost exclusively upon our laboratory computing facility. The advantages of immediate accessibility and direct control outweigh the disadvantages of small size and relatively difficult programming.

Our experience in digital computing began nearly 10 years ago when special-purpose devices were designed to convert data from our experiments to a form suitable for input to a large central computer (Poggio and Mountcastle, 1963; Mountcastle, Poggio, and Werner, 1963; Werner and Mountcastle, 1963). But this was a stopgap measure, limited by the requirement that data first be recorded on analog tape and then played back at greatly reduced speed for conversion into machine readable form. Only when we were given the opportunity to participate in the evaluation of the LINC computer,[1] a small machine specifically designed for laboratory use, were we able to begin to explore the advantages of real-time data collection and experimental control.

The LINC is very small and relatively slow. Its maximum memory size is 2048 12-bit words, only half of which are addressable as instructions. Memory cycle time is 8 μsec and most instructions require two to four cycles for execution. An adequate assembly language with excellent provisions for editing and manipulating source programs on magnetic tape and an absolute binary loader are the only widely available systems software for the machine (Wilkes, 1970). An unusually powerful instruction set to some extent compensates for the lack of compiler languages. In its basic configuration the computer is equipped with two small digital magnetic tape units, a multiplexed analog-to-

[1] Sponsored by the National Institutes of Health in conjunction with the National Aeronautics and Space Administration under NIH contract PH 45-63-540. Most of the physiological research referred to in this article has been supported by Public Health Service Grant NB-06828. Funds from this grant and from Air Force Contract No. 49 (638) 1305 have been used to purchase and construct interface and peripheral devices for the LINC.

digital converter, an input keyboard, and a display oscilloscope with facilities for automatic character generation. To these we have added an industry compatible seven-track digital tape recorder, a digital incremental plotter, a medium-speed teleprinter, and a specialized input/output interface for data collection and experimental control. This interface includes a 4096-word auxiliary core memory that is used specifically in data collection but may also be used at other times as a random-access data store.

The LINC's limitations impose constraints that would seem intolerable in a machine built today. Yet apart from complaints about scheduling that arises from our inability to service more than one laboratory at a time, and about the difficulty of writing complex programs for a machine with such a small memory, there has been little dissatisfaction with the role it has played in support of research in three neurophysiological laboratories.

Perhaps the reason that such a small computer system has been able to serve several laboratories is that the general research goals of these laboratories are similar and that a unified approach to data collection and analysis has been possible. This has reduced both the cost of interfacing the computer to the laboratory and the amount of time invested in programming. It has been more difficult to find common approaches to experimental control. Each laboratory contains highly specialized stimulating equipment, the use of which may change significantly as the research program progresses. Several years and a number of evolutionary steps have been required to bring us to our present position where a generalized output interface may be patchboard-connected to control most parameters of stimulation in each of the three laboratories and where a system of common programs performs most of the secondary tasks associated with data collection and experimental control. Our approach has not eliminated the need for hand coding real-time programs, but it has reduced the task to manageable proportions.

THE RESEARCH PROGRAM

The general aim of our research in neurosensory physiology is to discover the functional significance of the nerve impulse activity occurring in defined populations of nerve cells. Since methods do not exist for simultaneously recording impulses from all or even many of the neurons making up a natural population, we are obliged to study single cells serially and then to reconstruct from their recorded activity the responses to sensory stimulation of the populations from which they are drawn. Two methods are used to isolate the activity of a neural element from that of its neighbors: microdissection of peripheral nerve trunks physically isolates single conducting axons; microelectrode recording from the central nervous system electrically isolates nerve impulses from a single cell. In either case, what is recorded is the nerve impulse or spike action potential and not slower phenomena such as generator or synaptic potentials. Since the nerve impulse is an all-or-none event it is not necessary to record its time course or shape. A complete description of the impulse activity of a neuron is contained in a list of serially ordered interspike time intervals.

It is not enough, of course, merely to record the activity of single neurons, however precisely. One must seek to correlate the neural activity with parameters of stimulation, with the activity of other neurons nearby and at other levels of the nervous system, and with the sensory capacities of the organism revealed by psychophysical investigation. It is our hope that by such correlation we will be able to ascertain the nature of the neural codes used to transmit information about sensory stimuli from the periphery to the cortex and eventually to begin to understand the sensory process itself.

The simple task of data collection required by this experimental approach might by itself warrant the purchase of a laboratory computer. The complete study of a single neuron may take an hour or more, during which several "experiments" are performed, each of which requires that several hundred stimuli be presented to the animal. The permanent data record should make possible a temporal reconstruction of the course of each experiment. Not only must interspike time intervals be recorded, but also time intervals between stimulus "events" of interest such as the onset or termination of a flash of light or the beginning or end of a step indentation of the skin. When the time course of stimulation cannot be reconstructed from "events" alone, it may be necessary to make periodic measurements of time-varying stimulus analog voltages, to store them with the time interval data, and to provide a key that makes it possible to relate the two in time. Finally, the data record should specify all parameters of stimulation, both fixed and variable, and the identity of the neuron studied. The entire record from even a simple experiment may comprise many thousands of numbers. Yet, if one wishes to study single neurons quantitatively these are the data that are required. This is the problem of data collection.

But once that problem has been solved, the much more interesting problem of experimental control arises. Especially in studies of the central nervous system it is essential that an experiment be run with great efficiency, or else the precarious "grip" of the microelectrode will slip and a unit be lost before the experiment is completed. The urge to speed leads to mistakes, and unless great care is taken parts of an experiment will be useless because a switch was left unturned or turned too soon. Even a computer-based system that did nothing more than to reproduce manual control with unfailing speed and accuracy would greatly increase the amount of usable data that could be collected from a single neuron. Much more can be expected. It has been our experience that once a basic but flexible experimental control system has been developed, plans for new experiments expand to include approaches of a wholly new conceptual nature, approaches that would not have been considered if automatic control had not been available.

Finally, there is the problem of data analysis. Here, the importance of the laboratory computer depends upon the number and kinds of analyses performed. When analyses are mathematically complex or require large arrays of intermediate data, the raw computing power of massive general purpose machines may be required to execute them efficiently. For most of our work, the requirements are quite different. The state of our knowledge about the nervous system is often not sufficiently advanced to permit us to seek direct answers to questions of interest. Instead, we must reduce an unwieldy bulk of data to a form we can look at and then, on the basis of what we see, generate hypotheses that can be tested statistically. Even a small laboratory computer can be easily programmed to accomplish the desired data reduction. Although in principle the cost of performing data analysis is greater on a small machine than on a large one, once the small machine has been acquired for the specialized tasks of collection and control, analysis is almost free. Furthermore, appropriate programming gives the user interactive control over the analysis of large files of data, a privilege usually reserved for subscribers to very large time-sharing systems. Interactive control allows the user to test a variety of data reduction techniques in a short time and to select immediately the one that is most suitable for a particular set of data.

The purpose of this article is to discuss our use of a laboratory computer for these three tasks of data collection, experimental control, and data analysis and to describe the hardware and programming systems we have developed to help us. Particular stress is laid on techniques common to all of our laboratories. Attention is paid to the specific requirements of individual laboratories only in the discussion of experimental control. At this point, however, it seems advisable to review briefly the several research interests of our group in order to provide a scientific backdrop against which our use of the computer can be seen. No effort will be made to present detailed aims or justifications for this research, nor will there be any attempt to provide extended physical characterization of stimulating and recording apparatus. Instead, a simple operational description of each laboratory's stimulators will be combined with a summary of their typical experimental uses.

THERMAL SENSATION

In the laboratory of Dr. Ian Darian-Smith, an electronically controlled thermal stimulator is used to study the psychophysics and neurophysiology of thermal sensibility (Darian-Smith, 1970). At the time of writing, simple psychophysical measurements made in man are being compared with the responses of first-order thermoreceptive afferent fibers in monkey in order to obtain a better understanding of the neural codes by which information about skin temperature is transmitted to the central nervous system. The operation of the stimulator depends upon the fact that dilute electrolyte solutions can be subjected to rapid controlled heating by passing large electric currents through them. Chilled solutions are heated in this way just before passing over a silver-plate thermode, which is pressed against the skin. Both relatively warm and relatively cold stimuli can be delivered, the difference depending only on whether more current is passed during the stimulus or during the interstimulus period.

At present, this stimulator is used primarily in two experimental designs. In one, the responses to step changes of temperature are examined. The only parameters of the stimulus that are systematically varied are resting skin temperature, step amplitude, and step polarity (warming or cooling). This design permits study of intensity-response relations for both warming and cooling as well as the analysis of the influence of baseline temperature on the responses to thermal transients. In the second design, rate of change of skin temperature is a controlled parameter, making possible the direct study of some aspects of adaptation to thermal stimuli.

VISUAL SENSATION

In Dr. Gian Poggio's laboratory, a variety of experimental approaches are used to study single neurons of the visual system. The experimental use of two different photic stimulators are described here. The first is a conceptually simple cathode ray tube stimulator developed by a graduate student for his thesis research. The second is a complex optical bench stimulator used in the ongoing research of Dr. Poggio, Dr. Frank Baker, and their colleagues.

The cathode ray tube stimulator is built around a small television monitor tube selected because of the brightness, whiteness, and speed of its phosphor. Stimuli are sharply focused spots, the position and brightness of which are controlled parameters. Typical experiments test the effect of different temporal sequences of spot presentation upon the apparent shape of visual receptive fields.

The optical bench stimulator is actually two complete and independent ophthalmoscopic stimulators, one for each eye. In each, light from a single source is divided into three beams, one for background illumination of the eye and two for delivering patterned stimuli to selected regions of the retina. Color, pattern, intensity, and timing of stimuli are established by a combination of manual and automatic controls. This stimulator has been used to study the effects of temporal, spatial, and intensive parameters on the interaction of stimuli falling upon the retina (Poggio, Baker, Lamarre, and Riva Sanseverino, 1969; Baker, Lamarre, Riva Sanseverino, and Poggio, 1969). Recently, the introduction of an electromechanically controlled deflecting mirror into the path of one of the light beams has made it possible to study the influence of speed and extent of movement of photic stimuli upon the responses of neurons in the visual cortex. The many degrees of freedom provided by the stimulator make it particularly desirable that this laboratory be supplied with a sophisticated experimental control system.

TACTILE SENSATION

The group directed by Dr. Vernon Mountcastle is now principally concerned with the simultaneous psychophysical and neurophysiological analysis of tactile sensibility. Its effort for a number of years has been directed to the quantitative description of peripheral and central neural responses to mechanical distortion of the skin. Experiments generally have used one of two basic stimulus patterns. The first is a simple steplike indentation of the skin. Variable parameters of this pattern are rate, depth, and duration of indentation. The second pattern is like the first except that superimposed on the period of steady indentation is a period of sinusoidal modulation of indentation depth. Frequency and amplitude of the sine wave are controlled as well as the duration of the period of sinusoidal modulation and the time of its onset with respect to the beginning of the step. Two feedback controlled electromechanical stimulators have been constructed that are capable of delivering these stimulus patterns.

Typical neurophysiological uses of the mechanical stimulators have been to study the effect of step amplitude on the responses of slowly adapting cutaneous afferent fibers (Werner and Mountcastle, 1965; Mountcastle, Talbot, and Kornhuber, 1966) and to study the effects of sine wave frequency and amplitude on responses of a variety of peripheral and central neurons (Talbot, Darian-Smith, Kornhuber, and Mountcastle, 1968; Mountcastle, Talbot, Sakata, and Hyvärinen, 1969). Current experiments combine recording of nerve impulses from cortical neurons in restrained unanesthetized monkeys with the behavioral analysis of the relevant sensory capacities of the animals used (*cf.* Evarts, 1968 *a, b*). Experimental control and data collection must simultaneously serve the needs of the behavioral and physiological aspects of the work. In a typical experiment, a simple reaction-time paradigm is used to ascertain the psychophysical threshold for the detection of sinusoidal stimuli of different frequencies. The laboratory computer delivers stimuli, monitors key-pressing responses of the animal, provides feedback to the animal in the form of food reinforcers and a variety of visual and auditory signals, and collects inter-event time interval data that completely describe both the time course of the animal's key-pressing behavior and the responses of isolated single neurons.

THE LABORATORY COMPUTER SYSTEM: AN OVERALL VIEW

The block diagram of Figure 1 shows the logical connections that on the one hand relate the experimenter directly to his experimental preparation and

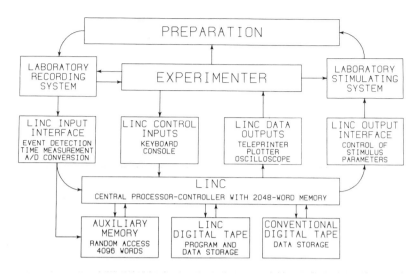

Figure 1. Diagram showing computer and its peripheral devices in their relationship to the laboratory during an on-line experiment.

laboratory equipment and on the other hand relate him to them indirectly through the laboratory computer and its interfaces. Physically, the computer is located in a central room close to all three physiological laboratories. Cables ranging in length from 40 to 90 ft run between the computer's interface and the stimulating and recording systems of each laboratory. All electronic circuitry in the three laboratories is grounded at a common point near the computer so that all that is required to transfer computer control from one laboratory to another is to unplug the connections of the first and plug in those of the second. Of course, each laboratory contains local control circuits that make possible off-line experiments. Tape recorded data from these experiments can be played back into the computer's input interface for digitalization and permanent storage.

The course of an on-line experiment is broken into a number of essentially independent periods of stimulation and data collection. Before each of these runs, manual intervention may be required to isolate a neuron or to preset fixed parameters of stimulation. Then, an experimental control program is loaded into the computer. Upon a signal from the laboratory the computer initiates stimulation and data collection. These continue until the programmed experimental design has been fulfilled or a signal from the laboratory requests a halt. The data collected during the 20 min or more of programmed stimulation are stored on magnetic tape together with a title record that combines identifying and descriptive information typed in by the user with similar information supplied by the control program.

Within each run there are a large number of trials, during each of which a single stimulus or pattern of stimuli is presented. Trials are grouped into classes.

Stimuli presented during the trials of any one class are identical in all parameters; between classes, stimuli differ in at least one parameter. Parameters for all stimulus classes are defined before the beginning of each run. During the run, the program may refer to a random-number table in order to select the class to which each trial will belong. This stimulus randomization helps to minimize systematic errors that might be introduced by time-dependent changes in the state of the animal or by the particular sequence in which trials of the various classes were presented.

Normally, data collection is interrupted briefly before the beginning of each trial. This affords time for the computer to transfer data from its memory to magnetic tape and makes possible the insertion of supplementary data in front of the inter-event time interval list for each trial. These supplementary data specify the serial number of the trial and the class to which it belongs, and may include measurements of analog voltages or other information required by a particular experimental design.

Data analysis may be performed between runs in order to provide information that may be used to modify the subsequent course of an experiment or it may be deferred until the experiment has been completed. Normally, data from each file are subjected to a number of analyses. These range from graphic representations of raw data to numerical evaluations of response statistics. Occasionally, methods of analysis are required that overtax the capacities of the laboratory computer. Input data for these analyses are prepared by the laboratory computer, written on industry compatible magnetic tape and carried to a larger computer. When desired, output data from the large computer can be returned to the laboratory on tape for automatic plotting.

Finally, data are transferred to industry compatible tape to form a permanent archive. This medium has been selected because it is cheaper and more compact than the LINC's own small tapes. A permanent archive is desired for two reasons: (1) digital magnetic tape contains the only record of the "raw" data from most of our experiments and (2) this record is sufficiently complete that it probably contains answers to questions we have not yet asked. The cost of maintaining an archive is relatively small; the cost of repeating any large number of experiments would be substantial.

THE COMPUTER'S LABORATORY INTERFACE

Even though the LINC was specifically designed as a laboratory computer for use in biomedical research, it was necessary for us to build a considerable amount of interface hardware in order to adapt it to our needs. Some of this hardware was required to simplify the programming problems associated with simultaneous data collection and experimental control, some to make possible continuous data collection, and the rest simply to provide the variety of input and output connections called for by our stimulating and recording equipment.

Because our use of the computer in data collection and experimental control is strongly influenced by the design of the interface hardware, the following pages describe this design in some detail. There is nothing particularly innovative in the design. It incorporates features that would be found in most on-line computer systems. But it has enabled us to create a fairly efficient and flexible system of automation for our laboratories. It is hoped that the reader who is planning a computer-based data collection and experimental control system for another laboratory may find here some juxtaposition of ideas that had not occurred to him before.

The major components of the laboratory interface may be divided fairly easily into three groups, which are used for experimental control, real-time measurement, and data collection (Figure 2). Because real-time measurement is required for both collection and control, this part of the interface will be described first. Examples of its use, however, are presented in connection with the discussion of the other two divisions.

The specific input/output characteristics of the LINC have to an unknown extent influenced the interface design we have implemented. Although relatively few direct references will be made to these characteristics in the discussion that follows, it seems advisable to review the most important of them here.

All data transmission between the LINC and the outside world is under program control. Of the six classes of input/output instructions, three control the LINC's magnetic tapes and display oscilloscope. They will not be mentioned further except to state that when magnetic tape is written or read, all other use of the computer is locked out. The lock-out can be broken only by an externally generated interrupt that causes the tape operation to be aborted. The LINC's inability to continue data collection and experimental control during tape transfers has affected both our interface design and the way we use the computer in experiments.

One class of input instructions controls the LINC's analog-to-digital converter. Thirty two microseconds are required to measure the input voltage on any of several input lines and to store the result in memory.

A separate class of instructions is used to test the state of 14 binary "sense" lines. Instructions of this class specify the line to be tested and the expected logical sense of the voltage on that line. These are conditional skip instructions that make it possible to omit single instructions or entire subroutines in response to conditions defined outside the computer. Eight microseconds are required to test one sense line.

The remaining class of instructions controls all transfers of bytes, words, and larger blocks of data in both directions between the computer and its environment. All transfers occur between the LINC Accumulator Register or Memory Buffer Register and selected peripheral devices. Device selection is controlled by the computer, direction and mode of transfer is determined peripherally, and the timing of the transfer is established by the interaction of the computer with the peripheral device. Unlike most other computers, the LINC decodes internally the binary number, which specificies the peripheral device for a transfer and sends out a "device select" signal on one of 16 wires leading to the interface. Accompanying the "device select" signal are a series of timing pulses that may be gated by the "device select" signals to provide specific synchronizing pulses for each peripheral device. Data are normally transmitted on 12-bit parallel input and output "buses".

Two types of single word transfers are distinguished by their timing. In one, timing is controlled exclusively by the computer: when a transfer instruction is executed the "device select" signal and timing pulses are emitted in a fixed sequence that effects the transfer in 16 μsec. In the other, the peripheral device may influence transfer timing: after sending the "device select" signal and one synchronizing pulse, the computer pauses until it receives a "ready" signal from the selected device and then sends out the remaining pulses to complete the transfer. The input/output pause, like the lock-out during tape operations, can be broken only by an externally generated interrupt.

When appropriate interface logic has been installed, multiple word transfers may be effected by the execution of a single instruction. These transfers exchange data between the computer's memory and the periphery through the Memory Buffer Register. The peripheral device supplies the initial memory address for the transfer and determines the number of words to be transmitted, the computer controls the sequential addressing of memory. A block transfer may be slowed by one or more input/output pauses or may progress at the maximum rate of one word every 8 μsec. In either case, all other use of the computer is suspended until the transfer is complete.

References have been made to externally generated interrupts. All peripheral devices use a common interrupt request line to generate a program interrupt. When a request occurs (and the interrupt system has been enabled) the ongoing program is interrupted at the completion of an instruction or within a pause or tape lockout and the computer forces the execution of the first instruction of a common interrupt service routine. This routine determines the cause of the interrupt, takes appropriate action, and then returns control to the mainline program. One hundred microseconds or more may be required to service an interrupt, depending upon the number of devices that must be polled to determine the cause of the interrupt and the complexity of the action required in response to it.

REAL-TIME MEASUREMENT

The rate at which a computer executes instructions is determined by internal timing circuits. If these circuits are controlled by a stable crystal oscillator, as they are in the LINC, it is possible to control the timing of input/output operations by writing programs that make use of repeated instruction sequences that require exactly one time unit for each iteration. But these "timed loops" are difficult to write for any but the most trivial of applications, are inappropriate for truly high-speed computer systems, and are irrelevant to computers in which internal timing is not rigorously controlled. It is hardly an exaggeration to state flatly that every laboratory computer requires a stable source of timing pulses that can be reliably counted in order to measure the time intervals between input events and to control the times at which the computer examines input lines or updates output lines.

When the interval between timing pulses is long with respect to the average execution time of the computer's instructions, counting may be performed by a program. When the interval between timing pulses is short with respect to instruction execution time, counting must be performed without program intervention. Some computers make it easy to implement interface hardware that directly increments the contents of specified memory locations; others make it necessary to build binary counters as part of the interface.

Our LINC interface includes two such counters: one is used primarily in data collection, the other in experimental control. The first, the Interval Timer, is cleared at the beginning of data collection and counts upward toward its

LABORATORY INTERFACE

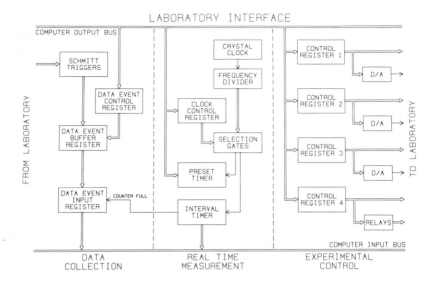

Figure 2. Block diagram of major components of laboratory interface. Broad arrows mark paths of parallel data flow; thin arrows mark single-wire paths. Sense lines, device selection lines, and synchronization lines have been omitted. *Data collection*: signals coming from the laboratory are sharpened by Schmitt Triggers and used to set bits of the Data Event Buffer Register if and only if corresponding bits of the Data Event Control Register are set to one. The contents of the Data Event Buffer Register are shifted to the Data Event Input Register before being transferred into the computer. This shift is synchronized with the computer's master clock to protect against data loss. *Real-time measurement*: the output frequency of a free-running Crystal Clock is successively halved by the Frequency Divider to provide a number of standard frequencies, one of which is selected as input to each of the binary counters by the Clock Control Register. The Preset Timer is loaded with a number by the computer and counts down to zero, at which time it generates a signal on one of the computer's sense lines (not shown). The Interval Timer is cleared by the computer and counts upward until its contents are transferred into the computer. *Experimental control*: each Control Register is loaded from the computer and provides parallel binary output lines to the laboratory. For three of the registers, digital-to-analog Converts provide an alternative control output; for the fourth register, general-purpose relays parallel the binary output lines.

maximum capacity until a data event occurs, then the count is transferred to memory and reset to zero so that the process can begin again. The second counter, the Preset Timer, is loaded with a number from the LINC accumulator and counts downward until zero is reached, then it generates a signal that notifies the computer that the requested time has elapsed.

Whenever time is measured with fixed length counters a trade-off must be established between the maximum time interval that can be measured and the temporal resolution of the measurement. It is helpful if this trade-off is not permanently established, but rather varied to fit the requirements of particular applications. The input pulse frequencies to the Interval Timer and Preset Timer are independently selected by the six-bit Clock Control Register (Figure 2), which is loaded from the LINC Accumulator. Six standard frequencies are generated from the 8000-Hz output of the master crystal clock by successive binary division. Three bits of the Clock Control Register select input to each counter. They are subjected to binary-to-octal decoding in order to enable one of eight AND gates whose outputs are ORed to provide input to the counter (Selection Gates, Figure 2). Six of these AND gates receive a standard clock frequency as their second input, one is connected to an external input for arbitrary pulse trains, and the last is disconnected to permit disabling of the counter.

Multiple input AND gates are used to detect the "all-ones" state of the Interval Timer and the "all-zeros" state of the Preset Timer. In data collection, a "no-event" time interval must be stored each time the Interval Timer reaches the all-ones state to avoid loss of time pulses; in experimental control, the all-zeros state of the Preset Timer indicates that it is time to change some parameter of stimulation.

Three minor points may be of interest. The first two concern alternatives to the design just described, the third concerns a problem that affects many aspects of the design of real time systems.

(1) The standard frequencies of our LINC interface are obtained by binary division of the output from a relatively low-frequency crystal oscillator (available frequencies are 8000, 4000, 2000, 1000, 500, and 250 Hz). I would now recommend decimal division of a much higher-source frequency. The high-source frequency permits finer grading even of relatively long intervals. Decimal division provides a more useful spacing between standard frequencies and can be easily made to provide a set of time units that is natural to the users.

(2) A useful addition to the design of a Preset Timer is the logic necessary to allow its contents to be read into the computer at any time without disturbing the countdown. Without this provision it is possible to control stereotyped experiments, but when the computer must respond dynamically to events in the laboratory by changing the temporal sequence of output commands it may be essential to determine where in the course of Preset Timer countdown the events have occurred.

(3) Unless interface timers are in some way synchronized with the computer's input/output commands, errors may occur in either of two ways. The first type of error is introduced by the "carry time" of ordinary binary ripple counters. Table 1 shows errors that might occur if the contents of such a counter were read by a computer at a number of inappropriate times following an input clock pulse. The second type of error may happen when a computer command to clear or preset a counter is coincident with an input clock pulse. Here, the clock pulse may be lost. Although the probability of collision between clock pulses and computer commands may be quite low, good system design must protect against these errors.

For the LINC interface, I have found it sufficient to place a synchronizing flip-flop at the input to each counter. The flip-flop is set by the input clock pulse and remains set until the end of any concurrent input/output command that affects the counter. Then, the flip-flop is cleared by a LINC master clock pulse. The transition from one to zero at the output of the synchronizing flip-flop provides the actual input to the counter. The LINC is sufficiently slow so that even if a command affecting the counter is initiated at the very instant that the synchronizing flip-flop is cleared there is sufficient time for a "carry" to be completed before the count is read by the computer. Faster computers require more elaborate solutions. "Carry time" can be eliminated by replacing ripple counters with more expensive synchronous transition counters, but protection against lost input pulses must be provided by synchronizing circuits appropriate to each computer's input/output structure.

Table 1. Errors Introduced by Reading Contents of a Binary Ripple Counter at Various Times after the Arrival of an Input Clock Pulse*

Time in Nano-Seconds	Binary Contents of Counter	Decimal Equivalent	Comments
0	011 111	31	Input pulse has arrived, but transition has not yet occurred at output of first flip-flop.
80	011 110	30	Transition has occured at first flip-flop output, but not yet at second.
160	011 100	28	Ripple has reached output of second flip-flop.
240	011 000	24	Ripple at output of third flip-flop.
320	010 000	16	Ripple at output of fourth flip-flop.
400	000 000	0	Ripple at output of fifth flip-flop.
480	100 000	32	Ripple complete, all outputs stable.

*A carry time of 80 nanoseconds per bit corresponds to that of several commercially available high-speed ripple counters. The initial contents of the counter are set for worst case carry time. Instantaneous reading has been assumed.

EXPERIMENTAL CONTROL

Because our computer system must serve three different laboratories it has been necessary to avoid undue specialization in the experimental control

Table 2. Interface Components for Experimental Control

Experimental Control Register 1	A 12-bit flip-flop register. Provides 12 binary output lines to the laboratory. In addition its lower six bits control a D/A converter to provide 64 different output voltages on a single output line.
Experimental Control Registers 2 and 3	Each is an 8-bit flip-flop register which provides 8 binary output lines and controls a D/A converter which can generate 256 different output voltages on a single analog line.
Experimental Control Register 4	A six-bit flip-flop register. Provides 6 binary output lines to the laboratories and controls six general-purpose single-pole double-throw relays.
External Sense Lines 1 and 2	Binary input lines to the computer.
External Device Synchronization Line	Binary output line (pulse) from computer.

interface. We have attempted to perform at the computer only functions that are required by two or more laboratories and to perform in each laboratory the functions that are unique to it. The common interface is very simple (Table 2). It contains flip-flop registers, digital-to-analog converters, relays, a pair of sense lines, and an output pulse line. The Control Registers are used to maintain control voltages that are established by computer output commands.[2] Each is supplied with a set of buffer amplifiers that drive binary control lines leading to the laboratories. The D/A converters and relays are operated from the same flip-flop registers that supply binary control. In each application, a choice must be made of the type of control desired. There is no logical necessity for this; the double duty was chosen for economy.

---

[2] ECR 1, ECR 2, and ECR 3 have been constructed as "jam transfer" registers in order to reduce the setting time of the D/A converters and to avoid undesired pulses on binary output lines that are not changed by particular output commands. ECR 4, which is part of the LINC's original equipment, is initially cleared by output commands that affect it and then loaded with its new contents. Since a 2 μsec pulse appears on each binary output line from ECR 4, which is a one both before and after an output command, this register is reserved for non-critical applications and is presently used only to control behavioral reward and punishment devices.

The four control registers are equipped with indicator lights that display the state of each flip-flop. Although not strictly necessary, these lights are helpful in tracing errors in experimental control programs and provide information to the user about the course of automatically controlled experiments.

A fairly complete picture of the control of our four physiological stimulators may be obtained from a study of Table 3. A few additional details are provided in the Appendix. Certain parameters of stimulation in each laboratory are set manually, others are under optional computer control. Automatic control of the thermal and cathode ray tube stimulators is effected entirely by analog voltages, that of the optical bench and tactile stimulators by a combination of analog and digital signals. For the former, the Experimental Control Registers provide input to the D/A converters; for the latter, one or more of the register is used to provide direct binary voltage levels to the laboratory.

Table 3. Summary of Control Functions for Four Physiological Stimulators

A. Thermal Stimulator

1. Position of stimulus on the on the skin.	Controlled manually.
2. Temperature range.	Controlled locally by adjusting the degree of chilling of the electrolyte solution directed to the thermode.
3. Instantaneous temperature	Controlled by feedback amplifier receiving its input from local circuits or from computer D/A converter.

B. Cathode Ray Tube Photic Stimulator

1. Gross position of stimulus.	Controlled manually by moving cathode ray tube with respect to eye.
2. Fine position of stimulus.	Controlled by X and Y voltage inputs derived from local circuits or from two of the computer's D/A converters.

3. Brightness of stimulus.	Controlled by Z voltage input derived from local circuits or the computer's third D/A converter.

C. Optical Bench Photic Stimulator

1. Gross position of stimulus. (Four beams)	Controlled manually by moving patterned mask in the path of light beam.
2. Fine position of stimulus. (Two beams)	Controlled by angle of deflecting mirror which is set by feedback amplifier receiving input from local circuits or from computer's D/A converter.
3. Brightness of background stimulus. (Two beams)	Controlled manually by inserting neutral density filters in path of light.
4. Brightness of patterned stimulus. (Four beams)	Controlled by settings of two neutral density wedges one of which is set manually, the other by an electric motor under computer control. Five binary output lines and one binary input line are used to provide computer control of the four wedge drive motors.
5. Color of stimulus. (Six beams)	Controlled manually by inserting colored filters in light path.
6. Pattern of stimulus. (Four beams)	Controlled manually by selection of mask to be inserted in light path.
7. Timing of stimulus. (Six beams)	Controlled by electromagnetic shutter driven by local circuit or by binary output line from computer (six lines for six shutters).

D. Tactile Stimulator

1. Position of stimulus.	Controlled manually.
2. Rate of onset of step indentation.	Controlled manually (continuously variable).
3. Step amplitude range.	Controlled manually (continuously variable).
4. Step amplitude fractionation.	Controlled by ladder attenuator. Four local toggle switches or four binary output lines from computer select desired attenuation.
5. Sine amplitude range.	Controlled manually (continuously variable).
6. Sine amplitude fractionation.	Controlled identical to that for step.
7. Sine frequency range.	Controlled manually (factors of ten).
8. Sine frequency vernier.	Controlled manually or by output of one of the computer's 8-bit D/A converters.
9. Step gate timing.	Controlled locally or by single binary output line from computer.
10. Sine gate timing.	Controlled locally or by single binary output line from computer.

A feedback controlled power amplifier is used to heat the electrolyte solution within the thermal stimulator. The control signal for this amplifier comes either from local analog circuits or from a D/A converter, the feedback signal comes from a thermosensor placed against the skin at the site of stimulation. Step stimuli can be delivered by suddenly changing the number in an Experimental Control Register by an amount that corresponds to the desired step amplitude. Rate of temperature change can be controlled by transmitting to

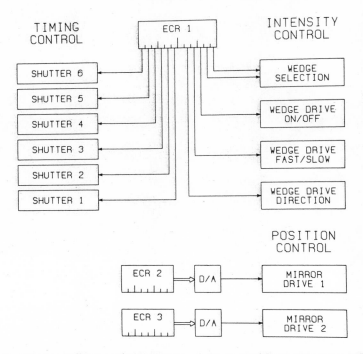

Figure 3. Use of Experimental Control Registers with Optical Bench Stimulator. Note that Experimental Control Register 1 (ECR 1) is used as a switch register to control a variety of functions, whereas ECR 2 and ECR 3 are used as input registers to the D/A Converters.

the control register a series of numbers intermediate in value between that corresponding to resting temperature and that corresponding to the desired final temperature; the particular number series used and the frequency of transmission determines the time course of thermal stimulation.

All three D/A converters are required to control the cathode ray tube stimulator. The two eight-bit converters define the horizontal and vertical co-ordinates of the illuminated spot; the six-bit converter defines its brightness. Normally, the position of the spot is established in darkness and then the spot is brightened.

Automatic control of stimulus timing, intensity, and position is provided for some or all of the beams of the optical bench stimulator (Figure 3). Each of the six light beams is interrupted by an electromagnetic shutter that is driven by a binary output line from ECR1, this provides *timing* control. Four of the light beams pass through motor-driven circular neutral density wedges. Five bits of ECR1 select the wedge to be rotated and the action of the drive motor in order to control *intensity*. For two beams, the angle of the deflecting mirror controls stimulus *position*. The angle for each mirror is established by a feedback amplifier, which receives its input from a D/A converter.

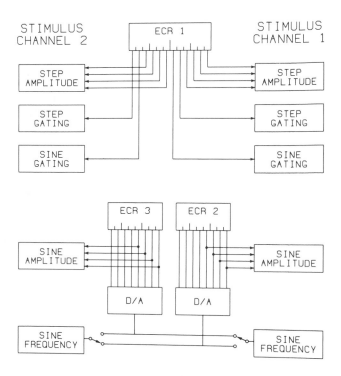

Figure 4. Automatic Control of Tactile Stimulators. Note that Sine Frequency may be independently controlled for the two stimulus channels or controlled for both by a single D/A converter releasing the other Control Register to select Sine Amplitude in one channel.

Since the rates of change required of the tactile stimulator are too great for effective direct computer control, these stimulators are driven exclusively from analog waveform generators within the laboratory. But the waveform generators may themselves be controlled from the computer (Figure 4). Automatic control of five parameters of stimulation can be provided for either stimulus channel when it is used alone. When the two stimulators are used simultaneously, the multiple connections of ECR1 and ECR2 make it necessary to set sine wave frequency or amplitude manually for one or both stimulus channels.

The foregoing indicates that automatic experimental control is effected for all four stimulators by transmitting numbers to the Experimental Control Registers. These numbers may be treated as arithmetic quantities and subjected to D/A conversion or treated as logical strings of bits, each of which controls a particular laboratory function. In either case, the pattern of stimulation occurring in the laboratory is determined by the sequence of numbers that is transferred to the control registers. The problem of the experimental control programmer is to establish the correct sequence and to make the transfers at the

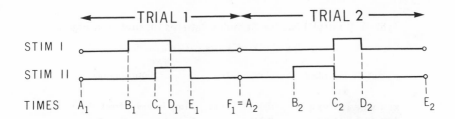

Figure 5. Timing diagram for stimulus presentation in a pair of trials from a simple experiment.

correct times. There is no single solution to this problem that is appropriate for all experimental designs, but one approach has proven useful in a number of different situations. It provides flexible experimental control with a minimum of programming effort. This approach will be illustrated for a simple experimental design involving the tactile stimulators before its more general use is discussed.

Figure 5 presents a timing diagram for two of the trials of an experimental series designed to test the interaction between step stimuli delivered to the skin. Parameters that are varied from trial to trial are the intensity (step amplitude) and duration of the two stimuli, the interstimulus delay, and the inter-trial period.

Figure 4 shows that step amplitude and timing are controlled from ECR1. What is required to generate the stimulus patterns of Figure 5, is to change the contents of ECR1 at the times indicated (A_1, B_1, etc.). In each trial, a maximum of five output commands must be given, one to preset intensities and one each to turn stimuli 1 and 2 "on" and "off". The computer program that executes these commands can be made very simple if we define the stimulus pattern for each trial in a *control list* stored in memory. This is an ordered list of number pairs. The first number of each pair is a time interval intended for the Preset Timer; the second number is a bit string intended for ECR1. The experiment is started by putting out the first time interval and "control word". Thereafter, each time the Preset Timer sends a "countdown complete" signal to the computer, a new time interval and control number are put out. Because the number of output commands may vary among trials, the length of the control list is not fixed. Instead, a zero time interval is used to mark the end of each list. Control lists for the two trials of Figure 5 are given in Table 4. Stimulus randomization is very easy to implement with control lists. A list is generated for each of the possible stimulus *classes*. At the beginning of each trial, a class number is selected from a random number table. This is used to select the control list for the upcoming trial. Figure 6 presents a flow diagram for a subroutine that uses control lists in just this way.

Minor changes in the control list structure and in the program that uses it make this approach applicable to experiments that require two or more

Table 4. Control Lists for Stimulus Patterns Illustrated in Figure 5*

Binary Number	Destination	Significance
xxx xxx xxx xxx	Preset Timer	Time interval from A_1 to B_1.
000 110 001 111	ECR 1	Preset intensities. Stim I = 15; Stim II = 6.
xxx xxx xxx xxx	Preset Timer	Time interval from B_1 to C_1.
000 110 101 111	ECR 1	Turn on Stim. I.
xxx xxx xxx xxx	Preset Timer	Time interval from C_1 to D_1.
100 110 101 111	ECR 1	Turn on Stim II.
xxx xxx xxx xxx	Preset Timer	Time interval from D_1 to E_1.
100 110 001 111	ECR 1	Turn off Stim I.
xxx xxx xxx xxx	Preset Timer	Time interval from E_1 to F_1.
000 110 001 111	ECR 1	Turn off Stim II.
000 000 000 000	Preset Timer	A zero time interval marks the end of the list.
xxx xxx xxx xxx	Preset Timer	Time interval from A_2 to B_2.
001 000 000 001	ECR 1	Preset Intensities. Stim I = 1; Stim II = 8.
xxx xxx xxx xxx	Preset Timer	Time interval from B_2 to C_2.
101 000 000 001	ECR 1	Turn on Stim II.
xxx xxx xxx xxx	Preset Timer	Time interval from C_2 to D_2.
001 000 100 001	ECR 1	Turn off Stim II; turn on Stim I.
xxx xxx xxx xxx	Preset Timer	Time interval from D_2 to E_2.
001 000 000 001	ECR 1	Turn off Stim I.
000 000 000 000	Preset Timer	A zero time interval marks the end of the list.

*Underlining has been used to emphasize changes in binary numbers intended for ECR 1. Figure 4 diagrams the connections which implement the control of tactile stimulators from ECR 1.

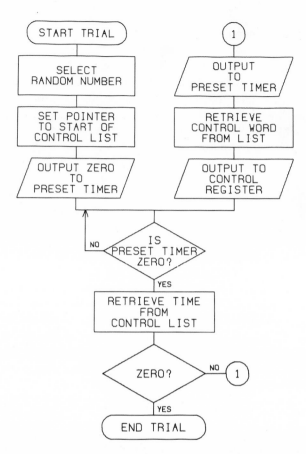

Figure 6. Flow diagram of simple subroutine sufficient to use control lists like those of Table 4 to Control an experiment like that in Figure 5. In general, the blocks of this diagram correspond to single machine-language instructions. For simplicity this diagram presents a *dedicated* control subroutine in which the state of the Preset Timer is determined by an iterative loop. In most cases, experimental control is effected in interrupt service routines that are entered when the Preset Timer counts down to zero.

Experimental Control Registers. In some cases, the contents of all but one of the Registers can be fixed at the beginning of each trial; these extra words can be put at the top of control lists like those of Table 4 to define these contents. In other cases, more than one Control Register must receive new contents at the end of each time interval; for these, we use control lists built of ordered triplets, quadruplets, or quintuplets. The primary advantage of the control list approach to programmed experimental design is that the computation required to determine the sequence of output commands may be carried out *off-line* so that the real-time control subroutine can be kept simple and fast.

EVENT DATA COLLECTION

Our principal objective in data collection is to create a list of labelled inter-event time intervals. The Interval Timer provides the intervals, the Event Data Interface generates the labels and either simplifies or eliminates the program required to create the list.

Several types of laboratory "event" are of interest in any of our experiments. The most important are nerve impulses, but a complete temporal history of an experiment also requires that attention be paid to stimulus events and sometimes to behavioral events as well. For most experiments, we are content if we know when stimuli have been turned on and off and when a behaving animal has depressed or released a telegraph key. Only occasionally is it necessary to make periodic A/D conversions of a stimulus analog voltage in order to trace the time course of stimulation. Since other chapters of this book describe A/D techniques in detail, the present discussion concentrates exclusively on event data collection.

Input signals come to the event data interface in the form of voltage steps. Signals from nerve impulse discriminators are pulses whose durations are meaningless, signals from stimulators or from a behavioral manipulandum are square waves, the duration of which marks the interval of stimulation or specific behavior. For the former, only voltage transitions from "low" to "high" are recognized as events; for the latter, both "low" to "high" and "high" to "low" transitions must be noted.

Since it is transitions and not steady state voltage levels that signal data events, flip-flops are required in the interface to store an indication of each event until it can be recognized by the computer. These flip-flops are organized into a Data Event Input Register, the contents of which can be transferred to the LINC Accumulator by a single input command. The individual bits of the word thus transferred specify the occurrence of particular data events. Table 5 lists the bit assignments in general terms. There are six independent input lines to the interface: four are "stimulus lines" on which both transitions are recognized, two are "nerve impulse lines" on which only "low" to "high" transitions are recognized.

Bits 9, 10, and 11 of the Data Event Input Register are given special treatment in order to make possible more compact and more flexible data storage. In all data collection systems, but particularly in one built around a computer with a very small memory, it is desirable to compress data storage as much as possible. One method of data storage that could be implemented with the parts of the LINC interface already described would be to respond to each data event by storing in consecutive memory locations a pair of numbers, the first of which comes from the Data Event Input Register, the second from the Interval Timer. This would generate a fully labelled list of time intervals in which we could distinguish labels from intervals by position (labels, for example,

Table 5. Event Coding by the Data Event Input Register

Bit	Significance of A "1"
0	An "ON" transition has occurred on stimulus input A.
1	An "OFF" transition has occurred on stimulus input A.
2	Stimulus B "ON"
3	Stimulus B "OFF"
4	Stimulus C "ON"
5	Stimulus C "OFF"
6	Stimulus D "ON"
7	Stimulus D "OFF"
8	An "ON" transition has occurred on nerve impulse input 2.
9	This bit is never set by the Data Collection Interface. It is used by the system to mark "special Codes".
10	An "ON" transition has occurred on nerve impulse input 1.
11	An event other than a primary nerve impulse has occurred. This bit is set by the logical OR of bits 0 to 8 and the "counter full" signal from the Elapsed Time Counter.

always being in even-numbered locations, intervals in odd). For most of our experiments, this method of data storage, though simple, is wasteful of memory. Normally, we record from a single neuron, and nerve impulses occur far more frequently than other data events. If we could eliminate the label for all intervals terminated by nerve impulses, we could reduce by almost half the length of the data list in memory. But to accomplish this, we must have an indicator other than position for distinguishing labels from intervals. Bit 11 of the Data Event Input Register is this indicator.

Bit 11 is the "sign bit" of a LINC data word. Simple high-speed instructions are available to determine whether it is a zero or a one. The Interval Timer was built with only 11 flip-flops so that bit 11 (the twelfth bit) of time intervals is always a zero. If all of the labels that are stored in the data list have a one in bit 11, there can be no confusion. The presence of a pair of time intervals in

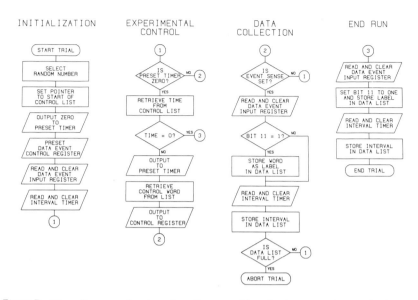

INITIALIZATION   EXPERIMENTAL   DATA   END RUN
                          CONTROL   COLLECTION

Figure 7. Flow diagram of subroutine that provides simultaneous data collection and experimental Control. This subroutine provides only for the collection of inter-event time intervals; any supplementary data (see below) must be inserted by the main program. The main program supplies the subroutine with the initial address and size of the memory area set aside for data storage; the subroutine supplies the main program with the address of the last data word it has stored. Normally, collection is terminated when the end of the control list is encountered; a final interval is stored even when no event has occurred, so that the recorded duration of collection will correspond to the duration of control. If the data list is filled before control is completed, the trial is aborted. The main program must include special provisions for recovering from an aborted trial. As in Figure 6, the blocks of this diagram with few exceptions correspond to single LINC instructions. In a modern high-speed computer, columns two and three of this diagram could correspond to interrupt service routines so that on-line analysis could progress concurrently with control and collection.

consecutive locations of the data list unambiguously indicates that the second was terminated by a nerve impulse.

Obviously, only one of the two nerve impulse input lines can be treated in this way. We have arbitrarily selected the line that sets bit 10 of the Input Register for label suppression. Logic has been provided in the interface that causes bit 11 of the Input Register to be set, if and only if, some event other than a bit-10 nerve impulse has occurred, but the LINC sense line that notifies the computer that a data event has occurred is activated by the logical OR of bits 10 and 11 of the Input Register. When the computer responds to the activation of this sense line, by reading the contents of the Data Event Input Register into its Accumulator, the sign of the number read determines whether it must be stored as a label. A simple program like that diagrammed in Figure 7 is sufficient to create a compact data list according to the conventions just described while carrying out simultaneous experimental control.

The block diagram of Figure 8 presents a number of details omitted from the preceding discussion. These details primarily concern event detection, suppression, and synchronization.

Transitions between voltage levels on the input lines are not necessarily clean and sharp enough to be used directly to set flip-flops within the interface. Schmitt triggers are used to standardize voltages, to eliminate noise, and to reduce the rise and fall times of the transitions. Inverters are included so that both signal rise and fall can be used to set flip-flops.

Irrelevant or redundant events can be suppressed by the action of the Input Pulse Gates, which are conditioned by the contents of the Data Event Control Register. The bits of this register, which is loaded from the Accumulator at the start of data collection, selectively enable inputs to the corresponding bits of the Data Event Buffer Register.

The Buffer Register is interposed between Schmitt Triggers and the Input Register in order to provide synchronization with the computer. The bits of the Buffer Register are set directly by input events without regard to synchronization. Synchronized transfer from Buffer Register to Input Register is required to prevent possible loss of data during the computer's response to an event. The outputs of Buffer Register flip-flops enable AND gates at the inputs of corresponding Input Register flip-flops (The Shift Gates of Figure 8). These gates are periodically sampled by "Shift Pulses" derived from the computer's master clock. Shift pulses are inhibited during the execution of the input command that transfers data from the

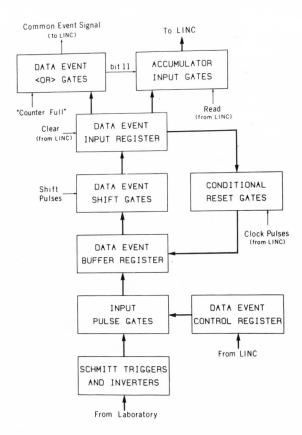

Figure 8. Detailed block diagram of data event collection system.

Input Register to the Accumulator and then clears the Input Register. Thus, it is impossible for the collection hardware to attempt to set a bit of the Input Register at the same time that the computer is clearing it. The corresponding bit of the Buffer Register retains the signal of the event until a shift pulse occurs to move the signal into the Input Register. Each bit of the Buffer Register is cleared by a LINC master clock pulse if and only if its Conditional Reset Gate is enabled by a one at the output of the corresponding bit of the Input Register. The combined synchronizing action of Shift Gates and Conditional Reset Gates ensures that each event will be detected and that no event will be detected more than once.

The parallel structure of the Data Event Collection System provides for correctly labelling intervals terminated by the simultaneous or nearly simultaneous occurrence of several data events. Two "event Gates" reduce to a minimum the computer operations required to determine whether an event has occurred and whether a label must be saved. The first performs an inclusive OR on the outputs of bits 0 to 8 of the Input Register and the "counter full" signal from the Interval Timer; its output corresponds to bit 11 of the Input Register. The second gate further ORs this bit-11 signal with the output of bit 10 of the Input Register to provide a common event signal on one of the LINC's sense lines. The connection of the "counter full" signal to the event gates causes the required "no event" time interval to be stored whenever counter overflow is about to occur.

Bit 9 of the Data Event Input Register is always read as a zero. Data collection can never, therefore, generate a word in which both bit 9 and bit 11 are ones. Such words are reserved as "special codes" used to mark the beginning and end of the data list for each trial and for separating supplementary data from inter-event time intervals.

All of the preceding discussion has presented data collection as a program-controlled process. Interface hardware has been described that generates time intervals and their labels, but a computer program has been postulated to store these data in memory. Because of rhe LINC's limitations, program controlled data collection is not fully satisfactory for neurophysiological research. Although simultaneous data collection and experimental control are possible, the time required to execute the latter degrades the temporal resolution of the former. Truly continuous data collection is made impossible by the lock-out of computer function that occurs whenever tape is written. To get around these limitations we have constructed a hardware controlled data collection system that creates in memory a compressed inter-event time interval list of the type discussed above. Because the LINC does not permit direct access to its own memory by peripheral devices we were obliged to add an auxiliary core memory to serve this collection system. The response time for data storage is a maximum of 16 μsec from the time an event occurs. All of the auxiliary memory may be used as an input buffer or half may be reserved to store control lists for experimental control. For continuous collection, the auxiliary memory is used as a "circular buffer" from which data are transferred to tape by the computer simultaneously with further data storage by the input system.

A similar hardware-controlled data collection system could be tied to the direct memory access channel, which is a standard feature of many modern computers. The speed of these computers will probably, however, make a simpler program-controlled system sufficient for most biological applications.

ON-LINE PROGRAMMING

A typical program for data collection and experimental control must include much more than a basic subroutine like that diagrammed in Figure 7. Provision must be made for interactive communication with the user to determine what experiment is to be performed and how the resulting data are to be titled, programmed checks of laboratory equipment must be carried out before the experiment begins, data must be transferred to tape and the transfers checked for accuracy, and a number of other tasks, major and minor, must be properly executed if the total system is to function as an efficient aid to the experimenter. Some of these tasks are highly specific to a particular laboratory, or even to a particular series of experiments within a laboratory; others are common to most or all on-line experiments. Unless a systematic approach is taken to on-line programming a great deal of effort may be wasted. Not only will there be redundant coding of solutions to the common on-line tasks, but incompatibilities in the data storage formats developed by different programmers are apt to necessitate further redundancy in analysis programming.

Other chapters of this book describe the development of compiler languages that make it possible for users to write collection-control programs in terms related to the laboratory instead of the computer. This approach does not seem practical for the LINC. The LINC's small memory size and relatively low speed frequently compel laborious optimization of the trade-off between execution time and program size in real-time programming. Simple compilers are notoriously bad at making such optimizations. We elected, therefore, to develop a standard data storage format and to write a system of programs that would take over many of the common responsibilities of collection-control programs, but to leave the preparation of the actual real-time code to assembly language programmers.

DATA STORAGE FORMAT

The object of a standard data storage format is to eliminate redundancy in analysis programming by making it possible to use one set of programs to analyze data from a number of different kinds of experiments. Yet it is important that the storage format not become a straight jacket that limits one's freedom to change experimental plans. This can be avoided by building flexibility into the standard format but establishing unchanging conventions by which analysis programs can find the data upon which they operate. Several years ago, we settled upon such a format which, with minor modifications, is serving all of our laboratories today.

The essential features of this format are diagrammed in Figure 9. A complete data file comprises at least three fixed-length tape blocks (256 words). The first two blocks constitute a title record; subsequent blocks contain trial

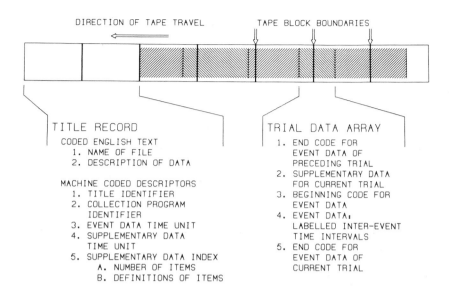

Figure 9. Characteristics of standard data storage format on LINC magnetic tape.

data records. There is no correlation between tape block boundaries and trial record boundaries; instead, the entire data array for the file is treated as a logically continuous string of numbers in which trial boundaries are recognized by unique beginning codes and end codes.

A fixed-title record structure and the common method of inter-event time interval storage that is imposed by data collection hardware provide the uniformity required to make stored data accessible to standard analysis programs. The supplementary data stored in each trial data array provide the flexibility required to adapt the format to different experiments. The number and order of supplementary data are fixed for each data file but may vary among files. Generalized analysis programs search the supplementary data index in the title record to find the serial positions of particular data they will use. The remaining supplementary data are skipped over by these programs. Special-purpose programs written to utilize the complete set of supplementary data produced by a particular collection program reject inappropriate data files on the basis of the Collection Program Identifier stored in the title record.

In addition to information required by analysis programs, the title record contains coded English language text, which may be displayed or printed in order to identify and describe for the user the data contained in the file. The Name of the file, which is assigned at the time data is collected, is printed with the results of all analyses. This name is normally a mnemonic character string that succinctly identifies the run, neuron, experiment, and experimental series.

Fixed-length tape blocks are imposed on us by the nature of the LINC's small magnetic tape system. But even if this were not the case, we would be inclined to use them for the following reasons: (1) they promote efficient use of tape by optimizing the relations between data-containing tape and inter-record gaps; (2) they promote efficient use of memory in analysis programming by establishing a fixed-length input buffer that is fully utilized by each tape-to-memory data transfer; and (3) they encourage users to make logical record boundaries independent of physical record boundaries, which eliminates size restrictions on logical records.

The beginning codes and end codes for trial data arrays are drawn from the set of binary numbers having ones in both bit 9 and bit 11. As noted above, these numbers cannot be generated by the event data collection system. They can, however, occur as supplementary data. For this reason, the number of supplementary data is fixed for each file and defined in the title record. When an analysis program that is scanning through inter-event time intervals encounters an end code, it must count through the supplementary data of the next trial to the beginning code for event data.

Special conventions affect the first and last trial data arrays for each file. Since the end code for event data of one trial is used to mark the beginning of supplementary data for the next, an end code for a fictitious zeroth trial precedes supplementary data for trial 1. The end code of the last trial is replaced with an end-of-file code that signals the end of meaningful data for that file.

A SYSTEM OF COLLECTION-CONTROL PROGRAMS

Our first systematic approach to collection-control programming was made by Dr. Frank Baker for the visual laboratory. Instead of embodying a specific experimental design in the instruction sequence of his program, he made use of control lists related to those of Table IV. Sets of these lists were prepared and stored in a file associated with the on-line program. Each *control set* defined parameters for all stimulus classes in a particular experimental design. It was loaded into the computer's memory with the on-line program and used in association with a random number table to determine the sequence of stimulation. A number of satellite programs were used to prepare control sets and random number tables, to maintain the file and its index, and to print index, control sets, and random number tables for visual reference.

Although this system provided considerable flexibility in the use of the optical bench stimulator, it embodied certain presuppositions about experimental control that were valid for only a limited set of experiments. And, as we looked toward the future, it seemed that this would always be the case. The use of control sets seemed to us to have wide applicability, but any particular control set structure could provide for only limited variation in experimental design. Our present on-line programming system was developed to minimize the amount of new code that would have to be written when a new control set structure was necessitated by changes in experimental programs.

At the heart of the system is an indexed magnetic tape file containing control sets, random number tables, specific subprograms that actually effect real-time experimental control, and a variety of English-language text arrays. These text arrays provide the means by which the generalized programs of the system, which have been written once for all, are tailored to the needs of a particular collection-control subprogram. The most important of them contain sets of questions to be directed to the user and sets of directives to the system

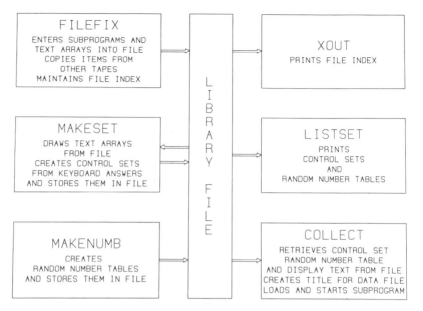

Figure 10. Relationship of on-line system programs to magnetic tape file used in data collection and experimental control.

that define the input conversion procedures to be carried out on the answers that are typed in by the user. Two such text arrays are associated with each collection-control subprogram: one contains questions used in the generation of control sets for the subprogram, the other contains questions asked during the initialization of the subprogram at the time of an experiment. A third text array specifies for each subprogram the table headings and output format to be used when hard copies of its control sets are printed by the system.

Six systems programs control the preparation, maintenance, and use of the file (Figure 10). Only one of these is normally executed during the actual course of an experiment; the others provide off-line functions. The exception is the supervisory program COLLECT, which is always loaded into the computer at the beginning of an experiment. Using the LINC's display oscilloscope, COLLECT asks the user to name the control set that defines the desired experimental design. COLLECT retrieves this control set from the file and is directed by it to retrieve three additional items. The first is the text array used by COLLECT to ask program-specific questions of the user. COLLECT converts the answers to binary numbers according to the directives contained in the text array and stores them in memory, along with the control set. Both questions and answers become part of the title record that is written onto tape by COLLECT. The remaining two items, which are retrieved from the file, are the random number table stored in memory and the subprogram that actually carries out experimental control and data collection. This is loaded into the computer by COLLECT, which destroys itself in the process. Thus, when the subprogram begins execution, it is in complete control of the computer and has in memory everything needed to specify the particular experimental design it is to implement. The tasks of communication with the user, title preparation, and file search and retrieval have been performed for it. The subprogram delivers stimuli, collects data, and writes data records on tape. When it has finished, it calls COLLECT back into memory so that a new control set may be specified without delay.

The benefits of this system are many. It is still difficult to write assembly language programs that provide real-time control of complex experiments, but the effort is spent where the interest is, on the real-time code itself. The laborious coding of the essentially trivial tasks of program initialization and user dialogue has been eliminated. The text arrays that control these tasks are almost as easy to prepare as free-style text. This ease of preparation has resulted in greatly increased use of man-oriented communication between computer and user. All questions are presented in the form of cathode ray tube displays so that wordiness is not penalized by slow output. Even our more machine-oriented programmers are now writing questions that are meaningful to physiologists who do not know a single LINC instruction. Finally, the presence of common features in the initialization and execution of different real-time programs makes it quite easy for the non-programmer who has been taught to use one to learn others by himself.

Because control sets are so important in our approach to experimental control, it is essential that the computer-naive physiologist be able to prepare them easily. While a flexible English language interactive communication between user and computer is necessary for this, it is not sufficient. Replacing the question "D/A?" with "What is the value of the number to be stored in the register which supplies the D/A converter controlling sine wave frequency?" certainly improves communication, but it still requires the user to have a fairly complete knowledge of the computer system. How much easier it is for the physiologist to answer "Sine Wave Frequency?". In general, it is necessary for experimental control programs to convert control sets from a form appropriate to the user to a form appropriate to the computer and its interface. This is not a task that can be performed by the system; the specific experimental problem will define the conversion algorithm. Normally, conversion subroutines form a significant part of the real-time subprograms stored in the system file. Conversion is carried out either once for all at the beginning of subprogram execution or on a trial-by-trial basis during the intertrial periods.

ANALYSIS PROGRAMMING

Most of our general-purpose analysis programs are written to operate solely upon the inter-event time-interval data that form the common part of our standard data storage files. There is no point in listing here the 20 or so most heavily used analysis programs in our library. But it may be useful to examine the basic features of a few categories of programs in order to reveal the kinds of assistance we obtain from the laboratory computer in analyzing data.

DATA EDITING PROGRAMS

Errors can occur even in data files produced by a collection system that includes numerous error detection subroutines. Some of these are innocuous but annoying, others may make it impossible to analyse an entire data file. Since errors rarely occur twice in exactly the same way, it is not worthwhile to write highly sophisticated correction routines. We have found that it is quite easy to find and correct data errors with the following set of simple programs: (1) a program that scans a data file and prints for each trial the times of occurrence of all "stimulus" events; (2) a search program that prints the location of each occurrence of a particular number; (3) display and print programs that allow the user to examine the contents of tape records as octal numbers, decimal numbers, and coded text; (4) an edit program that allows the user to replace any single word on tape with another word specified from the computer keyboard.

ROUTINE BOOKKEEPING PROGRAMS

The most important of these is a simple program that prints an index to the contents of each data tape. Names and tape block numbers are printed for all data files as well as the complete English language description from each file's title record.

DATA PREPARATION PROGRAMS

Most data reduction and statistical programs treat data from each stimulus class separately. The efficiency of these programs is greatly increased if the trial data arrays in each data file are grouped by class. A simple sorting program accomplishes this.

DATA RETRIEVAL SUBROUTINES

The numbers stored in an inter-event time interval list are not generally suitable for direct input to an analysis program. The list specifies time intervals between consecutive events without regard to the nature of the event. An analysis program requires time intervals between specific events. The list must be scanned for labels that correspond to the events of interest and the succession of time intervals between these events summed to determine the total elapsed time.

Throughout this process, memory address bookkeeping is required to determine whether it is necessary to read additional data from tape. Generalized subroutines have been written that perform these functions with as few instructions as possible in order to free most of the computer's memory for the analysis program itself.

DATA REDUCTION PROGRAMS

These are largely histogram generating programs. An approach that has proved particularly useful is to generate the histograms in memory and to store them on tape without plotting. Once on tape, the histograms can be manipulated arithmetically (scaled, accumulated, smoothed, *etc.*) without regard to the particular method used in generating them. Before, during, and after manipulation they may be displayed on the LINC's oscilloscope or drawn on the incremental plotter. Parameters used to initialize the histogram are stored with it on tape so that the graphic output can be unambiguously labelled. Plotting programs include a version that requires minimal initialization and is used to pack working copies of histograms onto standard notebook sized pages and a version in which almost every plotting parameter may be independently initialized in order to generate exactly the format desired for publication.

STATISTICAL PROGRAMS

These are of two kinds: those that operate directly on standard data files and those that operate on intermediate data produced by data reduction programs. Most produce output in the form of printed tables, a few are combined with plotting programs to produce graphic output. The LINC is poorly suited to statistical programming: its small word size necessitates multiple precision data storage; its lack of sophisticated arithmetic hardware necessitates space-consuming subroutines, yet its small memory size provides little room for either. Nonetheless, simple statistical processing is possible on the LINC, which greatly reduces the need to resort to computing facilities outside of the laboratory.

SOME GENERAL OBSERVATIONS

The laboratory that plans a computer installation in the 1970s has many advantages over one that planned such an installation in the early 1960s. In the first place, hardware is much cheaper. The hard compromises forced upon the designers of early small computers are no longer necessary. For much less than the actual cost of the system I have described, one can now buy a high-speed,

16-bit computer with a powerful instruction set, 8000 words of memory, and a reasonable complement of specifically designed interface logic. There are still difficult decisions to be made with respect to manufacturer-supplied peripheral equipment: both high-speed bulk storage devices and high-speed output printers continue to be quite expensive, but even these are less costly than they were a few years ago.

A second advantage is that reasonable software is more readily accessible. Few small computers are sold today without an adequate assembler, a package of arithmetic and input/output subroutines, some kind of FORTRAN, and perhaps an interactive programming language. The reliability of this software may be suspect and the power difficult to evaluate but at least few users are any longer tempted to write their first programs in absolute binary machine language and to enter them into memory via the computer's console switches!

Given these advantages, what can the reader learn from our experience with laboratory computing? In the first place he can take heart. Although we are well aware of the limitations of our computing system, we were quite satisfied with the job it has done. Our major problems have been associated with the extremely small memory of the LINC. By adding the auxiliary memory, we have improved our data-storage capacity, but programming problems continue to be aggravated by the necessity for segmenting programs into 1024-word overlays. The creator of the LINC Assembly Program has asserted that one third of the time required to prepare the most recent version of this program was devoted to condensing code so that it would fit the LINC's memory (Wilkes, 1970). We have found that more than half of the programming time for some on-line programs may be spent in this way. The relatively low cost of core memory modules for currently available laboratory computers should eliminate these problems for new installations.

None of the persons who had an active part in the design and construction of interface hardware for our system had any formal training in digital design. Each of us was trained as a physiologist or a physician and has learned what was needed from textbooks and particularly from design handbooks provided by manufacturers of digital logic modules. The use of commercial modules greatly simplifies hardware design and anyone who is reasonably compulsive about details can build an interface adequate for most laboratory requirements. Although it is not necessary for every research scientist to build his own interfaces, it is important that somebody in the laboratory understand both the scientific uses of the computer and the details of its operation. As a minimum, I would recommend that one permanent member of the scientific staff of a laboratory should become sufficiently familiar with the logical design of the computer and its interfaces to be able to evaluate thoroughly proposals for development and modification of the system.

Similar considerations apply to programming. Unless the scientists who use a computer are reasonably proficient programmers, they are utterly dependent upon the judgment and competence of someone who is probably uncertain about the goals and complexities of the experiments. The most difficult aspect of programming is not writing code but deciding what to do. To write even the simplest experimental control program requires making a number of decisions that were not foreseen when the problem was first defined—decisions that directly affect the course of the experiment. Again as a minimum, I suggest that one permanent member of the scientific staff should attain complete mastery of the programming system used with the laboratory computer in order to serve as liaison between users and programmers. Ideally, this should be the same man who has acquired an understanding of the physical system.

This dual role as scientific hardware and software specialist is non-trivial. Even the simplest laboratory computer installation gradually acquires enough interface hardware and a sufficiently large library of programs and subroutines to demand a considerable investment of time from the person who wishes to retain mastery over it. My experience in this role suggests that even if a competent full-time programmer-technician is available, the scientific supervisor of an active laboratory computer should expect to spend at least 20% of his time in computer-related activity. And, during periods of rapid development of the system, his investment may approach 100%.

What about other members of the scientific staff of a laboratory? Although it may be less precarious to depend on a scientific colleague than on a non-scientist programmer-technician, it is still a dependency. What can the physiologist do for himself without making his scientific activity secondary to computer-oriented activity? With an absolute minimum of effort he can learn to use existing programs. When programs have been written appropriately it can be rewarding and efficient for the scientist to operate the computer and to interact with it to control the course of his experiments and of his data analysis. We have found that a few hours of tutoring and a couple of days' experience are all that are required to give a computer-naive scientist considerable confidence in using well-documented LINC programs.

At the next level of involvement, the scientist acquires basic programming skills and learns at least one of the languages used on his computer. The amount of time required depends on the difficulty of the language: compiler languages are learned more quickly than assembly languages and assembly languages for machines with many instructions are learned more slowly than those for machines with few instructions. More than half of the staff members, graduate students, and fellows who have worked with us during the last six years have learned to write simple programs in the LINC assembly language. For those without previous programming experience, two or three weeks' hard work has been required to obtain a reasonable command of this language. Although many of these investigators have made no serious attempt to master the details of the laboratory computer system, all have acquired a better understanding of the computer's role in research and the ability to define problems in terms that can be understood by professional programmers.

Finally, there are scientists who attain sufficient competence to write any or all of the programs they use. Perhaps this group includes only those who have a natural aptitude for programming; it certainly is limited to those who are motivated to spend many weeks mastering the use of interface hardware and system software. Members of this group do not necessarily spend a great deal of time programming, but they are equipped to write particularly critical subroutines exactly the way they want them and to prepare whole programs when a shortage of professional programmers would otherwise make them wait. In our laboratory, this group is quite small, it numbers at most five out of a total of more than 20 scientists who have used the LINC. Possibly the fraction would be larger in a laboratory where greater research diversity made it more difficult to borrow programs, but it is unlikely that true system mastery can be expected of more than one third of the scientists who use any particular laboratory computer.

Perhaps the most painful part of our experience with laboratory computing has been the duplication of programming effort required by successive revisions of interface hardware. When the LINC was first acquired, we lacked the experience or counsel required for planning a "system" and instead elected to buy a minimum of interface hardware and to experiment with various uses of the computer. Hundreds of hours of programming effort went into this experimentation. After about a year, we made our first attempt to systematize data collection. A standard data format was defined, some interface hardware installed, and a number of collection-control programs were written. During the ensuing months a library of analysis programs was assembled to operate on data collected by this system. At the same time, however, defects in the system were becoming apparent. The data storage format was wasteful of memory and the interface hardware required such extensive software control that collection-control programming was unduly difficult. After much deliberation, we undertook the design and implementation of the system described in this chapter. This system required an entirely new set of programs not only for data collection and experimental control but also for analysis. The cost of preparing these programs greatly exceeds the cost of the interface hardware itself. If the book of which this chapter is a part can help other scientists to design systems that can grow painlessly with the growth of the research program they support, it will have served well. Our experience suggests that it is economically unsound to stint the investment of either time or money initially allocated to the laboratory computer. An adequate initial investment should not only increase the amount of useful work done by the computer but perhaps postpone the day when a thoroughly understood but limited system must be scrapped in favor of a largely unknown but potentially more flexible one.

APPENDIX: SPECIAL FEATURES OF THE CONTROL OF OPTICAL BENCH AND TACTILE STIMULATORS

Automatic control of the electromagnetic shutters and deflecting mirrors of the optical stimulator is straightforward: a shutter is opened by a zero-to-one transition of its control flip-flop and closed by a one-to-zero transition: the instantaneous deflection angle of a mirror is determined by the output voltage of a D/A converter. Computer control of the neutral density wedge motors requires further discussion. Although there are four motors, there is only one set of drive circuitry. One of four relays operated from a two-bit decoder on bits 0 and 1 of ECR 1 (Figure 3) selects the motor to be controlled. Other relays operated directly from bits 2, 3, and 4 of ECR1 turn the motor on and off and determine the speed and direction of its movement. The motors are simple variable-speed DC motors. Exact control of the extent of wedge rotation depends upon feedback from the selected motor to the computer. An opaque fan blade attached to the drive shaft of the motor interrupts a light beam directed onto a photocell four times during each revolution of the shaft (this light is unrelated to stimulating light beams). The voltage transitions at the output of the photocell are used to set a flip-flop that provides input to one of the computer's sense lines. The flip-flop assures that feedback signals from the wedge motor will be maintained until the computer has had time to recognize them. The computer clears the flip-flop as soon as it detects that it has been set. A control program starts the motor moving in the desired direction and counts feedback signals as they occur. When only a few counts separate the present wedge position from the desired one, the program switches motor speed from high to low in order to avoid overshoot. Speed-reducing gears between motor drive shaft and wedge have been selected to provide the desired precision of wedge positioning.

Custom-designed analog circuitry is used to shape the voltage inputs to the tactile stimulators that control step stimulation; commercial waveform generators produce sine wave input. Both sine wave and step function generators can be gated by binary control lines. The function of the vernier control of sine wave frequency can be assumed by an input voltage to the waveform generator derived from a D/A converter. Both step and sine wave voltages are generated at maximum amplitude and attenuated to provide stimulus intensity control. Separate relay operated resistive ladder attenuators control sine and step amplitude in each stimulus channel. Each attenuator is controlled by four relays and provides 16 attenuation factors ranging in steps of one fifteenth from zero to one.

We have found it advantageous to locate the relays that control stimulus intensity for these stimulators within the laboratory, rather than at the computer. On the one hand, this keeps the relatively noisy wedge motor control signals away from the computer's input/output lines; on the other hand, it eliminates the necessity for carrying the noise-sensitive input voltages to the tactile stimulators along long cables leading to and from the computer.

REFERENCES

Baker, F. H., Lamarre, Y., Riva Sanseverino, E., and Poggio, G. F. Excitatory responses of geniculate neurons of the cat. *Journal of Neurophysiology*, 1969, *32*, 916–929.

Darian-Smith, I. and Dykes, R. W. Peripheral neural mechanisms of thermal sensation. R. Dubner and Y. Kawamura (eds.) *Oral-facial sensory and motor mechanisms.* New York: Appleton-Century-Crofts, 1971.

Evarts, E. V. A technique for recording activity of subcortical neurons in moving animals. *Electroencephalography and Clinical Neurophysiology*, 1968, *24*, 83–86.

Evarts, E. V. Relation of pyramidal tract activity to force exerted during voluntary movement. *Journal of Neurophysiology*, 1968, *31*, 14–27.

Mountcastle, V. B., Poggio, G. F., and Werner, G. The relation of thalamic cell response to peripheral stimuli varied over an intensive continuum. *Journal of Neurophysiology*, 1963, *26*, 807–834.

Mountcastle, V. B., Talbot, W. H., and Kornhuber, H. H. The neural transformation of mechanical stimuli delivered to the monkey's hand. A. V. S. de Reuck and J. Knight (eds.) *Touch, heat and pain* (A Ciba Foundation Symposium). London: Churchill, 1966.

Mountcastle, V. B., Talbot, W. H., Sakata, H., and Hyvärinen, J. Cortical neuronal mechanisms in flutter-vibration studied in unanesthetized monkeys. Neuronal periodicity and frequency discrimination. *Journal of Neurophysiology*, 1969, *32*, 452–484.

Poggio, G. F., Lamarre, Y., Riva Sanseverino, E., and Baker, F. H. Afferent inhibition at input to visual cortex of the cat. *Journal of Neurophysiology*, 1969, *32*, 892–915.

Poggio, G. F., and Mountcastle, V. B. The functional properties of ventrobasal thalamic neurons studied in unanesthetized monkeys. *Journal of Neurophysiology,* 1963, *26*, 775–806.

Talbot, W. H., Darian-Smith, I., Kornhuber, H. H., and Mountcastle, V. B. The sense of flutter-vibration: Comparison of the human capacity with response patterns of mechanoreceptive afferents from the monkey hand. *Journal of Neurophysiology*, 1968, *31*, 301–334.

Werner, G. and Mountcastle, V. B. The variability of central neural activity in a sensory system, and its implications for the central reflection of sensory events. *Journal of Neurophysiology*, 1963, *26*, 958–977.

Werner, G. and Mountcastle, V. B. Neural activity in mechanoreceptive cutaneous afferents: Stimulus-response relations, Weber functions, and information transmission. *Journal of Neurophysiology*, 1965, *28*, 359–397.

Wilkes, M. A. Conversational access to a 2048-word machine. *Communications of the ACM*, 1970, *13*, 407–414.

CHAPTER EIGHT

COMPUTER CONTROL OF EXPERIMENTS IN PROBLEM SOLVING, PSYCHOPHYSICS, AND DECISION MAKING

LYLE V. JONES, EDWARD S. JOHNSON,
and FORREST W. YOUNG
University of North Carolina at Chapel Hill

[1] The development of the programming systems reported in this paper was supported in part by a PHS research grant No. M-10006 from the National Institute of Mental Health, Public Health Service. Mr. Richard Helwig provided engineering and systems support for all the programs referred to in this chapter.

Consider the apparatus needs of a laboratory pursuing psychological experiments that include studies of inductive problem solving, psychophysics, and decision making under conditions of uncertainty. For reasons to be made clear in this chapter, it is desirable to develop a computer facility for the control of these experiments. What are the relevant determinants of choice of laboratory design, and of hardware and software configuration?

The pertinent determinants of choice are bound to differ from one installation to another, even for experimental applications within the same problem area. They may be contingent upon budgetary constraints, or upon limitations in the physical space available. Certainly, the choice of equipment is unlikely to be the same now as it was several years ago or as it might be a year or two from now, as new computers, designed for real-time control, appear on the market. Yet, some considerations may change relatively little across different laboratories and over time. It may thus be of interest to share our experiences in developing a computer-controlled facility at the L. L. Thurstone Psychometric Laboratory at the University of North Carolina at Chapel Hill.

The Psychometric Laboratory at the University of North Carolina was founded by the late Prof. L. L. Thurstone in 1952 as a research unit within the Department of Psychology. Laboratory staff have engaged in research in a variety of problems of quantitative psychology and have participated in the graduate and undergraduate training programs of the Department. In 1959, the Psychometric Laboratory acquired an LGP-30, a small drum-memory computer that was made available on an open-shop basis to students and staff.[2]

Much effort was expended from 1959 to 1962 on the development of computer programs for the LGP-30 to meet needs of data analysis. Both univariate and multivariate statistical routines were written (e.g., Bock, 1960; 1961; 1963a; 1963b; Bock and Zyzanski, 1963). All graduate students who were training in quantitative psychology learned to program and to operate the LGP-30, and all became enthusiastic about the value of a small in-house computer. Soon after delivery of the LGP-30, a University Computation Center was established on campus. Largely as a result of the familiarity with computing gained by laboratory students and faculty, these personnel quickly became active users of services provided by the Computation Center. (The small Psychometric Laboratory has continued to be a large user of University data processing facilities.)

By 1962, the LGP-30 was used not only for data-processing applications, but served also as experimental apparatus for on-line psychological research. Subjects seated at the console device (a Friden Flexowriter) were presented stimuli in the form of alphanumerical strings that represented problems to be solved. Subjects' responses, typed on the Flexowriter, were recorded and saved

[2] The initial agreement was jointly supported by the Psychometric Laboratory and the Departments of Statistics and Biostatistics at the Chapel Hill campus of the University of North Carolina. Shortly thereafter, the Psychometric Laboratory assumed full responsibility for supporting the facility.

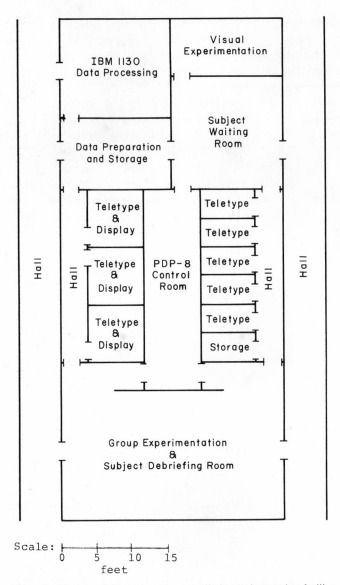

Figure 1. Diagram of the computer-controlled experimentation facility.

in the (drum) memory of the computer. Typical applications involved efforts to evaluate Bayesian models of human information processing (Rapoport, 1964; Wiesen, 1962; Wiesen and Shuford, 1962) and to study a class of descriptive and normative models for human decision making under conditions of uncertainty (Kahan and Jones, 1968; Messick, 1967; Rapoport, 1966a; 1966b; 1967a; 1967b; Rapoport and Jones, 1970; Rapoport, Jones, and Kahan, 1970).

By 1963, the Psychometric Laboratory was firmly committed to the proposition that a small computer in the psychological laboratory contributes greatly to effective training and research. Some effort was made by the senior author to proselyte his colleagues in his presidential address to the Psychometric Society that year (Jones, 1963).

The laboratory was scheduled to move to new quarters in 1967, and was able to contribute to the design of the space it was to occupy. Anticipating this move, funds were found in 1965 to acquire a computer that might be dedicated to the control of psychological experiments. Also, laboratory space suitable for computer-controlled experimentation was designed in the new building. In 1965, shopping for a laboratory computer (with a budget of $20,000) was simple; only one computer for laboratory control was being marketed within the price range. Therefore, an order was placed for a PDP-8, manufactured by Digital Equipment Corporation, Maynard, Massachusetts.

The new laboratory space was designed to provide for computer control of terminals in eight experimental cubicles. A diagram of this space appears as Figure 1. The group experimental room has proven useful as a reception room for meeting individual subjects before and after their experimental service. The larger experimental rooms accommodate a display scope and a teletypewriter, and one or more experimental subjects. The smaller rooms accommodate a teletype and a single subject.

Clearly, to achieve capability for multiple terminals on the PDP-8, it was necessary to develop suitable software systems, and also to augment the basic hardware configuration. The necessary additional components of equipment were acquired in 1967-68, and a concerted effort was made to develop adequate software.

WHY COMPUTER CONTROL OF EXPERIMENTS?

In recent years, the number of computer-controlled experiments reported in the literature has increased markedly. In addition to those mentioned earlier, Messick (1967) reported on the use of a computer to administer a complex decision-making task. Johnson (1966, 1967) and Johnson and Baker (1972) have reported on the differences between problem-solving performance under conditions of computer presentation of the task. Young (1967) used a time-shared terminal to run and analyze a 12-alternative probability learning task. Cooperband (1966) used a computer both for generating visual stimuli and for recording subjects' responses to them. Freeman (1971) developed a completely computerized procedure for studying recency effects in human probability learning. In a study of subjects' strategy in a two-person zero-sum game, Fox (1972) employed a computer as a standardized opponent against which all subjects played. Videbeck and Bates (1966) used a computer to present a verbal learning task in order to control for the possible biasing effects of a human experimenter. Mayzner (1968) and Haber (1968) developed and used systems for presenting subjects with visual stimuli using a computer-driven cathode ray tube. Many other examples could be given. In addition, this area of application has seen the appearance of its first textbook (Uttal, 1967), a survey of computer hardware and software appropriate for on-line psychological experimentation.

One obvious benefit to be achieved from computerizing the administration of an experiment is that the procedure thereby becomes more precise, standardized, and controlled. All subjects are treated in the same manner regardless of their sex, intelligence, appearance, or likeability. The subject-experimenter interaction, with its demonstrated susceptibility to unintentional biases, is eliminated. The net effect should be the elimination of several sources of nuisance variability and the consequent sharpening of experimental treatment effects.

Another set of advantages results from the power and speed of the computer. Subjects can be presented with stimuli that are selected on the basis of complex computations. Stimuli also may be dependent upon the subject's sequence of prior responses. In addition, subjects may be permitted a wide range of potential responses without fear that the computer will err in reacting to them. Under similar circumstances, a human experimenter would be more prone to error.

The computer's capabilities also may be harnessed to record subjects' responses either for immediate processing or for later input to data analysis programs. This procedure decreases the possibility of errors in the transcription and copying of data. Also, as a more subtle advantage, it forces the experimenter to be completely precise and objective in defining dependent variables.

A further increase in experimental efficiency may be realized if a time-sharing system is available that enables the computer to run several subjects simultaneously. With such a system, even for lengthy and complicated experiments, the experimenter may be able to accumulate a large quantity of data in a relatively short period of time. Such a time-sharing system has been developed at the Psychometric Laboratory and is described below.

HARDWARE CONFIGURATION

The basic component of our present system is a PDP-8 computer. The computer as delivered had a core memory of 4096 12-bit words with a memory cycle time of 1.5 μsec and was equipped with a Model ASR33 teletype and paper tape reader-punch (10 characters per second read and punch rate). Other input-output devices were added: a high-speed paper tape reader (300 characters per second), a high-speed paper tape punch (50 characters per second), and two magnetic "mini-tape" devices capable of storing 42 core loads apiece (7500 words per second transfer rate). To implement the time-sharing software system, the computer has been equipped with a second, 4096 words of core memory, an "extended arithmetic element" (to accomplish hardware multiply and divide), a serial line multiplexer that can handle up to 32 input-output channels, eight Model KSR33 teletypes, and two 32,000-word disks (with a core-to-disk transfer rate of about 15,000 words per second).

In addition, the computer has been equipped with a Model CC-300 display scope (manufactured by Computer Communications Incorporated, Inglewood, California). This device displays an 8 by 11 in. picture in either of two modes. In alphanumeric mode, up to 800 characters may be displayed in a 40-character by 20-line array. In graphic mode, any of 9180 discrete points on a 108 by 85 grid may be turned on. A slave scope mounted near the computer console displays whatever is shown on the portable CC-300 scope. (Four additional portable slave scopes were acquired in 1969.) Recently, an 80-column line printer capable of speeds up to 1110 lines per minute was added to the system. This has relieved a serious bottleneck in the utilization of the computer, that of obtaining a hard copy of programs, compilations, and data printouts.

The total cost of all these components at the time of purchase was $100,000. At current market prices the cost of comparable equipment would be less than $70,000.

SOFTWARE SYSTEMS

Since 1968, laboratory personnel have developed three software systems that have greatly enhanced the research productivity of the computer. The first of these is "RATSS" (Remote Access Time Sharing System) originally written by Conrad (1968) and later revised by Coston (1972). To make use of this system, an experimenter writes a program for administering a procedure to a single subject. Under RATSS it may be specified that up to eight copies of the program are to be created. All copies appear to communicate simultaneously with their respective subjects. The second software system, "SAVE" (System for Administering Visual Experiments) provides the experimenter with a simple method for designing and executing experiments in which subjects are presented with a sequence of visual stimuli. SAVE not only serves to guide the experimenter in designing the experiment but also handles the administration of the experiment to individual subjects. The third of these is "8TRAN" (Coston and Helwig, 1972), a compiler language combining the simplicity of FORTRAN syntax with the character-string and input-output features of PL/1. These three systems are described below and illustrated with examples of their use.

RATSS

Concern with cost efficiency may demand that a computer dedicated to the control of psychological experiments be capable of administering experimental procedures to more than one subject at a time. RATSS was developed to meet

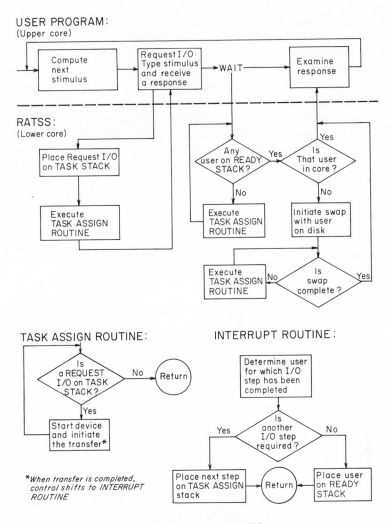

Figure 2. Flowchart of RATSS.

this demand. One feature of the typical computer-controlled experiment enables a system such as RATSS to exploit more fully the capabilities of the hardware: given the high speed of the computer, relative to the speed of the subject, most of the computer's time is spent waiting for the subject to respond. When a response is received, only a few milliseconds may be required to compute the next stimulus and to present it to the subject. Under these conditions, it is possible to create a system to capitalize on the computer's idle time so as to allow it to serve several subjects simultaneously.

The basic principle is simple. RATSS coordinates all communication between each subject and the program administering the experiment to that subject. Since only one of these programs can occupy the computer's core memory at a time, RATSS also acts as a program scheduler designed to minimize response delays (from the subject's perspective).

The program for each subject cycles repeatedly through three states. A small fraction of the time, the program is in core and actively engaged in computing the next stimulus message for its subject. When it has been formulated, the message is transferred to RATSS and the program enters a dormant state, during which it does not make use of the CPU. During this period, RATSS sends the message to the subject and checks to see if any other program can make use of the core. If so, the now dormant program is copied onto disk. When the dormant program's subject makes a response, the program enters the ready state. RATSS places the program on the bottom of a stack of programs awaiting their turn to compute.

A flowchart of RATSS is presented in Figure 2. The more detailed description below will be clearer if the reader first takes a moment to examine it.

RATSS occupies one of the two 4096-word core memory banks of the PDP-8 (the "lower" core). As many as eight subject programs are stored on the disk. At any given time, only one of these programs may be in core (the "upper" 4096 words). Figure 2 shows a segment of one such program. This particular program has been read into the upper core to examine the subject's last response (not shown) and to compute the next stimulus message. After the next message is prepared, the program executes a REQIO (for request input-output) command, instructing that RATSS print the message on the subject's teletype and allow the subject to type a response. The REQIO command is transferred to RATSS, which places it on the TASK STACK. The RATSS system retrieves from the program the specifications of the I/O request (the devices involved, the amount of data to be transferred, *etc.*), initiates the I/O task (*e.g.*, begins to send a string of print commands to the subject's teletype), and then jumps back to the program for possible further computation. (In the meantime, the I/O transfer is being carried to completion.) Typically, this computation requires no more than a few microseconds, since further progress usually is contingent upon receipt of the subject's response. Pending completion of the REQIO command, the user program issues a WAIT command, which transfers control again to the RATSS system. The program is now dormant while it awaits the subject's response.

While awaiting I/O completion for this program, RATSS determines if any other program can make use of upper core. RATSS first checks the READY STACK to see if the REQIO of any other program has been completed. If so, the current program is copied on disk, the next program is placed in core, and control is transferred to it.

All I/O requests and requests to transfer data from one terminal or storage device to another are initiated by the TASK ASSIGN routine in RATSS. With the completion of each such request, an interrupt signal stops the on-going processing of the CPU. Control then passes to the INTERRUPT routine or

RATSS, which determines which transfer was just completed and which program was involved. If a second transfer is required to satisfy the original REQIO (as would happen, for example, in a disk-to-magnetic tape transfer, which must pass through a core buffer) this second transfer is then initiated. If the original request has been fully satisfied, the appropriate program is placed on the READY STACK. In either case, the program that was interrupted is then allowed to resume.

Each subject's program repeatedly cycles through an active, a dormant, and a ready state. The length of time spent in each of these states determines the overall performance of the system.

One requirement for good performance is that the user program should spend relatively little time in the active state compared to the time spent waiting for the subject to reply. Response time will increase whenever a number of programs queue up on the READY STACK. Fortunately, the speed of the computer seldom makes it necessary to compute for more than a few milliseconds—enough time for several hundred commands to be executed.

The length of time spent in the dormant state is a joint function of the type of experiment being run and the subject's response time. System performance as a whole is better if the experiment requires relatively few responses and relatively long intervals during which the subject prepares his next response.

The length of time spent in the ready state is a joint function of the number of subjects being run simultaneously and of the general level of response activity. This time will be minimal when there are few other subjects competing for computer time, *i.e.*, if the other subjects are not actively responding. In the optimal case, the subject's program will still be in core when he makes a response. In this case, the presentation of the next stimulus message will appear to the subject to be instantaneous. If the subject's program is not in core (meaning that some other program has been active in the meantime) the following events occur. The interrupt alerts the RATSS system that the subject's response is ready to be processed. (If another program is computing, it is allowed to finish.) The program (now dormant) in core is copied onto disk, the ready program is read into upper core, and becomes active. The program then processes the subject's response and issues a reply, which RATSS immediately begins to print on the subject's teletype. The computation involved in this activity, except for the swapping of one subject's program for another, is fast enough to appear instantaneous. The swap time, however, requires 0.6 sec and represents the typical response lag if there is any lag at all.

On rare occasions, it may happen that a program is placed on the ready stack while there are several other programs ahead of it on the stack. Thus, the response lag will always be some multiple of 0.6 sec. It has been our experience with as many as eight subjects run simultaneously that the vast majority of response lags have been 0.6 sec or less. Only very rarely does a lag of 1.2 sec occur.

Programming for RATSS. Experimenters write programs (usually in the 8TRAN language) for use under the RATSS system as if only a single subject were involved. The object programs produced by a special version of the 8TRAN compiler are stored on magnetic tape. To run a program for an experiment requires only that the tape be mounted and that the program be called from the console teletype to run in the designated partitions. Typically, an experimenter makes use of all available teletypes and administers the same experiment on each. However, it is possible for several experimenters to share the facility, since any program written to run under RATSS may be run on any available teletype.

One partition of RATSS is reserved for a control system, FANTOM, which operates from the console teletype. Using the commands built in to FANTOM, the experimenter may orchestrate an entire experimental session. He may initiate and terminate any program in any partition. He may check the current status of each partition, receive indications of hardware and software failures, adjust the priorities with which the programs are allowed access to core, connect teletypes together into a communication network, and send messages to designated teletypes.

EXPERIMENTS USING THE RATSS SYSTEM

Most of the experiments administered using RATSS during the first three years of its operation may be grouped into three categories: multistage decision games, concept identification tasks, and bargaining tasks. For each of these classes of experiment, computer control has been found to be advantageous. In each case, the subject is presented a sequence of information that may be a function of his preceding responses, *i.e.*, the subject and the experimental conditions are in dynamic interaction of a form too complex for a human experimenter easily to cope with. Also, strict standardization of experimental procedure is highly desirable. Finally, all three classes of experiments require that subjects be run individually for about an hour. Without the capability of running more than one subject at a time, such experiments would require a very long time to complete.

Multistage Decision Making.[3] A variety of experiments have been performed to evaluate the adequacy of decision-making models for describing the behavior of subjects who are presented repeatedly with tasks requiring decision under conditions of uncertainty. The common property of *multistage* tasks is that each decision affects the state of the world, and thus influences the nature of subsequent tasks. The program of research on multistage decision making has investigated the degree to which normative models, that specify a sequence of optimal decisions, approximate descriptive models of subjects' performance.

---

[3] This project is under the direction of Amnon Rapoport and Lyle Jones. Lawrence Gordon has made substantial contributions to the programs used for this research.

Since optimality can be defined only with respect to some criterion utility function, the research also has been attentive to determining the form of the appropriate utility function.

A typical task studied with the aid of RATSS is a multistage betting game. In this game, the subject begins with a specified amount of capital in the form of money or points (that may be convertible into money). On each of many trials, he must allocate portions of his capital over a set of alternative events characterized by different probabilities of occurrence. One of these events then is randomly selected by the computer to be the outcome on that trial. The subject is rewarded in proportion to the amount of capital he has wagered on the outcome event. The game ends after a fixed number of trials (that may be unknown to the subject), or if he loses all accumulated capital.

A specimen dialogue between computer and player of a multistage betting game appears in Figure 3. The italicized characters represent a player's responses; all other typing is that of the computer. ("Comments" are presented for the reader of this report; they do not constitute part of the dialogue.)

Many variations of this game are possible. Among other parameters that the experimenter may assign are parameters to control the number of alternative events in the game, the reward multipliers for each alternative, the (stationary) win probability of each alternative, the number of games to be played, the number of trials in each game, the nominal unit of payoff, (dollars or points), the dollar equivalent of payoff units, the maximum winning allowed per game (with game to end after a trial on which accumulated capital reaches or exceeds the maximum), whether wagers must sum to or may be less than available capital, and whether a statement of subjective probabilities is to be requested at the termination of each game.

As many as eight subjects, in individual cubicles, may be controlled at one time by the multistage betting game program. Parameters may be the same or different for the several subjects. At the computer console, the human experimenter may monitor the progress of all subjects via the CCI scope display unit.

Data collected from subjects in the multistage betting game are retained in a block of core available to each subject. Periodically, as each block is filled, data are transferred to disk or magnetic tape for later detailed analysis by another set of programs.

With knowledge of (1) the probability with which each alternative event will occur, and (2) the player's utility function for money (or points), an optimal betting policy may be determined. In several studies, it has been shown that the performance of many subjects approximates that prescribed by an optimal policy, assuming that subjects have a logarithmic utility function for money. Systematic discrepancies from the optimal policy tend to appear, however, when capital size is very small (subjects take unusually high risks) or very large (some subjects are risky while others are highly conservative). Discrepancies also appear as a function of runs of successive failures or successes (as if influenced by "the

Teletype Dialogue	Comments
EXAMPLE GAME. INITIAL CAPITAL:	"Points" version of the
100 POINTS	game is being presented.
PLAY 1.	
BLUE: _60_	
BLACK: 40 POINTS --- OK? _Y_	
BLUE WINS! NEW CAPITAL, 060 POINTS	
PLAY 2.	
BLUE: _40_	
BLACK: 20 POINTS --- OK? _Y_	
BLACK WINS! NEW CAPITAL, 040 POINTS	
END OF EXAMPLE GAME.	Winnings in example
YOUR ACCUMULATED CAPITAL IS 000 POINTS	game do not accrue
WHAT PERCENTAGE OF TIMES DO YOU THINK	Request for estimates of
EACH EVENT WILL WIN IN FUTURE PLAYS?	subjective probability
BLUE: _50_	
BLACK: _50_ --- OK? _Y_	Off-line instructions
	are read here.
GAME NUMBER 1. INITIAL CAPITAL:	
200 POINTS	
PLAY 1.	
BLUE: _150_	
BLACK: 50 POINTS --- OK? _Y_	
BLUE WINS! NEW CAPITAL, 150 POINTS	Reward multiplier on Blue is 1.
PLAY 2.	
BLUE: _75_	
BLACK: 75 POINTS --- OK? _Y_	
BLACK WINS! NEW CAPITAL, 150 POINTS	Reward multiplier on BLACK is 2.
PLAY 3.	
BLUE: _50_	
BLACK: 100 POINTS --- OK? _Y_	
BLUE WINS! NEW CAPITAL, 050 POINTS	
PLAY 4.	
BLUE: _0_	
BLACK: 50 POINTS --- OK? _Y_	
BLACK WINS! NEW CAPITAL, 100 POINTS	Accumulate points for later payoff
WHAT PERCENTAGE OF TIMES DO YOU THINK	
EACH EVENT WILL WIN IN FUTURE PLAYS?	

Figure 3. Example of a multistage betting game. The subject's inputs are in italics.

Figure 3, cont.

BLUE: 50

BLACK: 50 --- OK? Y

GAME NUMBER 2. INITIAL CAPITAL:

300 POINTS

PLAY 1.

BLUE: 0

BLACK: 300 POINTS --- OK? Y

BLUE WINS! NEW CAPITAL, 000 POINTS   All capital exhausted; game ends

END OF GAME 2.

YOUR ACCUMULATED CAPITAL IS 100 POINTS.

WHAT PERCENTAGE OF TIMES DO YOU THINK

EACH EVENT WILL WIN IN FUTURE PLAYS?

BLUE: 60

BLACK: 40 --- OK? Y

YOUR WINNINGS FOR THIS SESSION ARE

100 POINTS. UNDER THE RULES STATED

EARLIER, THIS IS EQUIVALENT TO AN

ACTUAL PAYOFF OF $2.00, WHICH YOU

WILL NOW RECEIVE.

END OF EXPERIMENT!   S informed of payoff;

PLEASE CALL THE EXPERIMENTER.   payoff rate for this game

two cents per point

gambler's fallacy"). Ongoing research is investigating alternative utility functions, particularly the negative exponential (Rapoport, 1969), for which optimal policy is affected by amount of available capital. Other studies based upon multistage betting games have investigated Bayesian models for learning the probabilities of alternative events.

The Concept Identification Task.[4] In this task, which goes under the name "Zaps and Duds", the subject is required to examine a set of objects in order to deduce the rule that has served to classify some of the objects as positive instances (Zaps) and the others as negative instances (Duds). The objects consist of the 64 combinations that may be constructed using six Xs and Os, *e.g.*, XXOXOO and XOOOXX. The subject is told the set of possible solutions: two of the six positions are critical (there are 15 such pairs) and are linked with either a conjunctive or a disjunctive connector. There are thus 30 possible solutions. If the solution is "3 and 4", for example, then the positive instances,

[4] This project is under the direction of Edward S. Johnson, with the assistance of Robert Baker.

Problem 1. XXXXXX is a Zap and OOOOOO is a Dud.

Trial 1. *XXXOOO*   XXXOOO is a Zap.

Trial 2. *XXOOOO*   XXOOOO is a Zap.

Trial 3. *1 and 2*   1 and 2 is not the answer.

Trial 4. *XOOOOO*   XOOOOO is a Zap.

Trial 5. *OXOOOO*   OXOOOO is a Dud.

Trial 6. *1 or 2*   Impossible. 1 or 2 would make OXOOOO a Zap.

Trial 7. *OOOXXX*   OOOXXX is a Zap.

Trial 8. *OOOOOX*   OOOOOX is a Dud.

Trial 9. *1 or 4*   1 or 4 is not the answer.

Trial 10. *1 or 5*   correct!

Figure 4. A sample ZAPS and DUDS protocol. Subject's inputs are in italics.

the Zaps, are those patterns with Xs in both positions three and four. All other patterns would be classified as Duds. If the solution is "3 or 4," the Zaps are those patterns with an X in either position three or four or both. The subject must infer the rule by discovering how it classifies a number of patterns.

The subject begins a problem knowing only that pattern XXXXXX is a Zap and pattern OOOOOO is a Dud. At each trial thereafter, the subject may either inquire about the classification of any pattern he wishes, or try out a rule. The problem is solved when the subject types the correct rule. A sample solution is presented in Figure 4.

The task as thus far described could easily be administered by a human experimenter. A computer is required because of the complex manner in which the solution is selected. Unlike traditional concept formation tasks, a Zaps and Duds problem has no solution specified before the subject starts his search. Instead, the solution is selected during the subject's search in such a way as to maximize the number of trials required to find the solution. (The subject, on the other hand, is instructed to minimize the number of trials required.) The procedure for selecting the answer is termed Minimum Information Feedback (MIF) and operates as follows. A list of all possible solutions is kept by the computer. Initially, all of the 30 possible solutions are on this list. If the subject requests the classification of a particular pattern, the computer first calculates the number of answers that would remain logically tenable (a) if the pattern were called a positive instance (a Zap), or (b) if it were called a negative instance (a Dud). The classification is then reported to the subject so as to maximize this number. The solutions that have been eliminated are then crossed off the list. If the subject ventures a pattern that logically eliminates the same number of hypotheses regardless of classification (as happens in trial one of the solution presented in Figure 4), the computer decides upon the classification randomly.

When the subject types a proposed solution, the computer first searches for it on the list of possible solutions. If the solution is missing from the list, then the hypothesis logically contradicts information that has already been given to the subject. In this case, the contradiction is reported to the subject (see Figure 4, trial 6). If the hypothesis is on the list, then it is still a logically possible solution. If it is the only solution left on the list, the subject is told that he has solved the problem. Otherwise, the subject is told that his hypothesis is not the answer and the computer deletes it from the list of possible solutions.

As an example of the MIF procedure, suppose that on trial 1, where all 30 solutions are still viable, the subject inquires about pattern XOOOOO. If this pattern were to be classified as a Zap, then only the following five solutions would remain: 1 or 2, 1 or 3, 1 or 4, 1 or 5, and 1 or 6. The other 25 solutions would be eliminated. On the other hand, if this pattern were to be classified as a Dud, then the five solutions listed above would be the only ones eliminated and the other 25 would remain viable. Thus, pattern XOOOOO would be classified as a Dud.

As a second example, consider a subject who tries to out-guess the computer by typing in one hypothesis after another until he finds the solution. In this case, it will always be the thirtieth hypothesis that is called correct.

The Zaps and Duds program is used primarily as a vehicle for studying problem-solving strategy. For this purpose, the somewhat Machiavellian MIF technique has the advantage of extracting from the subject a maximum amount of information on each problem. The subject is more likely to reveal his strategy in his trial-by-trial behavior simply because more trials are required to discover the solution (an average of about 13 trials per problem as opposed to an average of seven trials when pre-determined solutions are used.)

Subjects in a Zaps and Duds experiment typically are asked to solve four problems and then answer a 10-item computer-administered questionnaire. The length of time required varies greatly from subject to subject, ranging from 15 to 100 min, with a mean of about 40 min. Two experimenters are employed, with eight subjects scheduled per hour. The first experimenter is responsible for instructing all subjects in the rules of the task and the use of the teletype. He also answers calls for assistance, which subjects may make from their cubicle. The second experimenter services the cubicles between their use by successive subjects. This involves requesting a data printout for the preceding subject and then initializing the program for the next subject.

In order to maintain as rapid a flow of subjects as possible, the CRT display scope at the computer console has been programmed to exhibit each cubicle's moment-to-moment status. This enables the second experimenter to know exactly when he must prepare a cubicle for the next subject and enables the first experimenter to know exactly when a cubicle has become available for another subject.

In addition to printing a full record of each subject's performance immediately after he has vacated the cubicle, the computer stores a table of summary data on magnetic tape. After each experimental session, these data are punched on paper tape in a format recognizable to the Laboratory's IBM 1130 computer. A program for this machine converts the paper tape data to punched cards and allows the experimenter to enter additional information about the subject via the console keyboard. The card data may then be transmitted from the 1130 to an IBM 360 Model 165 for analysis.

The Bargaining Game.[5]   One form of this task attempts to assess how various pressures on a bargainer will influence his effectiveness on negotiating a mock labor contract. The four subjects who play the game are informed that they will be assigned to play one of the following four roles: (1) the management spokesman who negotiates with (2) the labor spokesman; (3) the management constituent who observes the negotiations and who advises his spokesman; and (4) the labor constituent who also observes the negotiations and who advises the labor spokesman. The four subjects are then assigned to separate cubicles where each is told that he is to play the role of management spokesman. While each subject assumes that the other three roles are being played by his fellow subjects, in actuality the computer simulates the other three roles and performs a separate negotiation experiment with each subject simultaneously.

The experiment consists of 10 trials of negotiation between the subject and the simulated labor spokesman, with the issue of negotiation being hourly wages. Each trial consists of two parts: the latest wage demand from labor, together with a verbal message from the labor spokesman, are typed by the computer for the subject to read; the subject then decides upon a management counter-offer and a verbal message to be sent to the labor spokesman. Before trials 1, 4, 7, and 9, the subject receives a message from his (simulated) management constituent and the subject in turn selects a message to be sent back in response.

An example subject-computer exchange is presented in Figure 5. The messages that the subject sends to the other players are selected from a list of possible messages given to the subject at the outset of the experiment. Each message is identified by a code letter. The subject is told that by typing a code letter he may cause the equivalent message, in its entirety, to be printed on another subject's teletype. He also assumes that the messages that are printed on his teletype have been sent by other subjects who have been provided with similar sets of messages. The illusion that the subject is in communication with live subjects is heightened by random time delays that occur before each message is received and which, presumably, represent time spent by the other subjects in selecting their messages.

---

[5] This project is being carried out by James Kahan and Robert Frey.

All subjects receive the same initial message from management in which they are directed to begin the bargaining by offering $2.00 per hour and are advised to concede very little to labor. Labor's initial demand, $3.50 per hour, is also the same for each subject, as is the entire sequence of labor demands throughout the 10 trials of negotiation. The sequence of labor messages that accompanies the demands is not the same for all subjects. Half the subjects receive labor messages that are always demanding and exploitative in tone (the labor message in Figure 5 are of this type) while the other subjects receive labor messages that are uniformly cooperative and yielding.

Having received the first labor demand and its accompanying message, the subject exemplified in Figure 5 makes the initial offer which, of course, is the $2.00 per hour that was authorized by management. The subject also selects a message to send to labor by typing in the appropriate letter code, in this case, message A (see Figure 5). On the second trial, neither the labor spokesman nor the subject yield any ground in their wage offers; the subject selects a slightly firmer message. Trials 3 through 8 have been omitted from Figure 5. Before trial 9, a message is received from the management constituent (the fourth and last such message) and the subject selects rather hostile messages to send in reply to labor's increasingly demanding statements. The experiments ends with the subject offering $2.50 per hour and the simulated labor spokesman demanding $3.10 per hour.

All subjects receive the identical sequence of wage demand from labor. What varies is the tone of the messages that accompany the demands. The final labor message in the conciliatory sequence, for example, is: "Once again I am lowering our request against direct orders from my constituency not to do so. I am really trying to be as fair as possible both to management and to our own workers. We must both have an attitude of mutual give and take."

The data collected from each subject consist of his 10 offers, the 10 messages sent to labor, and the four messages sent to management. The messages have previously been scaled on a conciliatory-demanding continuum in order to make possible a quantitative statement about how subjects react to different kinds of labor messages. The results indicate the subjects tend to yield less in hourly wages to a conciliatory labor spokesman than to a demanding one. But while yielding less, the subjects display a very pronounced tendency to send conciliatory replies in response to conciliatory labor messages. This effect carries over to the subject's communications with management. Even though all subjects receive a uniformly demanding set of messages from management they tend to respond with conciliatory messages if that is the type of message they receive from labor.

In the bargaining game, as in the other experiments described, the computer's CRT display is used to keep track of each subject's progress in the experiment.

Other Applications. The three classes of experiment noted above represent uses of RATSS during the third year of the system's availability. Other

From management spokesman:

MAKE AN OFFER OF $2.00 FOR THE FIRST SESSION. REMEMBER THAT A SUB-
STANTIAL PAY RAISE WILL COST OUR COMPANY TOO MUCH MONEY. WE CANNOT
AFFORD TO GO MUCH HIGHER THAN $2.00. MAKE VERY FEW AND VERY SMALL
CONCESSIONS. CONVINCE THE UNION SPOKESMAN THAT THEY WILL HAVE TO
COME AROUND TO OUR POINT OF VIEW IF THEY REALLY WANT A NEW CONTRACT.

Trial 1. From labor:

OUR REQUEST FOR THIS SESSION IS $3.50. WE HAVE HAD A RECORD INCREASE
IN THE COST OF LIVING. YOUR COMPANY IS RESPONSIBLE FOR THE WORKERS'
WELFARE. JUST TAKE A LITTLE LESS PROFIT THIS YEAR. WE NEED A LARGE
RAISE AND WE INTEND TO GET IT ONE WAY OR ANOTHER.

OFFER TO UNION SPOKESMAN = *$2.00*. MESSAGE CODE TO UNION SPOKESMAN = *A*

Trial 2. From labor:

OUR REQUEST FOR THIS SESSION IS $3.50. FRANKLY WE WERE REALLY SHOCKED
AT YOUR RIDICULOUSLY LOW FIRST OFFER. WE WOULD ALL STRIKE RATHER THAN
ACCEPT SUCH A RATE. YOUR TROUBLES ARE NOT OUR CONCERN. THE ONLY THING
THAT WE CARE ABOUT IS FOR YOU TO GET YOUR OFFER UP TO A REALISTIC
LEVEL.

OFFER TO UNION SPOKESMAN = *$2.00*. MESSAGE CODE TO UNION SPOKESMAN = *B*

... (Trials 3 - 8 omitted) ...

From management spokesman:

THIS IS RIDICULOUS! YOU ARE SUPPOSED TO REPRESENT THE COMPANY'S BEST
INTERESTS. STOP LETTING THAT UNION SPOKESMAN WALK ALL OVER YOU. IF
HE DOESN'T START MAKING SOME GENUINE CONCESSIONS VERY SOON, GIVE HIM
HELL. WHOSE SIDE ARE YOU ON ANYWAY? MESSAGE CODE TO CONSTITUENT = *Z*

Trial 9. From labor:

OUR REQUEST FOR THIS SESSION IS $3.15. BOTH MY CONSTITUENCY AND
MYSELF HAVE JUST ABOUT HAD IT. YOU WILL NOT LISTEN TO REASON.
THEREFORE, WE ARE NO LONGER ASKING, RATHER, WE ARE--DEMANDING--A
DECENT RAISE. IT IS NOT GOING TO TAKE MUCH MORE FOR US TO SERIOUSLY
CONSIDER GOING ON STRIKE.

Figure 5. A sample protocol from the bargaining game. Subject's inputs are in italics.
Messages corresponding to the letter codes are given in the lower portion of the
figure.

Figure 5, cont.

OFFER TO UNION SPOKESMAN = $2.50. MESSAGE CODE TO UNION SPOKESMAN = P

Trial 10. From labor:

OUR REQUEST FOR THIS SESSION IS $3.10. WE ARE MAKING THIS ONE LAST
CONCESSION BUT I DON'T THINK IT WILL DO ANY GOOD. YOU ARE AN OBSTINATE
FOOL. WHATEVER HAPPENS FROM NOW ON IS YOUR OWN FAULT. IF YOU DON'T GET
UP TO THIS RATE VERY SOON, WE WILL KNOW THAT A STRIKE IS NECESSARY.

OFFER TO UNION SPOKESMAN = $2.50. MESSAGE CODE TO UNION SPOKESMAN = Q

YOU HAVE JUST FINISHED THE LAST SESSION OF THE EXPERIMENT. PLEASE
TURN ON THE SWITCH WHICH IS ON THE RIGHT SIDE OF YOUR TELETYPE IN
ORDER TO SIGNAL THE EXPERIMENTER.

Message A (to labor):

WE FEEL THAT THIS OFFER REPRESENTS A SUBSTANTIAL INCREASE IN SALARY
FOR THE WORKERS, AND IT SHOULD ENABLE THEM TO KEEP UP WITH THE COST
OF LIVING. IT IS A RATE WHICH IS VERY FAIR TO BOTH SIDES.

Message B (to labor):

YOUR WAGE REQUEST IS VERY HIGH. WE COULD NEVER AFFORD TO PAY SUCH A
RATE. HOWEVER, I AM WILLING TO RAISE MY OFFER IF YOU START LOWERING
YOUR REQUEST.

Message Z (to management):

REMEMBER, I DID NOT ASK TO BE THE SPOKESMAN. WHY DON'T YOU STOP
GIVING ME SUCH A HARD TIME AND TRY TO REALIZE THE POSITION I AM IN.
DO YOU EXPECT ME TO PERFORM MIRACLES?

Message P (to labor):

ARE YOU FOR REAL? WHERE DO YOU THINK SUCH OBNOXIOUS TALK IS GOING
TO GET YOU? IF YOU SERIOUSLY THINK WE COULD AFFORD TO PAY SUCH
BLOWN-UP WAGES, YOU HAVE A LOT TO LEARN. GET DOWN TO EARTH.

Message Q (to labor):

WHAT LOW-DOWN GALL YOU HAVE. DO YOU ACTUALLY THINK THAT YOUR CHILDISH
NAME CALLING IMPRESSES ME? YOU ARE ACTING JUST LIKE A UNION RADICAL.
EITHER GET DOWN TO BUSINESS OR WE WILL BREAK OFF NEGOTIATIONS. I AM
NOT GOING TO PUT UP WITH SUCH BEHAVIOR MUCH LONGER.

experiments are planned, in which greater use is to be made of the capabilities for dynamic interaction between subjects' responses and subsequent selection of stimuli. Examples of such studies are those of Rapoport (1966a, 1966b, 1967a, 1967b) applying a dynamic programming approach to several inventory control problems.

SAVE

SAVE is a system of programs that assists the experimenter in the design, implementation, and performance of experiments using visual stimuli. The system is oriented towards three particular goals: enough flexibility to make possible a wide range of visual experimentation, sufficient ease of use to minimize the need for any special knowledge of computers or programming, and simple, error-free recording of responses and response latencies. Since there is no necessity for programming in assembly language, SAVE enables investigators who may have never used a computer to computerize their experiments.

SAVE is composed of three programs. With them, the experimenter constructs stimuli, composes instructions, and then designs and executes the experiment. Each of these steps can be accomplished in separate sessions with the computer if desired. The information generated during one session is stored on the experimenter's reel of magnetic tape. At the start of the next session with the computer, the experimenter places his reel of tape on the tape unit and continues to construct the experiment.

The first program, DISP, is used to assist the experimenter in constructing stimulus and instructional displays. This program allows the experimenter to interact with the computer from a teletype terminal. By typing various commands and instructions, the experimenter constructs graphic stimulus and alphanumeric instructional displays on the CRT. When a display has been completely finished, he can then permanently store it on magnetic tape. The experimenter also may review and/or modify any or all of the displays he has constructed.

When the experimenter has constructed the full sequence of stimuli and instructions, he is ready to use the second SAVE program to design the experiment. This program, called DESI, enables the experimenter to design his experiment. The experimenter indicates the labels for the stimuli and instructions, the number of stimuli and instructional frames, the number of trials, the duration of the stimulus and response periods, the presentation order of the stimuli (or whether it is to be randomized), and the nature of allowable responses. This information is also stored on the experimenter's magnetic tape. Examples of specific designs and the interaction between DESI and the experimenter are presented in the next section.

When the experimenter is ready to execute the experiment, he uses the third SAVE program, an operating system for the information compiled during the use of the previous SAVE programs. The experimenter has only to determine that the hardware is ready to be used. He places his tape on the tape unit and transfers the SAVE operating system to core. The operating system then runs the experiment. During the experiment, the operating system determines which stimuli are to be presented and what form of feedback is to be presented (if any). It records and punches on paper tape the subject's responses and the response latencies. To administer the experiment again to another subject, the experimenter reloads the operating system into the core memory of the machine.

EXPERIMENTS USING THE SAVE SYSTEM

Psychophysics.[6] The psychophysical experiments that have been performed with SAVE have all involved simple geometric stimuli: lines or rectangles. One psychophysical experiment (Young, 1970) investigated relations between various kinds of human judgments concerning unidimensional stimuli (lines). Subjects were presented with one of the following two tasks. In the *similarity* task, the lines were presented in pairs for as long a time as the subject desired, and the subjects made category judgments about the similarity of each pair. In the *same-different* task, the lines were presented in pairs for very brief periods of time and subjects made judgments as to whether their lengths were the same or different.

Figure 6 shows the design phase of this experiment, in which DESI asks the experimenter for the design attributes. The italicized parts of Figure 6 were typed by the experimenter, the remainder by DESI. Both parts of the experiment involved all possible pairs of 14 lines, including each line paired with itself. There were, therefore, a total of 105 stimuli, as indicated by the experimenter on the first line of the printout. On the next line, the experimenter indicated that the stimuli had consecutive labels from 19 through 123. In both parts of the experiment the same stimuli were used, reducing effort in generating the displays.

For the similarity condition, the experimenter instructed DESI that the subject was to be self-paced, *i.e.*, that the subject could view the stimulus for as long as he desired, and that the stimulus would disappear following the subject's response. DESI also was instructed that the only responses the subject could make were the numbers 1 through 9. In the instructions to the subject, it was stated that he was to make category judgments of the similarity of the two lines, using nine categories labelled 1 through 9. If the subject typed any other character the operating system ignored it and the character was not allowed to print on the teletype.

---

[6] These projects are under the direction of Forrest Young and Lawrence Jones.

```
Designing the similarity task of the psychophysical experiment:
                    NUMBER OF STIMULI = 105.
                    THEY ARE LABELED: 19-123.
                    SELF-PACED (Y/N)?Y
                    RESPONSES: 123456789.
                    RANDOMIZE (Y/N)?N
                    NUMBER OF BLOCKS = 1.
                    INSTRUCTIONS (Y/N)?Y
                    THEY ARE LABELED: 5-7,10.
                    FEEDBACK (Y/N)?N
Designing the same-different task of the psychophysical experiment:
                    NUMBER OF STIMULI = 105.
                    THEY ARE LABELED: 19-123.
                    SELF-PACED (Y/N)?N
                    TIME INTERVAL = 0.16.
                    RESPONSE EXTENSION (Y/N)?Y
                    TIME INTERVAL = 4.84.
                    RESPONSES: SD@.
                    RANDOMIZE (Y/N)?N
                    NUMBER OF BLOCKS = 1.
                    INSTRUCTIONS (Y/N)?Y
                    THEY ARE LABELED: 8-10.
Designing the generalization experiment;
                    NUMBER OF STIMULI = 32.
                    THEY ARE LABELED: 31-62.
                    SELF-PACED (Y/N)?N
                    TIME INTERVAL = 5.00.
                    RESPONSE EXTENSION (Y/N)?N
                    RESPONSES: VM@.
                    RANDOMIZE (Y/N)?Y
                    NUMBER OF BLOCKS = 3.
                    INSTRUCTIONS (Y/N)?Y
                    THEY ARE LABELED: 291-299,307,308.
                    FEEDBACK (Y/N)?Y
                    TIME INTERVAL = 1.00.
                    TRIALS TO CRITERION = 10.
                    LABELS WITH RESPONSE V: 31-38,47-54.
                    LABELS WITH RESPONSE M: 39-46,55-62.
                    LABELS WITH RESPONSE @: .
```

Figure 6. Interaction with the DESI portion of SAVE. The experimenter's inputs are in italics.

For the same-different condition, the experimenter instructed DESI that the subject was not to be self-paced. Specifically, the subject was to view the stimulus for 0.16 sec and was to have an additional 4.84 sec to respond. DESI also was instructed that the only permissible responses were S and D. (The special character @ instructs DESI that the subject is allowed the option of no response.) In instructions to the subject, it was stated that he was to decide if the two stimuli were the same or different, and to respond with an S or D respectively.

For both conditions of the experiment, the stimuli were presented in the order indicated by the answer to the labelling question. However, when the stimuli were originally constructed by the experimenter they had been assigned numerical labels in a random sequence so that each subject saw the same randomized order. Finally, for both conditions of the experiment, the entire block of 105 stimuli was presented only once, the subject was instructed via the display, and there was no feedback contingent on the subject's behavior.

In summary, then, there were two conditions in this experiment. In one, the subject viewed each pair of lines for as long as desired and made a category similarity judgment. In the other condition, the subject viewed each pair of lines for a very brief period of time and decided whether the two lines were the same or different.

The analysis was performed on the category judgment data, and on the latency and percentage of correct same-different judgments. All three kinds of data revealed very similar psychophysical functions for line length, but it was concluded that the similarity judgments required the least amount of experimental effort and produced data with the least amount of error.

Several other psychophysical experiments have been performed using SAVE. One experiment investigated the effects upon category judgments and response latency of varying the probability that each of several stimuli would be presented. Twelve lines, varying in length from 1 to 2.8 cm, were displayed with varying probabilities of appearance over a block of 240 trials. The probability of presentation was manipulated by repeating the labels several times in response to DESI's question about the labels of the stimuli. For example, if the 12 stimuli were to be presented equally often, then each label would be repeated 20 times. If the six shortest stimuli were to be presented one-third as often as the six longest, then the six "short" labels would be repeated 10 times and the six "long" labels 30 times. The particular probability distribution was systematically varied over groups of subjects. By manipulating the form of the probability distributions (e.g., rectangular versus normal) judgemental data provide insight concerning the manner in which category judgments are generated.

Another experiment was designed to study the effects of a superimposed classification of judgemental scales and response latency. Twelve lines, varying in length from 11/16 in. to 4 13/16 in., were presented either horizontally or vertically (the superimposed classification). A perfect correlation was imposed between line length and orientation. Thus, the six shortest lines were presented horizontally and the six longest lines were presented vertically. The major experimental question pertained to how observers use the additional information of horizontal or vertical orientation in judging line length.

Discrimination and Generalization.[7] A series of experiments involved stimuli consisting of four points of light arrayed in the shape of a diamond. In these experiments, the subject was shown a standard stimulus at the beginning of the experiment and then a series of comparison stimuli. For each comparison stimulus, he was asked to indicate whether it appeared to be the same or different from the standard. The comparison stimuli varied either on the horizontal separation of two of the dots or the vertical displacement of the two dots, or both. The purpose of the experiment was to determine the relation between unidimensional and multidimensional generalization gradients. The experiment also involved a discrimination training phase to determine the effect of training on the various generalization gradients. Here, the subjects were informed via the CRT after each response whether that response was correct. The series of interactions between the experimenter and DESI for this training phase is presented in Figure 6.

There are two major ways in which this design differs from the two discussed in detail earlier. First, this experiment repeats the block of 32 stimuli up to three times, producing a maximum of 96 trials. Also, the order of presentation is randomized within each block. Note that if the experimenter had indicated that there were 96 stimuli, had repeated the labels three times, and had indicated that there was one block, then the randomizing would have been performed over all 96 trials.

The second major difference in this design is the presence of feedback concerning whether or not the subject's response was correct. The feedback is displayed for 1 sec, and if the subject makes 10 correct responses in a row, the experiment is terminated. The stimuli for which each of the responses is correct were indicated by the experimenter. The response @ (no response) is incorrect for all stimuli.

Concept Formation.[8] Several experiments were performed involving stimuli, each of which consists of five 3-in. lines. Each line may be either in horizontal or vertical orientation. The subject is informed that each stimulus is to be classified into one of two categories depending on the orientation of some unspecified one (or, in a different condition, three) of the lines. He is asked to type one of two letters to indicate in which of the two categories he thinks the stimulus belongs. After he responds, he is told via the CRT whether his response

[7] This project is being carried out by David McGourty.
[8] This project is being carried out by Robert Ochsman.

was right or wrong. The purpose of this experiment was to compare learning rates when there is one relevant line and when there are three relevant lines.

Evaluation of SAVE.   During its first year of operation, SAVE was used to run nine experiments. In addition 12 undergraduates successfully completed individual class projects. In all, approximately 250 subjects were run for a total of about 400 subject hours. Of the six graduate students and faculty members who performed experiments with SAVE, three had little prior contact with computers. Of the 12 undergraduates who completed class projects using SAVE, 10 had little or no computer experience. Thus, it appeared that two of the three goals, ease of use and simple recording of responses and latencies, were adequately met. The wide range of user sophistication attested to the ease with which SAVE could be used. The paper tape output of responses and latencies provided a simple means of access to the Laboratory's IBM 1130 computer for data analysis.

The year of experience with SAVE also indicated that the third goal, that of flexibility, was being met, but only through continued rewriting of the DESI program. DESI was designed to be a general purpose program for designing and executing visual experiments. However, its generality was somewhat limited, and frequent revisions were necessary to enable it to design different types of experiments. With the development of 8TRAN, it became obvious that each new experiment could just as easily be written in this language.

8TRAN

One of the major costs of operating a computerized laboratory is that of program development. We were motivated to produce our own language because no compiler language was available for the PDP-8 that allows efficient character-string manipulation, flexible I/O operations, and that produces efficient object code able to run either stand-alone or under the RATSS system.

8TRAN, based on ASA Full FORTRAN IV, is a comprehensive and efficient language that meets these requirements. Programmers are not intimidated by the language, since the syntax and structures are those of FORTRAN; indeed, many FORTRAN programs are able to compile directly and many others compile with only minor changes. However, the language is considerably more powerful than FORTRAN and includes many features found in PL/1.

In addition to the usual data forms (including single- or double-precision integers and floating point), 8TRAN provides for bit strings of fixed length, character strings of variable or fixed length, and pointers. Pointer operations often permit programs to be considerably smaller than they would be otherwise and allow the possibility of list processing.

Input and output may be formatted but need not be. Default formats exist for output, and free form may be used for input. Character manipulation and evaluation, including string extraction and comparison, are done as easily as are arithmetic operations. Comparison, concatenation, and Boolean operators are available, as are the other operators normally found in FORTRAN. Mixed-mode expressions may be used freely. Type conversion is done automatically.

These features alone provide great flexibility in programming and therefore in experimental design. Others have a similar effect in terms of data storage. 8TRAN permits the user to define INPUT, OUTPUT, or UPDATE files, the latter being used for both input and output. The files may be addressed either in stream (ASCII characters) or in record (internal format) form. Thus, it is as easy to write, say, from core to disk as it is to receive input from a teletype.

8TRAN makes efficient use of core storage, a feature especially desirable with a small computer. Thus, the linking loader puts together only those subroutines that are required by the program. Temporary buffer storage is allocated dynamically during the execution of a program. Non-trivial programs containing 200 to 300 lines of code have run in 4K of core.

8TRAN code is also time-efficient. Run-time routines typically execute from two to six times faster than comparable FORTRAN routines.

Although this description of 8TRAN is far from complete, it should provide some indication of its power and potential usefulness. Experience in our laboratory has already shown that when 8TRAN is employed, program development time is a fraction of what it would be otherwise. Also, 8TRAN is considerably easier to learn than assembly language, especially if one has any familiarity with FORTRAN or PL/1.

8TRAN Applications.   When 8TRAN became available it became relatively simple to design and implement experiments of considerable complexity. While it is possible (at least in principle) to write such programs in assembly language, in actuality the process is extremely time consuming.

Several 8TRAN programs have been developed to perform Interactive Scaling with Individual Subjects (ISIS), with the initial results reported by Young and Cliff (in press). ISIS represents the first attempt to develop a model for the gathering and analyzing of similarities data that is based on multidimensional scaling notions and that uses the computer interactively as a data gatherer and analyzer. With ISIS one can determine the perceived relations between all pairs of a large number of stimuli by gathering information concerning only a small subset of the pairs (for example, only 300 of the 1225 possible pairs of 50 stimuli). ISIS is a true interactive system, since the particular stimulus pairs that are judged by the subject are selected by the computer on the basis of judgments the subject made about pairs of stimuli previously presented. The computer's behavior is contingent on the subject's behavior, and conversely.

As a second example, we have developed an 8TRAN procedure for the study of game behavior. The game selected for study is Gomoku, a game of the tic-tac-toe family, but played on a 17 by 17 grid instead of a 3 by 3 grid. The object for each of two players is to be the first to place five of his own markers in a row. Gomoku is only slightly below checkers in terms of the complexity of strategy involved, yet the computations required to enable the computer to play a good game are relatively straightforward. Gomoku is an attractive vehicle for the study of strategies and their development. From the initial conception of the experiment to the running of the first subject required about one month of calendar time and 40 man-hours of program development. Most of this time was spent in fine-tuning the algorithm to play a good game.

The Gomoku program, when operated under RATSS, performs quite nicely. In addition to winning about 95% of the games, the program, when playing against eight subjects simultaneously, has an average response lag of less than 5 sec (even though 2 sec of compute time are required to compute the reply to a particular subject's move). The relatively fast response time is possible because the typical subject requires at least 15 sec to decide upon his own move.

THE OPERATION OF THE FACILITY

The PDP-8 facility is available to all laboratory personnel, both staff and graduate students. About 30 individuals are involved, with about half this number being frequent users. The staff, graduate and undergraduate students of the Department of Psychology, which houses the laboratory, also have access to the computer, although special permission is required.

Anyone wishing to use the computer is encouraged to learn 8TRAN programming as well as the operation of RATSS and the PDP-8's monitor system. Informal classes are held regularly for prospective users and systems programmers are available to provide assistance in writing new programs. Relatively little difficulty has been encountered in imparting a working knowledge of the PDP-8 and its software to potential users.

For scheduling purposes, the day is divided into three shifts. The hours 8:00 a.m. to 1:00 p.m. Monday through Friday are reserved for program development, and 2 hr a week are scheduled for preventative maintenance. The PDP-8 support personnel are guaranteed approximately half of this time for systems programming, with the rest of the time available on a sign-up basis to other users. The afternoon and evening hours until 10:00 p.m. are divided into three 3-hr blocks for running experiments. The available 60 blocks per month are allocated at a monthly meeting attended by all prospective users. During the night hours from 10:00 p.m. to 8:00 a.m. and on weekends, the facility may be used on a sign-up basis for any purpose. During periods of high demand, it has been necessary to create additional experiment-running blocks on weekends.

The PDP-8 has been in operation for several years, during which time it has grown into a sizable system in terms of both hardware and software. In view of the system's high productivity and the generally high level of user satisfaction, it may be instructive to review some of the detailed history of the installation.

The computer was originally delivered with a 4K memory and a teletype as the sole input-output device. During the first year of operation, much time was spent by laboratory personnel in learning how to program the computer. A large percentage of the time also was spent in developing and using data analysis programs. Toward the end of the first year's operation, we acquired the high-speed paper tape I/O device as well as a single magnetic tape unit. These additions made the computer much more convenient to use, and enhanced its capacity to accomplish a given job in much less time than previously. The released time was quickly consumed by an increased demand from a larger number of users. During the succeeding six months, a second magnetic tape was added and several more teletypes were acquired. The first experiment administering program was written and used to run 50 subjects, each separately. Over this first period of 18 months the computer was in operation for an average of about 5 hr a day. The daily usage was very little higher at the end of this period than at the beginning, although quite a bit more was being accomplished.

The demand for computer time increased markedly as development proceeded on the software systems described in this chapter. This demand was met by again increasing the capability of the machine. A second core and a disk memory were installed and a CRT display was added to the system. After slightly more than two years of operation, the SAVE and RATSS systems became available. During the second 18 months, the computer was in use an average of about 12 hr a day. This was well below the "saturation" at which individual users begin to feel dissatisfied and inconvenienced by the competition for computer time. During the following 18 months, however, additional user programs were developed and freer access to the facility was granted to non-laboratory personnel. As a result, the system became saturated toward the end of this period.

In an installation such as ours, with a limited number of potential users, the result of adding to the capability of the computer has a predictable effect on the demand for time. If the addition extends the computer's range of application (as did the acquisition of the CRT display and the development of RATSS, SAVE, and 8TRAN) then the result is an increased demand for computer time as the users seek to exploit the new capabilities. If, on the other hand, the addition results simply in enabling the same task to be accomplished in less time (as did the acquisition of the second core, the disk, and the line printer) then the improvement tends to result in a net time reduction in overall demand. The hardware facility cannot be upgraded indefinitely, however. Eventually, a point is reached at which it becomes more economical to acquire an entirely new system. Accordingly, in the fall of 1971 in an order was placed for a second computer facility centered around a PDP-11/45. Components will include a CPU with 24K words of 16-bit memory with a cycle time of 850 n.s. (interleaved), a memory management unit, floating point hardware, nine KSR teletypes, DECwriter, paper tape reader/punch, two DECtape transports, a 1.2 million word movable disk unit, and a programmable real-time clock.

The computer facility depicted in Figure 1 has been modified to accommodate the new equipment. Eight additional cubicles have been constructed in the group experiment room. The control room has been expanded to house the PDP-11, and an independent temperature and humidity control system has been installed to serve the PDP-8, the PDP-11, and the IBM 1130.

We anticipate that the addition of the PDP-11 to our facility (and the conversion of RATSS and 8TRAN to this machine) will meet our needs for the next several years. It is expected that from time to time, new components will have to be added either to provide new services or to enable the existing machines to provide faster service.

We have not yet remarked about one important practical feature of system development, that of possible system malfunction. It is a fact of life that computer hardware fails at awkward times and that computer software is slow to be developed and even more slowly becomes purged of errors. We have been fortunate in being able to employ personnel to keep these frustrations at a minimum. A part-time electronic technician and a systems manager have been employed to perform routine maintenance on the computer, attend to the infrequent hardware failures, and provide programming assistance to the students and the staff. Additionally, we have employed personnel to assist in the development of the major software systems. With this pool of talent, the first version of the time-sharing system, RATSS, was ready for use six months after the initial coding began. The reliability of both the hardware and software has been maintained at an excellent level. This is illustrated by the fact that the experimenters using the facility have had to reject data from less than 1% of their subjects because of system failure.

It is our advice, therefore, to those who wish to establish a computer-controlled experimentation facility, that appropriate personnel be employed to maintain the facility. At the very least, services of an electronics technician need to be assured, to keep the equipment in running condition. If a systems programmer can also be employed, then the users of the facility will find that their productivity is greatly enhanced.

We also recommend that attention be given to a schedule for acquiring additional hardware components. By gradually increasing the computer's capabilities, it is possible to keep pace with increasing demands for computer time and to prevent over-saturation from interfering with the research efforts of the users.

SUMMARY

It has become widely recognized that certain benefits are to be gained by computerizing psychological experiments. Among these benefits are standardization of procedures and the capacity for the presentation of stimuli determined by complex functions of prior responses. However, a major drawback to computer-controlled experimentation has been the cost, not only the capital investment in electronic hardware but also those costs of direct consequence to the experimenter, the time and effort spent in implementing an experiment-administering program.

In this chapter, we have described a working laboratory for computer-controlled experimentation that has effectively reduced both of these costs of experimentation. RATSS is a time-sharing system that permits a procedure written for a single subject, to be run for as many as eight subjects simultaneously, allowing each subject to proceed at his own rate. Alternatively, several experimenters may share the facility, each running subjects in his own experiment.

SAVE and 8TRAN are oriented toward the reduction of the other expense involved in computer-controlled experimentation, *i.e.*, the human effort involved in writing and debugging programs. Using the SAVE system, the experimenter may avoid much of the usual programming grief, for the system provides direct assistance in constructing and administering the experiment. Further, the experimenter need not master a programming language in order to use the system. Indeed, it has been found that undergraduates without previous training or experience can easily make use of the system to assist them in class projects. Using 8TRAN, the experimenter has a powerful and versatile system for creating any type of experiment consonant with the capabilities of the hardware. This language has brought about at least a five-fold reduction in program writing and debugging time as compared to the use of assembly language procedures.

The economies of time and effort to be realized from systems such as these are striking. It is noteworthy that such systems can be constructed successfully for a small and relatively inexpensive computer of the PDP-8 class. Using SAVE, an experimenter can convert an idea into a running experiment in as little as 2 hr, much shorter than the time required to implement the same experiment on a tachistoscope. Using RATSS, it is possible to complete in a matter of days a study that otherwise would have required weeks or months. By reducing the time an experimenter needs to spend in gathering data, the computer has increased the time available to analyze the data, interpret the findings, and to design new experiments. In this way, computer-controlled apparatus not only is likely to yield increased quantity of research, but also may provide conditions for improved quality of a psychological research program.

REFERENCES

Bock, R. D. Multivariate and univariate analysis of variance for any design—a computer program for the Royal McBee LGP-30. Chapel Hill, N. C.: *Psychometric Laboratory Research Memorandum No. 3*, May, 1960.

Bock, R. D. Rapid fixed-point matrix subroutines for multivariate statistical computation. *POOL News*, December, 1961.

Bock, R. D. Programming univariate and multivariate analysis of variance. *Technometrics*, 1963, *5*, 95–117. *(a)*

Bock, R. D. A computer program for univariate and multivariate analysis of variance. In H. Koenig (Ed.) *Proceedings of the IBM Scientific Computing Symposium in Statistics*, 1963, 69–111. *(b)*

Bock, R. D. and Zyzanski, S. J. A matrix interpretive subroutine system for the General Precision LGP-30 computer. Chapel Hill, N. C.: *Psychometric Laboratory Report No. 38*, December, 1963.

Conrad, M. The use of RATSS in an experimental environment. Chapel Hill, N. C.: *Psychometric Laboratory Computer Memorandum No. U4*, July, 1968.

Cooperband, A. S. The use of a computer in conducting psychological experiments. *Behavioral Science*, 1966, *11*, 307–312.

Coston, A. RATSS Users Manual. Chapel Hill, N. C.: *Psychometric Laboratory Research Memorandum No. 38*, 1972.

Coston, A. and Helwig, R. 8TRAN Programming Manual. Chapel Hill, N. C.: *Psychometric Laboratory Research Memorandum No. 37*, 1972.

Fox, J. The learning of strategies in a simple two-person zero-sum game without saddlepoint. *Behavioral Science*, 1972, *17*, 300–308.

Freeman, L. A computer controlled experiment on recency in probability learning. *Behavioral Science*, 1971, *16*, 174–179.

Haber, R. N. An on-line computer in a visual perception laboratory. *Behavioral Research Methods and Instrumentation*, 1968, *1*, 86–93.

Johnson, E. S. Can a computer adequately administer a complex problem solving task to individual human subjects. New Haven, Conn.: *Yale University, Department of Psychology, 1966, Tech. Rep. 11*, Contract Nonr 609 (20).

Johnson, E. S. The computer as experimenter. *Behavioral Science*, 1967, *12*, 484–489.

Johnson, E. S. and Baker, R. Some effects of computerizing an experiment in human problem solving. Chapel Hill, N. C.: *Psychometric Laboratory Report No. 105*, 1972.

Jones, L. V. Beyond Babbage. *Psychometrika*, 1963, *28*, 315–331.

Kahan, J. P. and Jones, L. V. Decision making in a four-choice multistage betting game. *Proceedings of the 76th Annual Convention of the American Psychological Association*, 1968, *3*, 217–218.

Mayzner, M. S. The research potential of a computer based cathode-ray tube display system. *Behavioral Research Methods and Instrumentation*, 1968, *1*, 41–43.

Messick, D. M. Interdependent decision strategies in zero sum games: A computer controlled study. *Behavioral Science*, 1967, *12*, 33–49.

Rapoport, A. Sequential decision making in a computer-controlled task. *Journal of Mathematical Psychology*, 1964, *1*, 351–374.

Rapoport, A. A study of human control in a stochastic multistage decision task. *Behavioral Science*, 1966, *11*, 18–32. *(a)*

Rapoport, A. A study of a multistage decision making task with an unknown duration. *Human Factors*, 1966, *8*, 54–61. *(b)*

Rapoport, A. Dynamic programming models for multistage decision-making tests. *Journal of Mathematical Psychology*, 1967, *4*, 48–71. *(a)*

Rapoport, A. Variables affecting decisions in a multistage inventory task. *Behavioral Science*, 1967, *12*, 194–204. *(b)*

Rapoport, A. Multistage betting games with an exponential utility function. Chapel Hill, N. C.: *Psychometric Laboratory Report No. 75*, 1969.

Rapoport, A. and Jones, L. V. Gambling behavior in two-outcome multistage betting games. *Journal of Mathematical Psychology*, 1970, *7*, 163–187.

Rapoport, A., Jones, L. V., and Kahan, J. P. Gambling behavior in multiple-choice betting games. *Journal of Mathematical Psychology*, 1970, *7*, 12–36.

Uttal, W. R. *Real-time computers.* New York: Harper and Row, 1967.

Videbeck, R. and Bates, H. D. Verbal conditioning by a simulated experimenter. *Psychological Record*, 1966, *16*, 145–152.

Wiesen, R. A. Bayes estimation of proportions: The effects of complete and partial feedback. Chapel Hill, N. C.: *Psychometric Laboratory Report No. 32*, December, 1962.

Wiesen, R. A. and Shuford, E. H. Bayes strategies as adaptive behavior. In E. E. Bernard and M. R. Klare (Eds.) *Biological prototypes and synthetic systems.* New York: Plenum Press, 1962, 303–310.

Young, F. W. Twelve-choice probability learning with payoffs. *Psychonomic Science*, 1967, *7*, 353—354.

Young, F. W. Nonmetric multidimensional scaling: Recovery of metric information. *Psychometrika*, 1970, *35*, 455—474.

Young, F. W. and Cliff, N. Interactive scaling with individual subjects. *Psychometrika*, (in press).

CHAPTER NINE

GENERATIVE COMPUTER-ASSISTED INSTRUCTION[1]

WILLIAM R. UTTAL, TIMOTHY PASICH,
MIRIAM ROGERS, and RAMELLE HIERONYMUS
The University of Michigan

[1] The research reported in this chapter was supported in part by a grant from the National Science Foundation (NSF GJ114). Before this paper was published, an expanded version was published as a separate monograph entitled "Generative CAI in Analytic Geometry" by the Enteled Press, Newburyport, Mass.

[Analytical geometry], far more than any of his metaphysical speculations, immortalized the name of Descartes, and constitutes the greatest single step ever made in the progress of the exact sciences.

John Stuart Mill

INTRODUCTION

The field of computer-assisted instruction or computer teaching machines can be classified along many different dimensions. Some (Zinn, 1967) have done so in terms of the types of teaching interaction between the student and the computer. Another dimension, oriented more toward computer technology itself, is based on differences in the logic of the programming systems used to organize and produce the materials presented to the student and to analyze the responses from the student. Computer-assisted instructional systems can be generally divided into three categories along this logical dimension. The first category, *degenerate computer teaching machines*, includes those devices that are simply not using a sufficient amount of the computer's information processing capability to be really regarded as anything more than automated page turners or error tabulation devices. The general characteristics of the degenerate computer teaching machine include such input media as simple multiple choice keyboards and display media such as microfilm or slide projectors. Systems like this reflect the fundamental fact that a high level of gadgetry is not the essence of a computer teaching machine. It is, rather, the adaptive logical processes executed that distinguish computer-assisted instruction from the older teaching machines. In other words, all teaching machines that have been computerized are not computer teaching machines.

Fortunately, there are not too many degenerate systems about any more. By far the largest number of today's computer-assisted instruction systems fall into the second category—*selective computer teaching machines*. Selective computer teaching machines are categorized by a programming logic in which all or most of the dialogue material is prescripted by authors and then stored in great randomly accessible memories. Usually, the assembling of this vast dictionary of canned comments makes use of one of the many "teacher's compiling languages" (see Uttal, 1968, for a complete definition of these terms) developed over the last few years as clerical aides to package properly the items in the dictionary for presentation to the student. The sequence of logic implicit in all of these selective systems is that a "canned" question will be asked of the student and his answer *compared* against a list of "canned" alternative correct and incorrect answers. The match (or partial match in some systems) that is finally made will lead to the computer's *selection* of an appropriate response statement. In this way, the student can converse with the computer in a relatively adaptive manner, in a simulation of the dialogue he might have with a human tutor, the model upon which the entirety of CAI is, of course, based.

In the context of the current state of the computer art, the selective computer teaching machine system represents a gross underutilization of the computer's capabilities. This is not to say that it is not possible to simulate a relatively comprehensible tutorial dialogue with selective machines, but rather, that this is the unesthetic and probably uneconomical way to proceed. There are several fundamental practical limitations, in addition to the esthetic one, involved in not operating at a sufficiently sophisticated level in an already sophisticated technology. Most limiting of all, the appropriateness of the sequence of tutorial statements is completely dependent upon the availability of the very large dictionary of canned material. In spite of the clerical aid of the currently available teacher's compiling languages, it has often been difficult to induce our best teachers to sit down to the remarkably tedious task of anticipating all the dialogue that might be necessary in a student-oriented conversation. This programming bottleneck has only occasionally been squeezed through, and even then by an almost brute-force approach that has seen marginally qualified people actually becoming the direct authors of widely distributed teaching materials. Few full semester-length courses are yet available. Yet, even if these logistic problems were solved, selective techniques could never allow completely adaptive conversation, for it is impossible to conceive of a complete anticipatory dictionary.

Selective computer teaching machines thus suffer from the same limitation that the pictographic languages of the orient do. There is little generality to the representational scheme, and there must be, as many characters (items) as there are concepts (student interactions). The coded languages of the west, however, use a very small number of symbols and a limited number of combination rules to form words representing a wide variety of concepts. This coded or algorithmic approach to language is far more efficient, economical and elegant, in addition to the fact that it possesses psychological advantages of considerable consequence. The mind-blasting consequences of memorizing 5000 to 10,000 weakly discriminable characters has to be experienced to be appreciated.

Emerging in various minor roles in the more conventional programming languages for selective computer teaching machines is a new approach that is neither degenerate nor selective, but more completely models the processes that the human tutor uses in his conversational interaction with the student. This new approach—our third category—is, in fact, *generative*, in that it uses algorithms to generate problems, answers, diagnostics, and remedial materials for transmission to the student, based upon his current status and recent responses. Generative computer teaching machines therefore, are organized quite differently than selective ones. There are no large dictionaries of canned dialogue, but rather, modest numbers of powerful algorithms or subroutines that operate on certain input information to generate the necessary dialogue items as they are required.

The idea of generation hinges completely upon the fact that some subject matters are amenable to algorithmic manipulation. The list of subject matters so amenable is small, currently including the mathematical course materials, other mathematically oriented subjects like the physical sciences, and some special subject matters such as chemistry or logic in which there is a formal system describing the relations between and among parts. Hopefully, as the computer sciences develop, information processing techniques capable of handling verbal materials will continue to evolve in a way that allows the generative approach to be used for unstructured subject matters. For the moment, however, to be realistic we must exclude verbally oriented subjects as possible items for a generative curriculum.

The notion of generative computer teaching has some attractive possibilities. The tedious drudgery of preparing the course materials will be greatly eased. There will simply be no need for complete anticipation. Algorithms, to a significant degree, will be able to generate material as needed. We can also expect a significant increase in the appropriateness of the dialogue generated by the computer, because it is to be expected that generative algorithms will be responsive in context as well as immediacy to the student's inputs. Perhaps most important is the fact that there will be a significant pyramiding of past accomplishments as algorithms developed for other programs are used in new tutorial contexts. It is almost certainly true that there is no such pyramiding effect in the selective approaches used today, as all dialogue must be regenerated anew during the development of each new programmed course.

In the particular case of the generative computer teaching machine, algorithms developed for use in another program can be called easily, as needed, in a new program. This is very much the flavor of the approach used in the modern procedure-oriented languages that represent the highest levels of current computer programming technology. On the other hand, the one-to-one representation of the machine language instructions in the assembler languages is more analogous to the selective computer teaching machine process.

Generative computer teaching machines can, in this context, be seen as also having another advantage. Since there will be, presumably, only a relatively small number of algorithms, peripheral bulk storage requirements for disc memory (now almost the *sine qua non* of selective computer teaching machines, with their huge lists of anticipated dialogue) will greatly decrease. However, this reduction in bulk storage will be compensated for by a drastic increase in the load on the central processor of the computer and its high-speed core memory.

Unfortunately, we must also acknowledge that this issue of increased central processing requirements is a most critical point which might, for simple practical and economic reasons, disqualify the generative approach in the long run. The algorithms for generation may be immensely more complicated than those simple subroutines that sequence the student through some compare-and-select branching tree. Thus, there will remain for a considerable period of time the question of whether or not generative programming, even if it is successful as an intellectual enterprise, can be an economical addition to our library of CAI techniques. There are, of course, several reasons of merit equal to concerns of practical applicability which justify our approach. First, and very important, in spite of the immense commercial overtones of computer-assisted instruction, it is esthetically pleasing to some of us to be pushing the limits of the computer technology, rather than to be applying the older paradigms that have already been shown to be modestly workable. Second, the model of the intellectual process called teaching, which will emerge as we develop a generative programming system, is going to be far more interesting and theoretically relevant to our understanding of the cognitive processes underlying human thinking. We must always remember that the human tutor does not operate in the fashion of a table scanning device, *i.e.*, he is not a dictionary user. Rather, he is an analyzer and generator who determines what his student's needs are, and then from some general set of rules or heuristics formulates a sentence, a problem, a diagnostic, or a remedial unit. It is our premise that the best possible model we could use for the development of a computer tutorial situation is exactly this—the human tutor. The generative computer teaching machine quite explicitly models tutorial cognition by a human teacher. The model used in selective computer tutoring, on the other hand, has been, in general, the dictionary or its descendant, the programmed text.

Nevertheless, we must also be aware of the practical goals of the work described below and therefore, must recognize the potential obstacles to practical application. Generative programs may simply be too complicated to put into a time-sharing operation so that the expenses of a single computer can be amortized across many students. But it is also important to note that the particularly ostentatious claim made by some enthusiasts, of multiple thousands of terminals attached to a single computer, while certainly possible, may in fact be based upon assumptions of simple if not trivial programming logics. Whether simplified branching logics can be used to good effect as educational tools is an open question. Such programs certainly will not operate on the same high interactive level as the generative routines discussed below.

The introductory material presented so far would be open to the most severe criticism as empirically unfounded speculation, if it were not based on demonstrations that algorithmic or generative procedures can be implemented in at least some contexts. It is the purpose of the rest of this chapter to make such demonstrations.

From 1968 to 1970, our laboratory had been exploring the possibilities of generative computer teaching programs. We chose analytical geometry as the vehicle curriculum item primarily because it is a small self-contained unit of knowledge, but also because the algorithms we are developing promise to have wide general applicability to other forms of mathematics teaching. Also important in our decision was the fact that analytical geometry is essentially the interface between high school and college, and it seemed that if we were successful, our contribution at this level would be most worthwhile. Nevertheless, remember that this curriculum chunk is but a vehicle. We are not really interested in analytical geometry *per se*, but rather, in the generative procedures that were to be developed. In the rest of this chapter we first shall briefly review the history of computer teaching devices and then will try to make explicit the progress made on this project. The details of the programming algorithms we have already developed or have immediate plans to implement are then discussed.

Although the specific nature of the hardware used is unimportant, it may be of interest to some readers to know that all of this work was carried out on a Digital Equipment Corporation PDP-9, first with magnetic tape and then with disc storage. Magnetic tapes, as is well known, are not adequate for this sort of random access application because of their long access time, and the acquisition of the disc system added enormously to the realism of our simulation of the tutor. No attempt at time sharing was made. We explored the logic of the generative process and did not want to concern ourselves with the complex housekeeping problems involved in multiple student operation. Our one tutorial station is a Computer Communications Incorporated CC-301 Television display with both alphanumeric and graphic capabilities. The graphic capabilities of this terminal are relatively modest. The dot matrix on which figures are drawn is 80 x 100 and this leads to some rough approximations to some of our conic sections. These problems are discussed in greater detail below.

HISTORY AND PRESENT STATUS OF RESEARCH ON COMPUTER TEACHING MACHINES

The history of computer teaching machines may be considered to have developed in several phases. The first phase includes those non-computerized teaching developments that grew out of the creative and imaginative minds of S. L. Pressy and B. F. Skinner. The development of the concept of the computerized conversational teaching machine depends greatly upon the earlier concepts of sequencing, frames, and the general idea of a program. It is our belief that, in large part, the differences between the older linear techniques and the new conversational, adaptive branching ones are attributable to the technology available to each investigator, rather than to formal bodies of comparative data.

The second phase of development of computer teaching machines involved two early explorations, both developing independently in 1958. The work of Coulsen (1962) and his colleagues at the Systems Development Corporation with the Bendix G-15 and a special purpose random access slide projector is one example. The other is the work of Rath, Anderson, and Brainerd (1959), in which an IBM 650 computer was used to teach binary arithmetic.

The third phase of computer teaching machine development, and the first major wave of serious development saw the rise of a number of important concepts, including time sharing of central computational facilities for use by groups of students and the use of dynamic visual displays, particularly the computer-operated cathode ray tube, for tutorial functions. The ideas of random access stored conversational materials and the full capability alphanumeric response mechanism also were important contributions made during this period. Additionally, several authors suggested the concept of the teacher's compiler language, a "clerical assistant" that could help to format and prepare tutorial dialogue for selective dictionaries.

Among the researchers participating in the field at this time were Licklider (1962), whose work emphasized the cathode ray tube and typewriter operation and motivational trapping; Uttal (1962), who investigated time sharing, random access memories, the logic of computer tutoring dialogues and the high motivating properties of conversational interaction; Bitzer and Braunfeld (1962), who were concerned with the instrumentation of displays for stored pictographic information, and Coulsen (1962) and his colleagues, who concerned themselves with the total system aspect of the computer in the school environment. It is of particular interest in the context of this chapter to note that Licklider had made the original demonstration of the computer teaching of analytical geometry.

A number of important controversies also clarified themselves during this phase. For example, there was a vigorous debate on the issue of the terminal device itself. Should the computer allow the student only to make a multiple-choice answer, or should it allow him full alphanumeric input capabilities? This was a question of major importance, due to the additional computer requirements demanded by the latter mode of operation. .

We now find ourselves in a fourth phase of computer teaching machine activity. It is a time of great activity, characteristic of a period of dissemination of the concept, and consolidation and application of the developments of the past to new curricular areas. The last few years, however, have not been marked as a particularly significant innovative period with regard to tutorial strategies or programming logics. Regardless of the type of display or input device, or the technology of the hardware, the paradigm for computer teaching usually remains the same—the entirety of the dialogue is generated by a human author in great detail in advance, for selective operation. These tediously developed tutorial materials are then stored either in random access general purpose computer memories or in special purpose audio and visual display devices for subsequent presentation to the student, when a specific match is achieved between an anticipated answer and a student response.

Feingold's (1967) description of the PLANIT programming system does make reference to problem generation routines embedded in their generally selective procedure, but the notion that a fully generative programming system is possible has not been sufficiently considered. To our knowledge, up to 1969 when this manuscript was prepared, in the last few years only Uhr (1964, 1967) has published a few brief but extremely suggestive notes expressing this point of view explicitly.

There has, however, been substantial progress in the state of related computer programming arts, which indicate that the necessary techniques for generative programming are available. Easley, Gelder, and Golden (1964) report techniques that process mathematical expressions, and Bennet (1965) has made progress on processing mathematical theorems. Weizenbaum's (1966) ELIZA program is also of considerable significance in suggesting that verbal material as well as mathematical material will ultimately prove amenable to algorithmic processing.

The work of Clapp and Cain (1963), in which a computer was used as an aid in symbolic mathematics, is particularly interesting to us. This is an example of the progress made in the manipulation of "literals" in mathematical computing. They demonstrated that a computer could be effectively used as a very intelligent assistant for a mathematician. The computer was programmed to display the result of algebraic manipulations and actually to perform many of the manipulations, such as substitution, factoring, and distribution. Culler and Fried (1965) developed a system that is specifically directed toward the goal of providing students with a powerful interactive computing facility, although it is not specifically tutorial.

Finally, a very important related area is the recent work in the field of operation-oriented computer languages for specialized purposes. Operation-oriented computer languages represent a step beyond compilers in that is is possible to program the computer to perform major operations by simply calling them up, rather than defining a set of subinstructions in complete detail. For example, Stowe, Wiesen, Yntema, and Forgie (1966) developed such an operation-oriented language for mathematical manipulations in which one instruction will cause two matrices to be multiplied by each other. The programmer gives but one command, rather than an elaborate subroutine, and all of the details are carried out automatically.

Thus, our goals seem to be in context with the current state of the art of computer programming and not unduly speculative. Our project therefore, is also a natural and timely continuation of this train of development. In the following section, the theoretical model underlying our approach is discussed as a further prelude to discussion of the specific details of the programmed algorithms.

A MODEL OF THE TUTOR

As indicated above, we believe that the human tutor functions in ways that are complex and creative. Modern biological science has not yet provided us with any neurophysiology upon which we can base a reductive model of the complex cognitive processes involved in sentence generation, problem solving, concept formation, and the other important functions involved in the simplest tutorial conversation. Therefore, the models that have been successfully called upon to describe such cognitive processes are descriptive and procedural, rather than structural. To begin this exploration of generative tutoring, we necessarily had to assume a conceptual model that describes the tutor's functions. It is obvious that there is an unending succession of levels to which we might have descended if we had not used some very arbitrary standards. We have, indeed, not gone too deeply into this hierarchy, but instead utilized a simplified, if not superficial, model of the human tutor. This model is presented in outline in Figure 1. The human tutor is seen, from our point of view, to be participating in a closed-loop interactive process with the student.

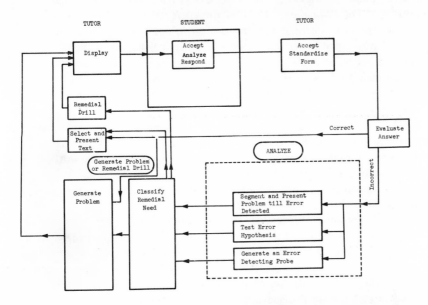

Figure 1. A flow chart of the processes involved in the tutorial conversation. This flow chart emphasizes the role of the tutor and the feedback loop between the student's responses and the tutor's generation of problem, diagnostic, and remedial materials.

The teacher, according to this model, has a number of explicit functions. There is no particular point more appropriate than any other at which to start our discussion, so let us quite arbitrarily consider the display of some new question or problem as the initial entry into this closed-loop feedback system. The student is presented with a question by the tutor. The question may come via a number of different media. It may be a string of words presented either verbally or in some written form. The student then perceives (accepts, acquires) the meaning of the question and fits it into the context of his previous experience so that it can be processed. Ultimately, an appropriate response will be selected and emitted by the student. All of the complicated actions underlying the selection of a particular response are beyond the realm of this discussion. We will consider the tutorial actions only. However, when the student responds, the situation changes for the tutor. What had been the destination of the question is now the source of the response directed at the tutor. The response from the student must be accepted and standardized by the tutor, just as it had been by the student.

Though simple data acquisition is one of the intrinsically less-interesting aspects of the computer model we will be discussing, it is, to a surprisingly large degree, the greatest single continuing obstacle to computer processing of verbal and other non-numeric information. There is a fundamental limitation of all modern computers that is all too infrequently made explicit. We might call this limitation *"The Principle of Limited Anticipation"*. This principle reflects the fact that computers cannot accept arbitrary strings of verbal or symbolic input and deal with them in the same way that human beings seem to handle complex patterns. Each and every input to which a computer successfully and appropriately responds must be a member of a class of inputs that the computer has been programmed to handle. Restrictions on input format in all computer programming systems are necessary concomitants of their logical organization.

The modern serial "von Neumann" computer and its programs are essentially syntactic machines and not semantic ones. They can process information for which synthesis and analysis routines have been preprogrammed. But without these prepared information handlers, no computer can begin to process generalized verbal strings, no matter how meaningful they are to humans.

All non-numeric processing by computers is done by algorithms that essentially are analogue, but not necessarily homologues, of organic thought processes. Simple tricks are used, which at this stage of our psychobiological knowledge at least, are thought to have no similarity to information processing in the brain. Thus, the utility of the list processing languages is in large part due to the fact that they provide a "trick" method by which semantic similarities can be mimicked. Position in a list can represent semantic similarity. However, few enthusiasts of the "dynamic modeling approach" assume that there is some biological equivalent of a list structure in the human thought process. Some other unknown means of linking similar concepts almost certainly is used in our brains. If it turns out that some great neurophysiologist of the future does discover list processing in the human brain, probably no one would be more surprised than some of the most ardent champions of this modelling approach today. Nevertheless, our particular model is based upon a list processing procedure. We do not, however, take this particularly convenient programming mechanism any more seriously than any other analogue that might exhibit similar functional characteristics.

As we have pointed out, the series of responses from the student must be anticipated by input handling routines that are prepared to accept and format them according to the data processing structure of our model. And, indeed, the acceptance and standardization routines in our programs quickly evolved into what would have been called a string or list processing language if they had had general applicability. Algebraic formulae and answers composed of more than a single character are entered, stored, and accessed in strings of the constituent symbols, numbers, and letters.

Another result of the principle of limited anticipation is that, in general, all computer teaching machines and, in fact, almost all non-numeric processing done by computers limit the human conversant to very brief responses. The grammatic, syntactic, and semantic complications of a simple sentence string can quickly overtax the ability of some of the most complicated input string handlers. Conversations between a computer and a human thus take on one of two stereotyped modes. The first mode is one in which the computer, using prestored dialogues, chatters merrily on, essentially dominating the conversation and allowing only the most limited one- or two-word inputs from the human conversant. By directing the conversation in this way, the computer may adapt its dialogue to the needs of the student rather well, using key information in the few words uttered by the student, but still not allowing him elongated responses. On the other hand, a second mode of processing is possible. This is usually based upon the detection and flagging of key words in the student's responses by the computer program, all but ignoring the context in which these words came. The result of this type of processing is characteristically the non-directive dialogue typified by Weizenbaum's (1966) ELIZA psychotherapeutic conversation. In this case, there is an almost complete absence of direction in the computer's contribution to the conversation, but the human conversant is able to make elongated responses.

Once the student's response, however limited it might be, has been acquired it must be evaluated. At the simplest "selective" level this stage of processing would be reduced to direct, character-by-character comparision with a list of prestored items. In a generative system, such as the human tutor, however, there are other more interesting possibilities. Once the answer has been accepted, it must be standardized and formatted, or in more psychological terms, fitted into the system concept structure in spite of the fact that it might not be in the most desirable canonical form.

The set of decisions made at each of the many stages of a computer tutorial program corresponds to the tutorial model of a human tutor used by the designer of the system. There is a large set of questions of which "considering where the program is now, what is to be done next?" is the prototype. The sum total of these implicit questions is, in fact, a major portion of the model of the tutor. Since decisions of this sort are built into all levels of the tutorial program, it is difficult to abstract each one and thus make our model completely explicit. To do so would involve a complete recapitulation of our program. This is a continuing problem in reporting models of this sort. We can, however, emphasize some of the major decision nodes that, either by enlightened insight or by the rough school of experimentation, have been brought to our attention as important considerations in this model of the tutor.

The first of these decision nodes occurs when it has been determined that an answer to a problem is correct or incorrect. If correct, the tutor, following some appropriate signals to the student, typically moves on to the next step in the curriculum. If an error has been made, however, the situation is far more complicated, for the tutor, most desirably, would diagnose the difficulty and remedy it before proceeding on to more complex material. Unlike the older work of Skinner, in which the teaching programs were designed to minimize errors, our programs with their diagnostic and remedial algorithms will be seen to dote on errors as the major guide to the tutorial sequence. This is, in fact, a reasonable analogue of the ideal tutorial conversation. Diagnostic tests of all kinds are made by the human tutor, ranging from direct questions such as: "What are you having trouble with—do you know?" to a step-by-step processing of the student's responses to track down a deficiency that the student could not identify. Once identified, some remedial process is called into play to fill the gaps in the student's understanding of the nature of the problem, or to give him a necessary skill. Once a deficiency has been identified and remedied, the student is usually directed by his tutor to return to the main stream of the curriculum and once again is tested to determine if he has corrected the trouble. The remedial process itself may involve the presentation of text or of problems of a simpler sort, as well as calling on the diagnostic and remedial techniques used by the tutor on the more complex problem itself. The whole process is thus seen to be recursive, with some functions calling other functions, and in turn themselves being called within other functions as needed.

The act of information presentation (of text containing new concepts, problems, or remedial drills) finally closed the feedback loop between the tutor and the student. When the tutorial process is looked at from this point of view, it can be seen that in addition to the display and input acceptance processes, there are only a few general processes that are used over and over again recursively. Diagnosis, remediation, problem generation, and a few other somewhat less-general procedures, each of which can call up the others as needed, constitute an almost complete set of the functions involved in the tutorial process. If this initially oversimplistic point of view holds, it then becomes possible to model the tutor's functions by simulating each of the members of this small set of generative processes, rather than by the alternative procedure of compiling a dictionary of dialogue.

The organization of our tutorial program is presented in Figure 2. In one sense, this can be seen to be simply a reproduction of the major features in Figure 1. However, Figure 2 emphasizes the organization of the computer programming system, pointing out the specific programming blocks and subroutine names where appropriate, rather than the pieces of the tutorial act.

Our generative model of the human tutor has evolved into a programming system in which a master executive routine (DEAN) calls up, as required, particular procedural subroutines required in the tutorial process. The overall organization of DEAN thus embodies a large part (but not all) of the decision logic of the tutorial process as it sequences the program through the various subroutines. DEAN also handles management and bookkeeping functions. Each student's name and status are stored and updated as necessary automatically

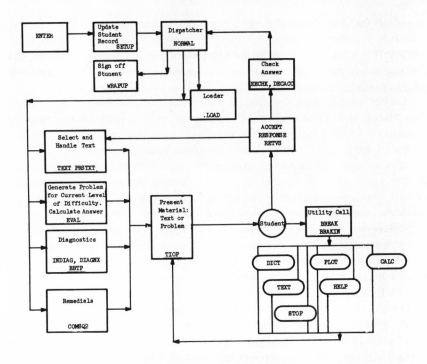

Figure 2. A flow chart of *our simulation* of the tutorial process flow charted in Figure 1. Unlike Figure 1, this model emphasizes the different program segments and the organization of the programming system we have developed, rather than the tutorial acts themselves.

assuring that he will be dealing with the appropriate problems. However, the algorithmic nature of the problem generators assures an endless supply of different problems that may even be graded in difficulty according to the status of the student. Thus, problems may be appropriate and similar, but not identical for each student. Also, individual students can have different problems repeated until the generality of the formulation is a matter of deep and intuitive understanding, rather than a superficial association of a method and a specific problem. All of this is possible without the extensive repetitive production of diagnostic dialogue necessary in selective computer teaching machines. Internally generated problems, both verbal and numerical, must of course then be automatically evaluated so that the answer processing programs will be provided with a criterion with which to evaluate the correctness or incorrectness of the student's answer.

Diagnostic routines comprise a major part of our programming effort. It has been our goal to develop diagnostic routines that can be used on a wide variety of different problems. Specific information must necessarily be communicated from the problem generating routines to the diagnostics so that it is not necessary for the diagnostic program exhaustively to query the problem generator. We describe below our current diagnostic segmentation procedures. Remedial routines are another major category of our simulated tutor. They, like the diagnostics, are concatenations of text, problem generation, diagnostics, and recursive calls to remedials.

Certain specific characteristics of this model must be emphasized. Rather than dealing with the particular details of each problem item, we are trying to find general and generative algorithms that can be called up as needed in a wide variety of contexts for application to particular cases. Programmed routines of this sort will produce a pyramiding of effort quite unlike the selective dictionary operation. We hope to be able to advance quickly into an algebra or calculus tutorial, with only a small effort at additional programming, when this analytical geometry teaching system is completed. Within the context of our current curriculum we have already begun to appreciate this pyramiding effect. In several instances, complex functions have been developed by merely writing a list of JMS (jump to subroutine) instructions. Each of these instructions is responsible for calling upon a subfunction. A major additional requirement for each part of this very large programming task has thus been to maintain a high level of generality so that each routine may be used in other contexts.

A large number of minor subroutines (in the sense that they are housekeeping routines rather than a fundamental part of our simulation of the tutor) is also required. The simple presentation of materials on the CRT required a moderately elaborate set of subroutines that can be called by any part of the system to display text and figures. Answer acceptance routines were also necessary to retrieve information from the student's keyboard and properly format it for processing by other major portions of the program. In the next section, we consider some of these housekeeping routines in detail.

HOUSEKEEPING AND OTHER USEFUL SUBROUTINES

The development of a generative teaching machine system such as we have undertaken is a much more complex task than the preparation of a simple teaching program using one of the more conventional editorial systems. It was, indeed, necessary to go through many of the steps required in the development of a new compiler or procedure-oriented metalanguage. Before we could begin the development of specific generative tutorials, it was necessary to develop a system of housekeeping routines that could handle input and output and format translations within the computer. These housekeeping routines are common to all of the various teaching routines and often act as communication links through which the tutorial segments can communicate with each other. In the early stages of the development of our system, it became clear that we were in the process of developing a string or list processing language. Algebraic equations, text materials, and even graphs were processed as data strings and required a list organization not unlike some of the other more general list processing languages. Many of the housekeeping subroutines that we subsequently developed turned out to be analogs of instructions in those languages. Unfortunately, even though we realized that this was the case rather early in the game, there were no list processing languages available for our small computer and no possibility of doing the sort of things we wanted to do on a larger time-sharing system. Lest there be any misunderstanding about this, it is our belief that the best of the large time-sharing systems still does not allow the type of interactive control we knew we were ultimately to require.

A number of different formats are required for the representation of data strings at various stages in our system. Algebraic expressions must necessarily be subject to manipulations that both separate out the relevant elements and also maintain in one way or another the important arithmetic relations between elements. Thus, when a student typed in some algebraic expression at the teaching console, the string of characters was stored in what quickly came to be called R-Format (raw format). R-Format was a storage technique in which each character was stored in sequential core memory locations as it came in from the keyboard. A termination character was placed at the end of each input string to indicate to other programs the end of the expression. R-Format expressions were always produced by keyboard operation through the medium of special input handler programs for each type of device. RETVS, for example, was a program to bring in a string of R-Format characters from the television keyboard.

Many of the tutorial programs developed to handle algebraic expressions that might be generated by the student required a more specific format, however, than R-Format. An intermediate stage of date organization called I-Format was developed to simplify these operations. I-Format expressions were produced from R-Format expressions by a special program (PSCS) that evaluated the nature of each element of the R-Format expression. Although each element was still stored one character per word, each word had certain of the high-order bits set to indicate the type of element represented. For example, while alphabetic characters were stored with none of the high-order bits set, operators such as addition, subtraction, parentheses and random variable indicators (among others) had the highest order bit (the left most significant bit in our machine) set to one, to indicate that the character was an operator. Operators were not stored in their raw form, but by a coded scheme that helped to simplify some of the later manipulations. If the second highest order bit was set, the character stored in a given word was identified as a constant. Once again, rather than storing the constant itself, only the address of an element in a remote constant table was indicated. Finally, setting the third highest order bit indicated that the element so tagged was one that should be assigned a random value at the time it was displayed. Random variables were also assigned locations in a random variable table and it was again only their addresses in the table that were actually present in the I-Format string.

A number of new concepts have been introduced here. The constant table, the random variable table, and symbol tables were developed as integral parts of our teaching system. This tabular (or list) structure introduced early in the game simplified many later functions to a significant degree.

Manipulations of algebraic expressions in some of the diagnostic routines required a special format that emphasized the unity of a triplet composed of two operands and an operator. We used a technique similar to some of those used in algebraic compilers like FORTRAN. This format was called the TT (triple table) Format. TT-Format tables were produced by a program called JSCS, from I-Format expressions. A triple table for an expression is a convenient form emphasizing the series of operations to be performed on the set of constants and variables. Another program, TTIS, actually carries out these operations, giving numerical value to the expression.

Finally, the expressions represented in this system of data representation had on occasion to be transferred back out to the outside world via the television display or the teletypewriter. This data output operation was the function of another program called DISEX, which converts from I-Format to ASCII codes. The entire family of formats and conversion programs is summarized in Figure 3.

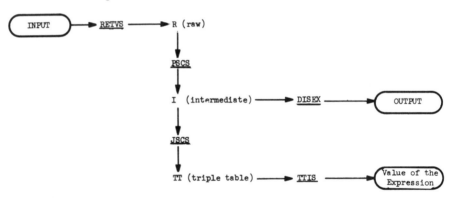

Figure 3. The family of formats and format conversion routines described in detail in the text. (Program names are underlined.)

As can also be inferred from the preceding discussion, many of our problems involved the substitution of random numbers in formatted expressions. Therefore, we also developed another group of utility programs capable of generating quasi random numbers (RANDOM) or ones that were constrained between given limits (RIBEL). Further, many of the binary coded ASCII coded input characters represented numbers that had to be encoded in a pure binary form before they could be processed either by some of the programs devised in our laboratory or by the mathematical subroutine library provided by the computer manufacturer. Programs had to be developed that converted ASCII coded numbers to their equivalent binary codes (BCDBN2) and *vice versa*

(BNBCD2). Use of the manufacturer's mathematical library required additional amounts of preliminary processing. For example, the double precision fixed point (two computer word) binary numbers resulting from the execution of BCDBN2 were not in the format required by the manufacturer's library. Those subroutines require a normalized triple computer word floating point format. Routines called SCISTB and SCISTR were developed to allow us to convert back and forth between these two formats. The use of our special TV display also required an input-output handling system. TIOP was our television input-output package, standardizing all instructions with mnemonics as well as setting up certain standard functions (such as "print out a whole line") that could be called with a single instruction. RETVS was another subroutine that used TIOP to access an entire string of characters from the television keyboard. A special set of subroutines (SSRE) had to be developed simply to store strings of symbols and operators in specially designed tables. Blocks could be located, stored, and deleted from the string storage area by a system of string addresses and element numbers. The major storage area for this system of strings was accessed via an intermediary string address table.

In addition to the items mentioned above, a large number of other minor functions had to be programmed. EQTE changed equations (a string containing an equal sign) to expressions (a string not containing an equal sign); MATCH searched out a specific item in a table or determined that the element or sub-string was not in the table. MB moved a block of core memory backward or forward; and NCHK determined whether an ASCII character was a numerical digit or an alphabetic character. This list, though not complete, helps to define the magnitude of the task upon which we had embarked. These housekeeping functions are mentioned not to describe any novel approach or to present a usable algorithm, but rather to indicate the importance that housekeeping problems have assumed in our first year of work on this project.

Another useful housekeeping subroutine of particular importance is our equivalent expression checker (EECHK). It is a very difficult task to determine rigorously the equivalence of two algebraic expressions in a general way. However, the teaching procedure that we are using is not intended to be a rigorous and formal procedure, but a practical and effective one. Therefore, by ignoring certain criteria for rigor, we have been able to develop a subroutine that successfully distinguishes between equivalent and nonequivalent algebraic forms most of the time. This routine, called EECHK, can be fooled, but hopefully infrequently enough so that no serious damage will be done in our tutorial environment.

EECHK declares two expressions algebraically equivalent if the two functions are numerically equal for two different randomly selected sets of values for the variable. It evaluates the functions in the following manner: for each symbol in the symbol table, EECHK randomly generates an integer value between -5 and 5 and then determines if the numerical difference between the two functions is less than some arbitrarily small number. If it is not, EECHK declares the two expressions to be nonequivalent. If it is, EECHK generates a second set of random values and again determines if the numerical difference is less than that small number. If it is, EECHK declares the two expressions to be equivalent. (EECHK also determines if an expression is equivalent to the negative of the other by changing the sign of the value of one of the functions before testing for numerical equality.) Subsequent experiences will tell us whether this dual check is sufficient or whether it is necessary to use a more thorough testing procedure. Some routine checks for trivial cases have also been built into EECHK, and other checks are found in the mathematical subroutines that are called by EECHK itself.

EECHK and advanced versions of it will allow us to track a student step-by-step through a literal derivation, determining at each step whether his algebra has been correct. This should prove to be extremely important. It will also allow us to determine if the answer to a question requiring the student to respond with an algebraic expression is acceptable. Although there exist standard forms for all analytical geometrical expressions, not all answers should be expected to be in the standard form and EECHK will allow us to accept unstandardized, yet correct answers.

THE EXECUTIVE—*DEAN*

The most important housekeeping program of all is the executive system, which organizes the calls to the family of tutorial subroutines. As described above, our system generally operates by calling a sequence of subroutines, one after another, to perform specific functions. The logic involved in the determination of what that sequence is to be, and the mechanics of loading and linking those subroutines are the major responsibilities of the executive. We have named the executive DEAN after a suggestion made almost 10 yr ago by Mrs. Lenore Selfridge, one of the creative pioneers in the development of special programming systems for computer assisted instruction.

The package of programs that makes up DEAN performs many functions. Since the core memory capacity of the computer we are using is relatively modest, a system for swapping the contents of this high-speed memory with specified blocks of our bulk memory had to be developed. Each time a new tutorial subroutine is loaded into core from the bulk storage, the new material overlays the previous core load. An area of memory, therefore, had to be reserved and protected to communicate between sequential core loads. For example, the problem generator must necessarily leave some information behind when it is over-written so that the diagnostician subsequently loaded will be able to determine the current status of the program.

Simply loading the various programs as needed was a complicated job. Programs translated from source code to object code by the PDP-9 assembler are in a convenient relocatable form and thus can be placed in any available blocks of core memory locations. This means, however, that when relocatable programs are loaded, a certain amount of processing is necessary to make final address assignments throughout the program. Furthermore, loaded programs themselves, by defining external subroutines (globals) can automatically call these globals from the various user and system libraries and link them with the original programs. Our job in developing a program to load our programs (LOAD) was greatly simplified, however, by using a modified form of the linking loader program supplied by the manufacturer. Many of the functions of the manufacturer's systems loader were dropped and the program was altered to turn control over to the program just called in a way somewhat different than that usually used.

Another important loading function was specified by certain features of our system (described below) that allowed the student to break away on demand from the ongoing tutorial dialogue for certain kinds of assistance. In the event of a student-originated interrupt, the entire portion of the memory associated with the ongoing operation had to be saved. This was done by loading the entire program into a block of bulk storage. When the student exited from the utility routine, this entire block of information was read back into the computer's high-speed core memory and the tutorial conversation continued from the point at which it had been interrupted. SAVEM was the name of the program responsible for the storing and restoration of the core memory load.

The problem of transferring control from one program to another turned out to be also relatively complicated. The processes of communication, linking, and initializing the various programs as a student passed from one stage to another required the combined operation of several utility programs. NORMAL processed the more usual kind of return to the executive and was the subroutine in which many of the decisions defining the tutorial sequence were actually embodied. NORMAL kept track of which stage of the tutorial system had been operating and on the basis of this information and the final status of the current program, could decide where it was to go next. For example, if a problem generated by the problem generation routines had been answered incorrectly, NORMAL would select as the next tutorial program to be loaded, the master diagnostic routine that is responsible for finding out why the student made that error.

BRAKIN was a special subroutine designed specifically to handle the calls to the utility routines requested by the student, and certain additional requests such as QUIT, which terminated the student's activities for the day, or STOP, which terminated the use of the calculator or plotting utility routines.

Another important function of the package of subroutines that we have collectively called DEAN was the maintenance of student records. In preliminary stages of development, a student's records were simple, consisting of only one computer word containing a binary number indicating his position in the curriculum. SETUP was a program designed to handle student identifications. Depending upon whether the student was new or old, SETUP would either set up a new student record word or determine the status of the old student from his existing record word. When a student typed QUIT on the keyboard, another program (WRAPUP) signed him off and updated his record word.

The responsibilities of DEAN are certain to change as our system develops, but the programs mentioned do illustrate the type of functions that have to be handled and, most importantly, the ways in which some of the more subtle aspects of the decision logic underlying the tutorial sequence are embedded in our programming system. Figure 4 a flow chart of NORMAL, is particularly instructive in this regard, for it embodies very explicitly the overall sequence of an important part of our model of the tutor. On the other hand, it should also

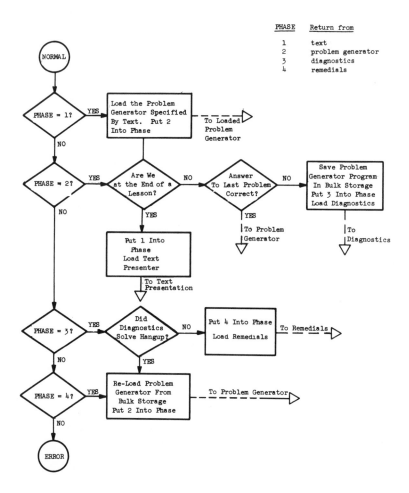

Figure 4. A flow chart of the dispatching routine, NORMAL, which maintains continuity as the system sequences from one generative program to another.

be noted that many of the programs we have so briefly mentioned are really manifestations of the computer configuration we use and are not essential to our argument that generative tutoring can be accomplished or to our specific model of the tutor. The various loading, linking, and communication routines all fall into this category and are merely reflections of the fact that our core memory simply was not large enough to contain all of the important programs at one time. If it had been, or if we had been time sharing this system among many users, a substantially different organization for DEAN would have been required.

DEAN was also responsible for coordinating the presentation of new text information, using the CCI television display.[2] The television display of text was chosen after consideration of other possible alternatives, including some sort of loose-leaf text book so that pages could be changed easily as our procedures improved. Such a book would have had two advantages. First, books allow the reader to skip ahead or go back as he chooses; second, loose-leaf books in particular, are not rigid documents and can be altered as needed. Both of these advantages were achievable, however, with the TV display. Students could be given control over the display so that they could back up or advance a specified number of paragraphs. Text information was stored on eraseable and updatable magnetic tape. In early stages of program development this a particularly useful and important feature.

There were, furthermore, other advantages to be gained from the use of the dynamic TV, which the more static book could not offer. Text presentations could be interrupted with calls to plotting routines, so that the student could explore the effects of changing a particular parameter almost as soon as it was defined. Questions could be asked, periodically to control reading comprehension as the student progressed through the text. In this way, attention was guaranteed and at least a first level of understanding of the newly presented material could also be depended upon. The algebraic format used by the TV text was similar to that used by the tutorial routines. This point may seem trivial, but since the TV display used did not have lower-case characters or half lines for super- or subscription, the formats in which information was presented took a little "getting used to". A different, even if superior format in a printed text would not have alleviated but rather would have compounded this difficulty. Figure 5 is a photograph of a typical "frame" of text as it is presented to the student on the TV. DEAN also allowed the student to call back previous text material for review at some later time. In the near future we hope also to have an automated dictionary available for call.

With this introduction to the general housekeeping details, we now can consider the type of algorithms designed for problem generation.

[2] We use the word television here, rather than the more technically appropriate term Cathode Ray Tube, for the simple reason that the display used in this commercially available system is, in fact, a standard and very inexpensive television unit. Its raster circuitry is used rather than point-by-point digital control, for character and figure placement, achieving a remarkable degree of power at modest cost.

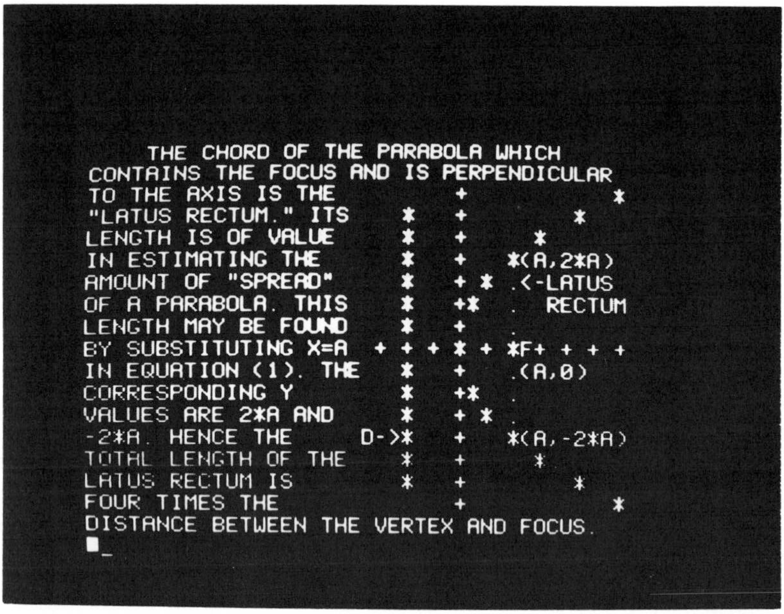

```
THE CHORD OF THE PARABOLA WHICH
CONTAINS THE FOCUS AND IS PERPENDICULAR
TO THE AXIS IS THE         +         *
"LATUS RECTUM." ITS     *  +      *
LENGTH IS OF VALUE      *  +     *
IN ESTIMATING THE       *  +    *(A,2*A)
AMOUNT OF "SPREAD"      *  + *  .<-LATUS
OF A PARABOLA. THIS     *  +*   .  RECTUM
LENGTH MAY BE FOUND     *  +    .
BY SUBSTITUTING X=A  + + + * + *F+ + + +
IN EQUATION (1). THE    *  +    .(A,0)
CORRESPONDING Y         *  +*   .
VALUES ARE 2*A AND      *  + *  .
-2*A. HENCE THE     D->*  +   *(A,-2*A)
TOTAL LENGTH OF THE     *  +    *
LATUS RECTUM IS         *  +      *
FOUR TIMES THE             +        *
DISTANCE BETWEEN THE VERTEX AND FOCUS.
_
```

Figure 5. A typical frame of text as presented on the television display. The graph presented in this figure does not use the same general purpose plotting procedure described in this chapter, but the student could call that general routine (PLOT) at this or any other time, and observe the effects of changing a given parameter on a family of curves.

PROBLEM GENERATION

As one glances through a text of analytical geometry, it is obvious that it is possible to classify the kinds of questions that are asked into a limited number of categories. Each category includes a set of questions of the same general format but different from instance to instance with regard to the specific constants or the particular type of conic section under consideration. The following list, while not complete, does include a surprisingly large number of the questions that might be asked in this restricted subject matter:

   a. Find the distance between two points along a curve.
   b. Draw a graph.
   c. Find the critical characteristics of a given curve, such as slope, directrix, foci, intercepts, etc.
   d. Find a missing coordinate, given other coordinates and a specific type of curve.
   e. Does a given figure fit a given algebraic expression?
   f. Given a figure, find an equation.
   g. Does a given point fall on a given curve?

  h. Given standard characteristics, give the equation.
  i. Derive one equation from another.
  j. Simplify, rotate and otherwise transform equations.
  k. Use and understanding of the cartesian coordinate system.

The only problem category that is not easy to implement on our computer configuration is b—draw a graph. We have therefore excluded this category and substituted some simple problem types that ask, for example, for the y coordinate given the x coordinate.

We have developed a set of programs, called by the generic name of PROGEN (problem generators), that can produce problems involving any of the conic sections that make up the realm of analytical geometry. These routines work, in general, by random generation of coefficients and constants to fill in various values in the general quadratic equation representing the conic sections:

$$AX^2 + BY^2 + CX + DY + E = 0^3$$

By setting various coefficients to zero and randomly selecting the others, a large family of specific conic sections can be produced. In fact, the family of expressions so produced can be virtually infinite. Not only can purely random expressions be produced, but it is possible to graduate the degree of difficulty of the expressions by constraining the random selection procedures in one way or another.

To illustrate several of these points, consider that a need has been established for expressions representing circles at a certain stage of the curriculum. In order to generate an expression for any conic, the random number generator must fill in certain of the coefficients of the general quadratic as indicated above. To make the resulting expression specifically into a circle, for example, the coefficients A and B must be equal, *i.e.*;

$$AX^2 + AY^2 + CX + DY + E = 0$$

To understand the further limitations that have to be placed on the coefficients to specify circles of specific degrees of complexity, it is desirable that we convert this general equation into a different standard form. Moving the constant term to the right side of the equal sign and factoring out the A gives:

$$A(X^2 + \frac{C}{A}X) + A(Y^2 + \frac{D}{A}Y) = -E$$

---

[3] Actually the fully general quadratic expression is $AX^2 + BXY + CY^2 + DX + EY + F = 0$, *i.e.*, it contains a cross-product term of X and Y. We have ignored this possibility in most of our subroutines at this stage. The effect of a non-zero XY term would be to rotate the particular conic about its center. At some later time we may generalize our presentation with no great difficulty, to include this aspect of the quadratic.

Dividing by A and completing the square gives:

$$\left[X^2 + \frac{C}{A}X + (\frac{C}{2A})^2\right] + \left[Y^2 + \frac{D}{A}Y + (\frac{D}{2A})^2\right] = \frac{-E}{A} + (\frac{C}{2A})^2 + (\frac{D}{2A})^2$$

$$(X + \frac{C}{2A})^2 + (Y + \frac{D}{2A})^2 = \frac{-E}{A} + (\frac{C}{2A})^2 + (\frac{D}{2A})^2$$

This equation is now in the standard form for the circle:

$$(X - p)^2 + (Y - q)^2 = r^2$$

where (p,q) is the point of origin and r is the radius of the circle. Thus, the origin of our generalized circle is:

$$(\frac{-C}{2A}, \frac{-D}{2A})$$

and the radius is:

$$\sqrt{\frac{-E}{A} + (\frac{C}{2A})^2 + (\frac{D}{2A})^2}$$

So if the circle is to be centered at (0,0), then the following must hold: $\frac{-C}{2A} = 0$ and $\frac{-D}{2A} = 0$, implying $C = D = 0$. Furthermore, with $C = D = 0$, the limitation $\frac{-E}{A} > 0$ (i.e., E and A must have different signs) is necessary in order for the radius term to have a solution, since we cannot take the square root of a negative number.

In all of the routines that generate expressions representing conics, we designed three clearly defined levels of difficulty. In the present example, the expression generator for the circle, three levels of difficulty were defined in the following way: Level One, the "easiest", circles were all expressions of the form:

$$X^2 + Y^2 = r^2$$

Thus, $A = B = 1$, $C = D = 0$. Furthermore, r was constrained by the use of RIBEL, to lie within a range varying from 10 to 36. For Level Two, the intermediate level of circle difficulty, A could have some value between 1 and 5 and r could vary between 22.6 and a number a little over 39.[4] The equation of a circle of difficulty Level Two was therefore, of the following form:

$$AX^2 + AY^2 = r^2$$

[4] The magnitude of these numbers had no special significance other than our attempt to scale the circles so that they looked "good" to the student.

Both Level One and Level Two are, therefore, circles centered at the origin of our axis system. The third level of difficulty introduced the additional complication of circles that were not necessarily centered at the origin. Their general form was, therefore:

$$AX^2 + AY^2 + CX + DY = -E$$

Limitations were placed on the choice of C, D, and $-E$ so that the expression would factor easily for the student. To do this, we constrained $C = 2AC_1$, $D = 2AD_1$, and $+E = AC_1{}^2 + AD_1{}^2 - MA$, where C_1, D_1, and M were random numbers generated by RIBEL. These values will allow the general form to be factorable into the form:

$$(X + C_1)^2 + (Y + D_1)^2 = M$$

To constrain further the size and placement of the circle, only coefficients with the following limits were allowed:

$$1 \leqslant A \leqslant 5, -15 \leqslant C_1 \leqslant 15, -15 \leqslant D_1 \leqslant 15, 100 \leqslant M \leqslant 728.$$

The following equations are samples for circles of varying levels of difficulty generated by the PROGEN routines:

Level One:	$X^2 + Y^2 = 1024$
	$X^2 + Y^2 = 324$
Level Two:	$2X^2 + 2Y^2 = 910$
	$5X^2 + 5Y^2 = 576$
Level Three:	$3X^2 + 3Y^2 - 24X + 90Y = 780.$

Similar techniques were applied to the other conic forms to produce graduated levels of difficulty for lines, ellipses, parabolae, and hyperbolae. Expressions so generated could be used in many different ways. One routine asked the student to determine whether or not a given point was on the generated curve.

Once a problem had been generated, however, it was necessary to know the answer to that problem. Producing general problem solving routines is, of course, a programming task of great complexity. But once again, within the practical context of our tutorial environment, considerable progress can be attained with simple expedients.

For example, we have a useful problem solving routine of modest complexity called EVAL. EVAL substitutes the values of a given X and Y coordinate into any algebraic equation and determines whether or not the equation is satisfied. This general purpose routine can thus be used in conjunction with some of the problem generation routines described above, to generate automatically the answer to a problem that has been asked of the student. For example, to determine if a randomly generated point (X,Y) falls on the locus represented by a generated equation, EVAL carries out the substitutions and arithmetic to see if the equation is satisfied.

Other more specialized answer generators were also programmed to work in conjunction with specific problem generators. In some cases, the expression generators above might themselves be considered to also be answer generators. For example, a question asking for the equation of a circle centered at the origin with a radius r would have as its answer an expression of the form described above.

Once a problem has been generated and the answer to it calculated, the executive DEAN is in a position to present the problem to the student and accept his answer. Once the answer from the student is accepted, it can be compared directly with the generated answer. If the answer is itself an expression, EECHK, the equivalent expression checker, could be used to determine if it is an equivalent form of the correct answer. A failure to match within certain limits of decimal accuracy (also a parameter specifiable in advance) would define an error. Once an error is defined, the diagnostic routines described in the following section would be called by the executive DEAN to identify the specific cause.

THE DIAGNOSTIC PACKAGE

Diagnostic dialogues to determine the kind and source of student errors, can also be produced by generative algorithms. In the following section we shall concentrate on one such generative diagnostic routine (BBTP), which illustrates this point. BBTP is a general purpose algorithm for tracing algebraic and arithmetic errors committed during the evaluation of an algebraic expression. BBTP operates as a *binary branching tree partitioner* or segmenter to decompose sequentially an expression into subproblems. Each subproblem is presented to the student until a specific location of the error is determined. This technique had originally been suggested by several people in the last decade, but, like so many other good ideas, it was not possible to apply it generally in the selective mode of computer assisted instruction. Each and every possible program that might have had to be segmented would have required advance scripting of all possible dialogue. The labor of prescripting these materials and the amount of storage required would have been astronomical. As an alternative but equally undesirable compromise, the number of problems so segmented would have had to be kept very small. For these reasons, the automatic segmentation techniques were vital if this promising and interesting diagnostic technique was to be used in the CAI environment.

What is binary tree partitioning or segmentation? It is the process the human tutor uses when he wants to locate an error in a calculation. It is the functional embodiment of the statement: "Now let's go through this together." Consider that a student had been asked to evaluate the simple expression[5]:

$$(A + (B * C))/(3 + (D - A)^2)$$

and had given an incorrect answer. BBTP would dissect this expression into component parts until an error was identified. The student might first be presented with the left side of the expression:

$$A + (B * C).$$

If he correctly provided the answer to that portion of the problem, the partitioner would go to the other branch and present:

$$3 + (D - A)^2.$$

If that part were incorrectly answered, the partitioner would break it down into its components and separately present:

$$(D - A)^2 \text{ or } D - A \text{ or even } D$$

until a discrepancy was found indicating that the student did not have the correct value assigned to a symbol, did not know how to square a term, or was not combining the parts correctly because of an arithmetic error. Figure 6 shows the full branching tree for this expression with all possible subdivisions indicated.

BBTP is designed so that as errors are made, the errors guide the descent into the branching tree. As the student provides correct answers, BBTP begins to recompose the parts of the expression in sequential recombinations until the initial expression is once again presented in its entirety. If an error is made at any stage, BBTP will reverse its direction and start down the tree again. In this fashion, BBTP is able to pinpoint the locus of specific deficiencies and guide the student step-by-step through the evaluation of a specific formula. But it is, we believe, only the first of a necessary family of diagnostic routines that will handle the general problems of error detection and correction. Other planned generative diagnostics will perform such functions as carrying on an interrogative conversation with the student to make him identify his own deficiency in a case in which strategy is more important than mechanics.

The important fact is that BBTP is a general algorithm that can perform this same function for all algebraic expressions and thus is the equivalent of an enormous amount of preprogrammed material stored for selective operation.

Figure 7 (composed of several plates) is a sample program that shows an elaborate application of BBTP as it dissects a relatively complicated expression.

[5] * = multiply, / = divide

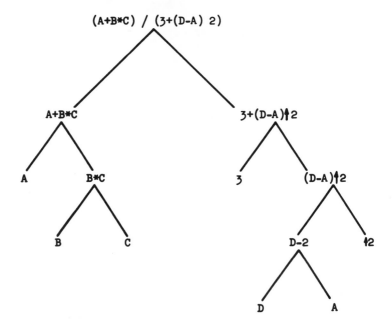

Figure 6. A full branching tree illustrating the way in which a typical expression is dissected by BBTP—the binary branching tree partitioner.

REMEDIAL TECHNIQUES

Once an error or deficiency has been diagnosed, some remedy must be applied to correct that deficiency in the student's repertoire of skills. At the time this chapter was being written, we had not yet prepared a specific set of remedial routines. It is clear, however, that the development of remedial techniques will be a process very similar to the development of the overall tutorial program itself, and that many of the subroutines developed for the main program will be directly transferable to the remedial section. Remediation, of course, is nothing more than tutoring on materials that are prerequisites for the current subject matter. Although some of this material may be in a far more fragmented form than the main curriculum material, we expect that there will be no major differences in the generative logics used in each case. We imagine that a course in algebra could be, in one sense, the first remedial block for our analytical geometry course, as well as being our next major curricular development item. From another point of view, there will, however, also necessarily be a need for briefer remedial routines to update the student on trigonometric functions, logarithms, and probably even arithmetic operations such as exponentiation. Previous experience unfortunately indicates that we also must plan for remedial drills in multiplication and division.

a

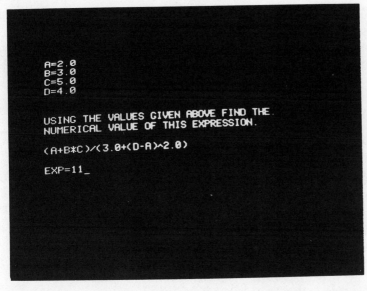

b

Figure 7. A series of photographs of the television display of the sequential parts of a BBTP process for a typical algebraic expression. In this sample display, some of the chatter (Wrong; Right) and answer stages are not shown. They would add little towards the solution of the major problem in a figure of this sort, *i.e.*, we are not able to demonstrate the dynamic action inherent in this tutorial conversation. (Nine frames, a — i.)

c

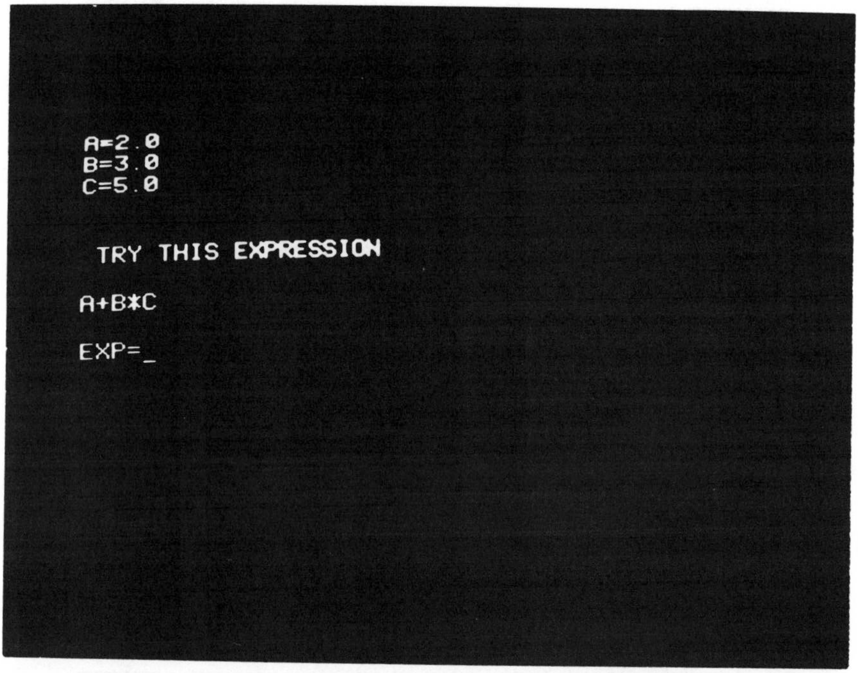

```
A=2.0
B=3.0
C=5.0

  TRY THIS EXPRESSION

A+B*C

EXP=_
```

d

```
    REALLY_
```

e

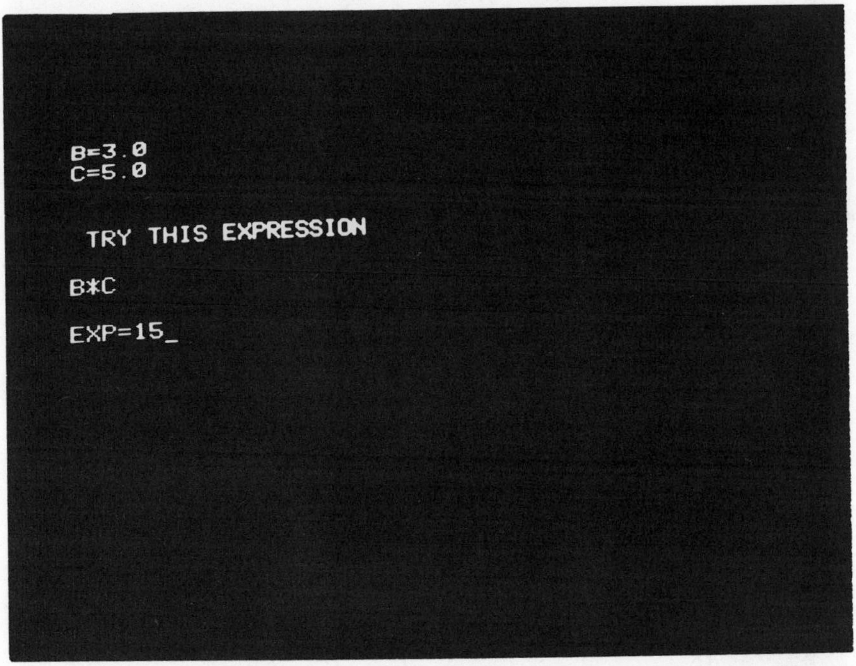

```
B=3.0
C=5.0

  TRY THIS EXPRESSION

B*C

EXP=15_
```

f

```
A=2.0
B=3.0
C=5.0

GOOD, TRY THIS ONE.

A+B*C

EXP=_
```

g

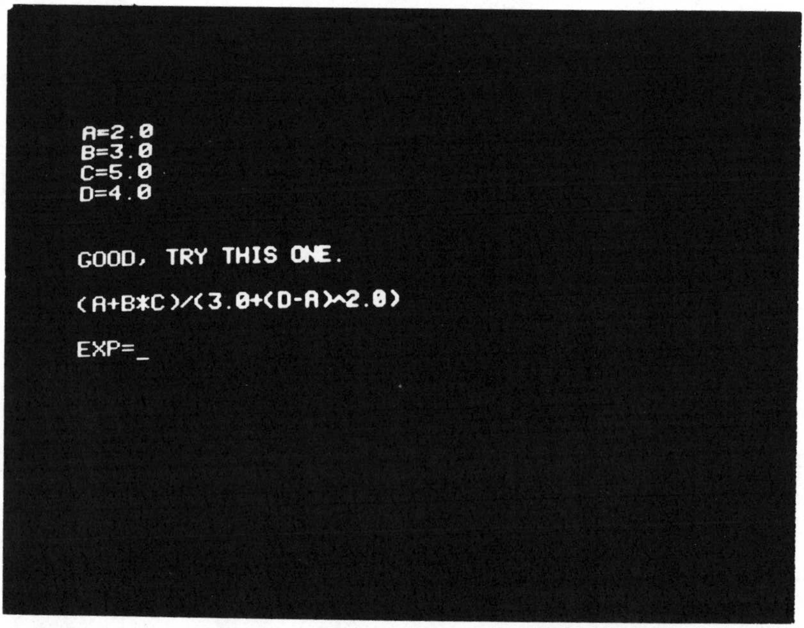

```
A=2.0
B=3.0
C=5.0
D=4.0

GOOD, TRY THIS ONE.

(A+B*C)/(3.0+(D-A)^2.0)

EXP=_
```

h

```
        INCORRECT_
```

i

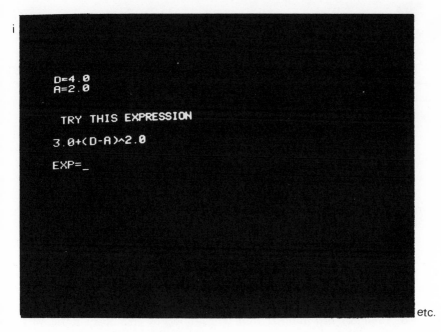

```
D=4.0
A=2.0

TRY THIS EXPRESSION

3.0+(D-A)^2.0

EXP=_
```

etc.

STUDENT-CALLED UTILITY ROUTINES

In addition to those generative routines that are specifically tutorial, a full simulation of the student-teacher interaction also requires that certain other types of utility functions be made available to the student. The availability of an arithmetic calculation aide (CALC), for example, has long been appreciated by students who would otherwise have to carry out long-hand calculations incidental to the main curricular thrust. Hand calculation is not itself an ignoble sport, but it is in the context of analytical geometry, calculus, algebra or any of the other substantive mathematical content matters, necessarily irrelevant and can be impeding. Similarily, the tedious plotting of each point on a graph is an interesting elementary exercise, but the routine mechanics of graph construction are not particularly germane even to analytical geometry, once one is aware of the specific strategy. A more fruitful expenditure of the student's energy would involve repeated observations of the specific effects of changing individual parameters on the shape of the curve. From our point of view, it is better to observe the effects of a single parameter on many different curves, than to spend one's time cranking out the individual points on a single curve. A graphical plotting routine (PLOT) was thus also made available to the student.

Many of the constituent parts of the program we call PLOT are generative subroutines themselves and can help to explain further what we mean by this term. PLOT was written as a subroutine in such a way that graphs could be plotted either by the student or as needed by the tutorial system.

PLOT is a general purpose graph plotter capable of handling the second-order (quadratic) equations of plane analytical geometry, as well as polynomials of higher order in X and Y. Equations may be entered into the PLOT routines using either one of two formats. The first format, Y = f(X), assumes equations that begin with "Y = " and contain no other variable other than X on the right-hand side of the equation. The general form used in the problem routines,

$$AX^2 + BY^2 + CX + DY + E = 0$$

can also be used as an input format. In fact, the plotting operations of PLOT are based upon the Y = f(x) format and all equations of the general quadratic form are converted to the Y = f(X) form by means of another program (PLOTIT) before being processed.

Points plotted on the TV screen are limited to rather narrow ranges because of the coarse grain of this display device. For the same reason, some special processing routines had to be developed that clean up the appearance of some of the graphs. For example, lines with slight slopes tend to appear like a shallow staircase rather than a monotonically increasing series of dots, because of the rounding error implicit in the coarse grain of the display. Therefore, to be plotted, a number had to differ from its neighbors by an amount sufficient to assure that it would not fall on the same level. Graphs therefore, tended to be composed of unequal distributions of dots depending upon the derivative of the function at any given point. Figure 8a shows the equation for a circle as it is typed in both of the acceptable formats, while Figure 8b shows the circle as it is plotted on the TV screen. This plotted figure shows some of the limitations of our current plotting scheme. This limitation is, of course, easily overcome by the technical expedient of using a somewhat differently organized visual display system.

CALC and PLOT are two of the major utility routines that have already been implemented in our system. The student calls them by typing the four-letter call words PLOT or CALC into the terminal keyboard at any point in the tutorial program. They are immediately trapped by the BREAK routine, and dispatched by BRAKIN. Other four-letter calls are planned that will operate in the same way to provide other utility functions to the student. Shortly, we expect to have completed a subroutine that will allow the student to call up any portion of the text at any time for review. It will be called by typing in the word TEXT. The call DICT is planned to allow the student to make contact with a dictionary of definitions. Finally, we expect that we shall also need to have a term like HELP, so that a student can ask for the human tutor to assist him in those situations in which no available subroutine can solve a human-generated difficulty.

Figure 8 (opposite). (a.) The equation for a circle as it is typed in either of the two proper formats for PLOT. (b.) The circle represented by the expression(s) in a.

CONCLUSION

In the preceding sections of this chapter we have presented a progress report on our development of a generative computer-assisted instruction system for tutoring students in analytical geometry. We have tried to emphasize, by example, the novelty of the generative approach in contrast with the more conventional selective computer teaching machine techniques. The main point to be made is that, for a number of reasons of practical applicability and logistics, the selective computer teaching machine has many of the same limitations possessed by a nonautomated teaching machine and few of the advantages of a talented human tutor. The result is that rather rigid and inflexible procedures have often tended to be ritualistically implemented in today's selective computer teaching machines. The computer, however, is a powerful tool, capable of far more than the simple dictionary or table scanning procedures characteristic of selective computer teaching machine operations. It is our thesis that a more effective and economical generative teaching system can be developed by establishing an explicit model of the human tutor who operates in a generative, algorithmic, or creative fashion, and then simulating these operations. Where some would use a dictionary, we would propose that a simulated cognitive process would be applicable. Where some would avoid errors because they cannot be handled, we believe that one's mistakes play an important role in the shaping of individual behavior. Where some would let the student's behavior be constrained by the limits of the computer's repertoire, we believe the notion of a generative computer environment adaptively responsive to the varieties of human personality is a realistic goal.

Yet all of this belief is without substance unless adequate demonstrations of the realized potential are given. It is for this reason that we have gone into considerable detail in discussing the operations performed by some of our generative algorithms. Substantial progress has been made in the housekeeping organization of a generative system, the development of problem generation systems, and the diagnostics. In summary, we are convinced that the notion of generative computer tutoring is a valid step forward for subject matters that have the degree of logical organization necessary for algorithmic evaluation.

REFERENCES

Bennett, J. H., W. B. Easton, J. R. Guard, and T. H. Mott, Jr., *Toward semi-automated mathematics: the language* and *logic of SAM III*. Princeton, N. J.: Applied Logic Corp., 1965.

Bitzer, D. L., Braunfeld, P. G., and Lichtenberger, W. W. Plato III: a multiple-student, computer-controlled, automatic teaching device. *In:* J. E. Coulsen, (Ed.) *Programmed learning and computer-based instruction.* New York: John Wiley, 1962. PP. 205–216.

Clapp, J. E. and Cain, D. A computer aid for symbolic mathematics. *In: AFIPS Conference Proceedings,* 24: Pp. 509–518. 1963 Fall Joint Computer Conference. Baltimore: Spartan Books, 1963.

Coulsen, J. E. (Ed.) *Programmed learning and computer-based instruction.* New York: John Wiley, 1962.

Coulsen, J. E. A computer-based laboratory for research and development in education. *In:* J. E. Coulsen, (Ed.) *Programmed learning and computer-based instruction.* New York: John Wiley, 1962. Pp. 191—204.

Culler, G. J. and Fried, B. D. The TRW two station, on line scientific computer: General description. *In:* M. Sass and W. D. Wilkinson, (Eds.) *Computer augmentation of human reasoning.* Washington, D.C.: Spartan Books, 1965.

Feingold, S. L. PLANIT—A flexible language designed for computer-human interaction. *AFIPS Conference Proceedings.* FJCC, 1967.

Licklider, J. R. C. Preliminary experiments in computer-aided teaching. *In:* J. E. Coulsen (Ed.) *Programmed learning and computer-based instruction.* New York: John Wiley, 1962. Pp. 217—239.

Rath, G. J., Anderson, N. S., and Brainerd, R. C. The IBM research center teaching machine project. *In:* E. Galanter, *Automatic teaching: the state of the art.* New York: John Wiley, 1959. Pp. 117—130.

Stowe, A. N., Wiesen, R. A., Yntema, D., and Forgie, J. W. The Lincoln Reckoner: An operation oriented facility with distributed control. *Proceedings of Fall Joint Computer Conference,* 1966, *29,* 433—444.

Uhr, L. E. The compilation of natural language text into teaching machine programs. *AFIPS Conference Proceedings of the FJCC,* 26, 1964.

Uhr, L. E. Toward the compilation of books into teaching machine programs. *IEEE Transactions on Human Factors in Electronics,* 1967, *8,* 81—84.

Uttal, W. R. On conversational interaction. *In:* J. E. Coulsen, (Ed.) *Programmed learning and computer-based instruction.* New York: John Wiley, 1962. Pp. 171—190.

Uttal, W. R. *Real-time computers: technique and applications in the psychological sciences.* New York: Harper and Row, 1968.

Weizenbaum, J. ELIZA—A computer program for the study of natural language communication between man and machine. *Communication of Association of Computing Machinery.* 1966, *9,* 36—45.

Zinn, K. Computer technology for teaching and research on instruction. *Review of Educational Research,* 1967, *37,* 618—634.

CHAPTER TEN

COMPUTER-AIDED QUANTITATIVE NEUROANATOMY[1]

PAUL D. COLEMAN, MARK J. WEST,
and URS R. WYSS

The University of Rochester
and University of Zurich

[1] Aided by Grant NS 07870 from the National Institute of Neurological Diseases and Stroke, Grant 3.133.69 from the Swiss National Foundation for Scientific Research and by funds from the Faigel Leah Foundation. The authors are indebted to W. Simon, Division of Biomathematics, L. Siegel, Behavioral Biology Laboratory and Conrad Stenton, Institute of Optics, University of Rochester, for help and advice.

The system described here has been developed in a neuro-biological laboratory over a period of approximately five years. Our uses started with relatively simple neurophysiologically oriented programs involving the derivation of sets of average evoked responses or peristimulus time histograms of single-unit activity obtained in response to auditory stimuli whose parameters were randomly varied under computer control. Over the years, the program library and hardware have expanded to include an extensive system for analysis of single and multi-unit spike trains, and a system for the measurement and analysis of certain types of microscope slides, electron microscope plates, and other biological images. Since these latter uses are relatively unique, the material presented here deals with these image-processing applications.

A need for reliable quantitative data on the structure of the nervous system is increasingly evident. The dynamic aspects of growth and the topological and quantitative treatment of the complex interweaving of nerve cell processes aimed at understanding neuronal information processing are of significant current interest. Instrumentation is a severe limitation to the amount of quantitative morphologic data that can be gathered within a reasonable time. The analysis of morphologic structures by visual inspection of microscopic preparations and by measurements taken with respect to a reference graticule is very cumbersome and yields results with tenuous statistics. To relieve the morphologist of tedious routine tasks a variety of devices have been described, most of which use image magnification techniques to prevent eye fatigue, and either pure mechanical or electro-mechanical coordinate transducers to improve accuracy and to reduce the amount of counting and calculation. It has been our intention to develop a system that takes advantage of the facilities offered by a variety of small digital laboratory computers that in general do not provide extremely large fast direct-access memory. The flying spot scanner developed for this purpose is described here.

HARDWARE

The system originally consisted of a Digital Equipment Corporation PDP-5 computer with the standard options of ASR-33 Teletype, 137 A-D converter, and 34B oscilloscope display. To these were added, within a month, a four-channel input multiplexer, four-channel stimulus pulse generator (both built with standard DEC System Modules), and a standard DEC 370 light pen. At later times were added: interface for driving a stepping motor, a sample and hold amplifier, computer controlled (by means of a stepping switch) attenuators, level setting potentiometers, CRT intensify circuitry for independent control of the intensity of a number of oscilloscopes (all designed and built in our laboratories), and two standard addressable tape units.

The PDP-5 is a 12-bit word machine with 4K of core memory. Its general organization and instruction set are essentially the same as that of its successor

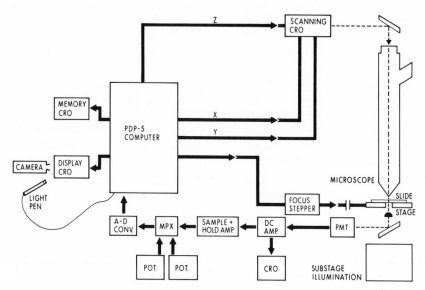

Figure 1. Block diagram of scanning system. X, Y deflection and intensification (Z) of the scanning cathode ray oscilloscope (CRO) are controlled by the PDP-5 computer. The light beam from the scanning CRO is deflected by a mirror to pass through the microscope optics in reverse direction. After passing through the slide to be scanned, light from the scanning beam is collected by the substage optics and reflected out of focus, onto a photomultiplier tube (PMT) by a mirror. This latter mirror may be moved out of the optical path to allow projection of the image on the slide onto the face of the scanning cathode ray tube utilizing the substage illumination. The electrical signal from the PMT passes through a dc amplifier, sample-and-hold amplifier, multiplexer (MPX), and analog-to-digital converter (A-D conv) to the PDP-5 computer.

PDP-8 minicomputers. Cycle time is 6 μsec, with three cycles required for the execution of most memory reference instructions. Thus, the add time is 18 μsec. Although this is significantly slower than the new minicomputers, it has been adequate for our applications in image processing and on-line analysis of extracellularly recorded spike trains. The core size of 4K in conjunction with magnetic tape has also been adequate for our spike train analyses, but has been a significant limitation in our image processing programs.

Of particular benefit in the use of this computer as a laboratory instrument has been the great ease of interface due to accessibility of output IOT pulses, memory buffer register, and accumulator output levels for control of external devices. Accumulator inputs and memory buffer inputs are also easily accessible for direct input to the computer, although most of our input is via the A-D converter. Other I/O control pulses, such as input-output skip and program interrupt, contribute to interfacing. We have found it convenient to bring 15 IOT pulse lines as well as accumulator input and output lines to an external patch panel for rapid connection to the computer of a variety of input-output devices. Analog inputs and outputs are also brought to patch panels. Figure 1 outlines the basic hardware configuration used in our image processing application.

The basic optical portions of the scanner consist of a scanning oscilloscope whose X,Y beam position and intensity are under computer control, a microscope, and a multiplier phototube (PMT). The light from the oscilloscope beam is reflected into a microscope eyepiece by the mirror indicated in Figure 1. After minification by reverse passage through the microscope optics, this light beam falls on the specimen on the slide. Alternately, for scanning electron microscope plates, the plate to be scanned can be placed directly in front of the scanning oscilloscope. After passing through the specimen or plate, the light is collected by the microscope substage optics and reflected, out of focus, to the PMT. The output of the PMT is amplified and input to the computer through appropriate interface. Dense portions of the slide or plate being scanning interrupt the passage of the scanning beam from oscilloscope to PMT, resulting in lower output voltage from the PMT.

The oscilloscope used for scanning is a standard Tektronix 503 oscilloscope with a cathode ray tube that has a P-16 phosphor. The P-16 phosphor light emission decays to 10% within 0.12 μsec, which makes it compatible with high-speed scanning. In the system described here the major limitation on resolution lies in the spot size of the scanning oscilloscope. Resolution is approximately four lines per millimeter, on an electron micrograph, and 160 lines per millimeter on a microscope slide when using a 22X oil objective. Objects smaller than this resolution can, of course, be detected, and in practice we have no trouble detecting the smallest neuronal processes (somewhat less than one micron) stained by the Golgi-Cox stain. Both resolution and minimum detectable objects are related to signal-to-noise ratio, which may be manipulated by averaging, as described below. They are also related to threshold of PMT voltages accepted as representing "signal" from material on a slide or plate, which is itself obviously also related to signal/noise ratio. These, as well as size and brightness of the scanning spot, interrelate in such a way that the statements about line pairs resolvable and minimum detectable represent not absolute limits, but limits that can be achieved with a reasonable degree of averaging and a reasonable threshold. The degree of apparent resolution "improvement" obtainable by these methods is very limited. Resolution could also be increased in the hardware by generating a smaller spot size. Commercial oscilloscopes are available at prices from $10,000 to $15,000 that generate quite small spots. Similar oscilloscopes may be constructed in the laboratory for approximately $5,000 exclusive of labor. It *may* be possible to decrease the apparent spot size of a standard oscilloscope by removing 60-cycle ripple from the deflection plates of the cathode ray tube itself. Vetter (1969) described a method of increasing resolution that would be useful in many applications. Image dissectors can also serve as useful input devices.

The microscope used in the system is a Leitz Orthoplan. This microscope was chosen because of its large field size, which could contain the whole dendritic extent of most neurons in a field at a magnification sufficient to accurately resolve a dendrite. With this microscope, we often find it useful to use oil-immersion objectives at powers of 22X and above to cut down light loss in the scanning beam at the slide surface that would occur at comparable magnifications with dry objectives. We also use a wide-field eyepiece to collect the light from the scanning oscilloscope whenever possible, not only for the wider field of view, but also for the greater amount of light it can collect. These steps to increase light reaching the PMT all increase the signal/noise ratio. One other strategem considered was the placing of a collector lens between the face of the cathode ray tube and the microscope eyepiece. It developed, however, that the distortions introduced by any reasonably priced lens of the necessary size rendered this step inadvisable.

The multiplier phototube used in the system is a classic 1P21. This tube has a spectral sensitivity closely matched to that emitted by the P16 phosphor of the scanning oscilloscope. Its signal/noise ratio (as well as other characteristics) is poorer than that of some of the more modern, more expensive phototubes. Improved performance could undoubtedly be obtained with a tube such as the RCA 8645.

The PMT output is amplified by a Tektronix 3A9 amplifier—a dc amplifier with low drift. The amplified PMT output is input to the computer through a sample-and-hold amplifier, an input multiplexer and A-D converter, as shown in Figure 1. The sample and hold amplifier is controlled by two IOT pulses. One IOT pulse ("sample" or "track") goes to one input of a flip-flop, setting the 0 output of the flip-flop to -3 v. This -3 v level on the control input of the sample and hold amplifier puts the amplifier in the sample (or track) mode. Another IOT pulse ("hold") sets the 0 output of the flip-flop to 0 v (after a short delay), which puts the sample and hold amplifier in the hold mode.

The input multiplexer consists of four single-pole solid-state switches that switch analog inputs to the A-D converter. One input is the amplified PMT output. Others are dc voltages controlled by the level-setting potentiometers. The closing of each of the four switches of the multiplexer requires the simultaneous appearance at an AND gate of: (1) a 5-mHz square wave and (2) a -3 v level on each of three control inputs. The 5-mHz square wave is derived from an internal clock. One -3-v control input is derived from a flip-flop whose output level is set at -3-v by a "select and enable" IOT pulse from the computer or at 0 v by a "clear and disable" IOT pulse from the computer. Another -3-v control input is derived from a quadruple flip-flop internally wired as a shift register, but also with provision for external read-in of ones. These four "ones" (one to each flip-flop) are taken from the accumulator output bus and are read in by "ANDing" these accumulator output levels with a read-in pulse, which is the "select and enable" IOT pulse. The last control input is always clamped at -3 v. Thus, any of the four inputs to the multiplexer may be enabled by a program that first sets one of four appropriate accumulator bits to 1 (usually done by adding a constant to a previously cleared accumulator) and then delivers the "select and enable" IOT pulse. Since the quadruple flip-flop is wired as a shift register, it is also possible to enable sequentially or step through the multiplexer inputs without setting accumulator bits by delivering a IOT pulse to the step input of the shift register.

Separate control of the intensification of a number of oscilloscopes is achieved by using a separate IOT pulse for each oscilloscope (or set of oscilloscopes) whose intensity is to be separately controlled. We generally control the intensification of the scanning oscilloscope separately from that of the display oscilloscopes (one memory oscilloscope, one short persistence phosphor oscilloscope for use with the light pen, and at times a long-persistence phosphor oscilloscope). The X, Y beam position of all oscilloscopes in the system is driven in common from the same pair of D-A converters without any necessity for buffer amplifiers between the D-A converter output and the oscilloscope terminals. Each separate intensify IOT pulse drives first a delay monostable multivibrator, whose pulse output drives another monostable multivibrator, whose level output controls an oscilloscope intensifier module. Setting the duration of the level output of the second multivibrator controls spot intensity.

The focus stepping motor is controlled by two IOT outputs: "forward" and "reverse." These IOT outputs are connected to a switch-tail ring counter and high-current driver module in standard form.

The level-setting potentiometers indicated in Figure 1 are 10,000 ohms. They have a zener stabilized voltage of 10 v across them. The voltage across the wiper arm can be input to the computer through one of the A-D channels.

Recently, the scanner has been moved to a DEC PDP-7. This machine is an 18-bit word machine with 8K of core. The cycle time is 1.75 μsec with an add time of 3.5 μsec. The PDP-7 contains an analog input section more complex than that of the PDP-5, with 64 channels of multiplexed analog input and an integral sample and hold amplifier. Moving the scanner to the PDP-7 was accomplished easily, requiring only that IOT pulses from the PDP-7 be brought to the focus stepping motor and oscilloscope intensify interface of the scanner. The sample and hold amplifier and associated control interface utilized with the PDP-5 were not necessary by virtue of the internal sample and hold on the PDP-7. The analog input could then be taken directly from the Tektronix amplifier into one of the multiplexed inputs of the PDP-7. For purposes of image processing programs, the 18-bit word and 8K core of the PDP-7 have represented a significant improvement over the 12-bit word and 4K core of the PDP-5. All desired information to specify one or a series of picture points can be packed into one word in ways to be outlined below. The 8K of core still cannot hold all the picture information in one microscope field, even in our most efficient programs, and requires resorting to swapping between tape and core in some picture processing programs. Another 4-8K of core would be useful.

SOFTWARE

In descriptions of programs below, most programs are presented as written for a 12-bit 4K machine. These are all relatively easily reprogrammed for a larger machine. Programs written for an 18-bit 8K machine require more extensive reprogramming for a 12-bit 4K machine both by virtue of the way in which information is packed into the 18-bit word and of the more limited number of words for storage of picture data.

The general goal of our programming activities is to develop a library of programs that will produce quantitative data from a wide variety of biological images with as little operator intervention as possible. Current development is revolving around quantification of dendritic fields in Golgi-Cox stained material and counting and sizing of synapses in electron microscope plates of tissue stained by the Aghajanian-Bloom technique (1967). The latter stain is selective for synaptic contacts. The Golgi preparations on which the analyses are carried out are 100-μ thick. Cell bodies and dendrites are stained selectively, with surrounding tissues unstained. About 2% of all neurons available are included in the staining process. Thus, the elective property of the Golgi-Cox method provides preparations that are not densely black, even if thick sections have been cut. The dendrites, the perikaryon, and sometimes the axon appear as a black-brown pattern on light background; branches out of focus are blurred. Since the dendrite system of one cell may have an extent up to 1 mm, there are limitations in completeness of scan of the dendrites of a single cell related to the thickness of the section and to the diameter of the microscope field. This latter limitation may be circumvented by means of a computer-controlled, motor-driven stage.

As a first approach to the classification of image processing programs, we may categorize programs as having either a predetermined fixed scan, or a scan that is interactive (or adaptive) with the material being scanned. A typical fixed, non-adaptive scan would be a raster, like a television scan, which proceeds to completion regardless of the information it produces and deposits image information (in the form of PMT output amplitude as a function of coordinate location) into computer memory for further processing. The fixed scan pattern need not, of course, be linear.

Examples of scans interactive with the material being scanned include line following, edge following, and focusing routines. Scans of this type can obviate the necessity of storing in core (and auxilliary storage) a complete representation of the image being scanned. One can, for example, extract desired summary information (such as length) during the course of a line following program by simply incrementing a "length" register as the line is followed. Coordinates of regions of special interest on the line may be stored and returned to later for further processing. In a sense, it is appropriate to say that the image being

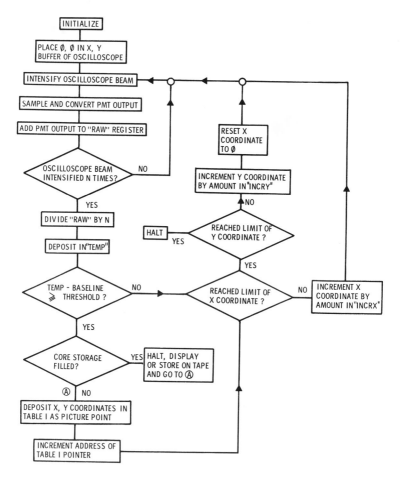

Figure 2. Algorithm for basic fixed scan with averaging and adjustable X and Y increments. See text for further explanation.

scanned serves as an auxillary memory. Our use of adaptive scans in measuring dendrites is covered in a later section.

FIXED SCAN PROGRAMS

A basic fixed scan program scans a field in a linear raster. An X, Y point is probed, and the magnitude of the PMT output is deposited in temporary storage. If the magnitude of PMT output exceeds a threshold amount, the current X, Y coordinates are stored. Whether or not threshold is exceeded, the X and Y coordinates are then incremented and the next point probed. This process is

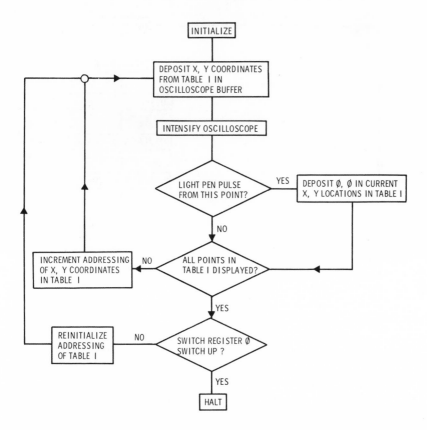

Figure 3. Algorithm for display of picture deposited in core by the scan of Figure 2. There is provision for operator "erasure" of unwanted points by means of a light pen. See text for further explanation.

repeated until the limits of X and Y are reached. It is convenient to have the limits of X and Y, as well as the magnitude of ΔX and ΔY, easily altered. An algorithm for this simple scan is shown in Figure 2.

When the specified field has been scanned (*i.e.*, X and Y have reached predetermined values) a picture display may be formed by intensifying the beam of the display oscilloscope at points whose coordinates were deposited in storage. It is also possible at this stage for the operator to pick points, by means of a light pen, for erasure or other manipulation. An algorithm for a display with erasure is shown in Figure 3.

Within the framework of this very simple program, a number of general problems emerge. These are: (1) the definition of threshold, (2) the definition of the baseline from which the threshold is taken, (3) the reduction of noise (both electronic and biological) and (4) packing as much required image data into core memory as possible.

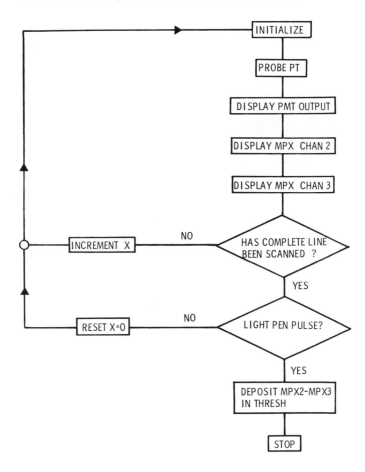

Figure 4. A. (above) Algorithm for setting baseline and threshold by means of operator adjustment of two potentiometers. The voltage drop across each of these two potentiometers is switched to the computer input via multiplexer (MPX) channels 2 and 3. Pt = Point on Scan pattern. See text for further explanation. B. (opposite) Effect of threshold on the picture stored. Scan is of a cell from a light microscope preparation of the cerebral cortex of a rat stained according to the Golgi-Cox Technique. As threshold moves closer to the baseline (top to bottom) out of focus elements start to appear, thinner or smaller elements also appear (*i.e.,* minimum detectable becomes smaller) and the line pairs resolvable per millimeter becomes smaller. Further change of threshold toward baseline than is illustrated here will result in the appearance of electrical noise as randomly placed dots in the picture. The bottom picture is "chopped off" at the bottom in comparison to

DEFINITION OF THRESHOLD

Definition of threshold is easily accomplished by a subroutine that scans one line of the field and presents the level of the PMT output on a display oscilloscope with position along the scan line represented as a time-varying

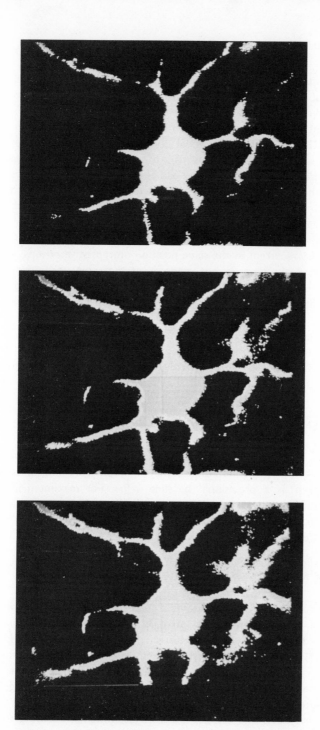

the other two pictures because the 8K core of the PDP-7 was filled before the complete field was scanned. The scan utilized to obtain these pictures was the maximally efficient one (in terms of core utilization) diagrammed in Figure 8.

function. Interlaced into this display of PMT output are two horizontal lines. The level of each of these is controlled by a level-setting potentiometer. The operator adjusts these two potentiometers so that one produces a horizontal line whose height corresponds to the baseline PMT output while the other produces a line whose height is above electrical noise but below signal peaks. When the operator is satisfied with the adjustment of the potentiometers, he may so signal to the computer by means of a light pen or console switches. The computer will then take the voltage difference represented by these two lines as threshhold. This adjustment of the potentiometers with respect to PMT output is easier if the computer scans one line of the image repetitively and presents a synchronous display of the PMT output. The operator can then define signal as PMT output peaks that are recurrent at the same position on repetitive sweeps, and noise as PMT output peaks that do not reappear at the same position on repetitive sweeps. An algorithm for this threshold program is shown in Figure 4A. An alternate method for definition of threshold that we have also used is to display immediately points exceeding a threshold set in the switch register. Repetitive sweeps of the field by the scanner as the operator manipulates the switch register shows the effect of various threshold settings on the definition of picture elements. The effect of alteration of threshold on the picture stored in the computer is illustrated in Figure 4B.

DEFINITION OF BASELINE

Baseline may be established more accurately by a small subroutine that pre-scans the image and determines the minimum PMT output voltage. This value is taken as a provisional baseline value. For maximum efficiency in detecting suprathreshold peaks of PMT output, this baseline value may be altered under program control to compensate for variations in background density and/or for vignetting.

REDUCTION OF NOISE

The reduction of noise represents a great deal of the programming effort in obtaining a clear representation of the image. Reduction of noise may be accomplished in several ways: (1) averaging, (2) integration, (3) neighbor analysis, and (4) operator erasure of noisy points, which is easily accomplished by means of a light pen. The first two methods are directed at reduction of electrical noise exclusively, which in our system originates largely in the photomultiplier tube. The latter two noise reduction methods are directed at both electrical noise and "noise" on the slide, which in our Golgi-Cox stained material consists of random, small deposits, *etc.*

Applying the usual process of averaging to image data simply involves repeated intensification of the beam of the scanning oscilloscope N times at any

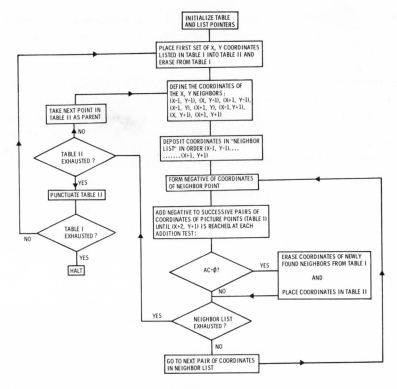

Figure 5. Algorithm for neighbor analysis. This algorithm separately examines each X, Y point in a picture. The neighbor analysis algorithm shown in Figure 13, in contrast, examines lines of picture elements.

given X, Y coordinate, converting N outputs from the PMT, summing these N values, and dividing by N. In practice, we find averaging about seven times represents a trade between time and noise reduction that gives a reasonably noise-free picture.

In addition, to or instead of, averaging (or summing) it is possible in a scanning application to reduce noise by the related process of integration.[2] This is accomplished by repeated intensification of the scanner beam at a constant X, Y location. We perform the integration by passing the amplified PMT output through a low-pass filter whose band pass is set to produce a time-constant approximating the time over which repeated intensifications of the scanning beam take place.

Once a picture has been obtained with the use of averaging and/or integrating, noise will still be present in the picture to some degree. Some of this noise can be eliminated by a neighbor analysis (Rosenfeld, 1969). This algorithm

---

[2] The use of integration was suggested by Dr. W. Simon.

asks of each point in the picture whether there exists a neighboring point that has been defined as a picture element (*i.e.*, has exceeded threshold). This query may be propagated through a set of connected elements to produce a definition of each picture element, which consists of a set of N "connected" points. The operator may define a size threshold for N; then any picture element in which N falls below the threshold N may be treated as noise and erased. With slight modification, one can utilize this algorithm to count the number of picture elements containing more than a threshold number of connected points, as described below in the section on analysis of electron micrographs. The basic principles involved in neighbor analysis may be discussed in relation to the simplified algorithm shown in Figure 5.

The neighbor analysis illustrated in Figure 5 utilizes the original orderly deposition of picture coordinate information into an area of storage that will be called Table 1. The nature of this orderliness is such that in the original scanning of the picture by a linear, TV-like scan, successive picture points encountered as X was incremented were deposited in successive locations in Table I. When X reached its limit, Y was incremented and X reset to 0 and once again incremented repetitively with picture points being deposited in Table I successively as they were encountered. The goal of the neighbor analysis is to reorganize the coordinate information in Table I so that points listed in Table I that are part of the same picture element are in successive locations in another region of memory that will be called Table II. The first point defined in Table I represents the lower, left-most picture element. The coordinates defining this point are used to define neighbors. Neighbors of this point are defined in the order in which they would be encountered in the linear scan: $(X-1, Y-1)$, $(X, Y-1)$, $(X+1, Y-1)$, $(X-1, Y)$, $(X+1, Y)$, $(X-1, Y+1)$, $(X, Y+1)$, $(X+1, Y+1)$. Negative numbers, as would be formed at a picture edge or corner are not allowed. These neighbor coordinates are deposited in a "neighbor list". The negative of the first pair of coordinates in the list is added to successive pairs of coordinates in Table I until $Y+1$, $X+2$ (the point at and beyond which points are no longer neighbors) is reached. If none of these comparisons produces a match, *i.e.*, if in no case is the sum zero, the next pair of coordinates in the "neighbor list" is similarly compared with coordinates in Table I. When a match between a pair of coordinates in the "neighbor list" is found with a pair of coordinates in Table I, the "neighbor" is added to Table II and erased from Table I. When all neighbors of the parent point have been found, each successive pair of coordinates in Table II is taken as a parent point and any new neighbors are added to Table II and erased from Table I. The process continues until all pairs of coordinates in Table II have been used as parent points and no more neighbors can be found. Table I is now exhausted of neighbors for the group in Table II, and Table II is punctuated, indicating the end of the coordinate list for one picture element. This punctuation may be accomplished in any convenient way.

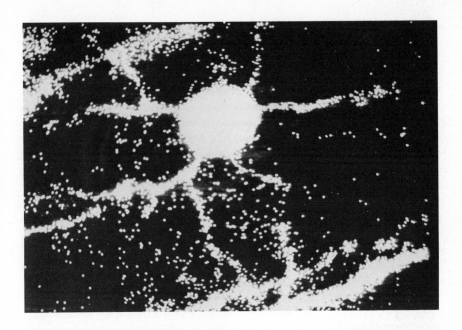

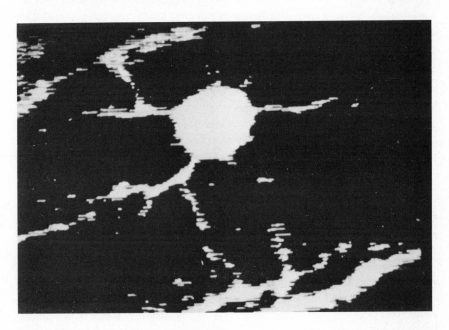

Figure 6. Elimination of noise by neighbor analysis from the data obtained from a scan of a cortical neuron of a rat stained according to the Golgi-Cox technique. It is apparent that portions of desired picture elements that are not solidly defined are also eliminated by this analysis. A method for dealing with this is suggested in the text.

The first remaining picture element in Table I now becomes the new parent point, which is inserted into Table II immediately after the punctuation mark, forming the origin of another neighbor hunt. This neighbor-hunt process is repeated until Table I is exhausted. Table II will then contain all points originally in Table I, but reorganized so that "connected" points are in successive locations in the table, separated from non-connected points by the punctuation marks. One can then to some degree eliminate noise from the picture data in Table II, by "erasing" any set of connected points that contains fewer than an operator-defined minimum number of points. One can also count the number of picture elements simply by counting punctuation marks. In addition, dimensions of picture elements and areas can be obtained. The results that can be obtained in the eliminating of noise by a neighbor analysis are illustrated in Figure 6. It is apparent that the noise-elimination program would be further improved by the addition of a distance routine that would accept as neighbors points that fell within a specified distance of each other, whether or not they were connected. Such a "distance routine" would save portions of dendrites currently eliminated in our analysis. Further details of the analysis of the picture data in Table II to obtain counts of picture elements, areas, *etc.*, are discussed below with reference to analysis of electron micrographs, as is also the adaptation of this algorithm for the class of alternate storage schemes that do not explicitly store all X, Y coordinates (described below).

PACKING IMAGE DATA INTO CORE MEMORY

The problem of packing as much required image data into core as possible derives from the fact that a reasonably complex picture cannot fit into the 4K of core available if one takes the simple and obvious approach of storing the X, Y coordinates of every picture point. In an 18-bit word machine, 9-bit X and Y coordinates may both be packed in one word. Overflow can, of course, be put on DEC tape but this is slow and somewhat inconvenient for refreshing a picture display, as well as for certain other manipulations that may require extensive swapping between tape and core, such as neighbor analysis. A disk would be more suitable for this purpose than tape.

Resolution, or the possible number of points in the picture grid (not necessarily the same depending on size of the scanning spot, quality of the optical system, *etc.*) is one of the basic factors in determining the storage requirements (the other being percentage of scanned area taken up by picture elements.) We have found the 9-bit specification of X and Y coordinates, which produces a 512- by 512-point picture grid yielding a scan containing 262,144 points to be more than ample for our purposes. With 9-bit coordinates, our resolution is still limited by the spot size on our scanning oscilloscope.

Given that storage of the X, Y coordinates of all suprathreshold picture points does not store sufficient picture information, other possibilities have been

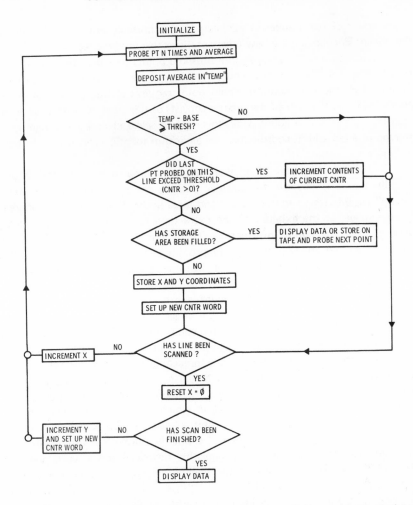

Figure 7. Algorithm for scan that does not explicitly store all X coordinates of picture elements. Leading edges of picture elements are defined with both X and Y coordinates and consecutive connected picture points along the X axis are counted. The termination of the count defines a trailing edge.

considered. Representation in core of PMT output of each point scanned as a 0 or 1, depending on whether PMT output at that point was above or below threshold (with no storage of coordinates *per se*), is obviously not feasible for a 262,144-point picture in a 4K 12-bit machine. Even an 8K 18-bit machine does not provide the memory capacity for this storage scheme.

Black and white picture data can be stored more efficiently in core by the use of coordinate storage algorithms that do not explicitly store the X and Y coordinates of all points. Assuming a linear, fixed scan, one storage algorithm stores the X and Y coordinates of the leading edge of a suprathreshold region and a count of the number of connected suprathreshold points on that line of the sweep. Encountering a new edge entails setting up three registers, an X, a Y, and a count register. Successive suprathreshold points are stored by incrementing the content of the current count register. Once a subthreshold point is encountered, the next suprathreshold point requires setting up new X, Y and count registers. If much of the picture consists of thin lines perpendicular to the scan that are only one count wide, this method is less advantageous than simple storage of all X and Y coordinates. An algorithm for this type of scan is shown in Figure 7.

If only nine bits of a 12-bit word are being used to specify either X or Y coordinates, it is possible to consider packing the count information in the "spare" six bits (three in the X word and three in the Y) for a one-third increase in core usage, at the expense of the extra time required for the packing and unpacking of the count information. The count is, in the case of a 12-bit machine, limited to 77_8 or 56_{10} (approximately 10% of the picture width) which may be too severe a limitation in some applications, such as displaying some cell bodies in our Golgi preparations. One can, of course, program so that in the event of overflow of the count another set of registers is set up to continue the count. In computers with a larger word length, such as the 18-bit PDP-7, eight bits may be allocated to the count, (yielding a limit of 377_8) in the algorithm described in the next paragraph. If 9-bit X and Y coordinates are both explicitly stored, as described in the preceding paragraph, 18 bits may be allocated to the count—nine from the X registers and nine from the Y register. This unnecessarily makes provision for a count greater than the picture width.

Still assuming a fixed linear scan, in which Y is always incremented by a fixed amount whenever X reaches its limit, all necessary black and white picture information can be stored without ever explicitly storing Y coordinates.[3]. This algorithm is related to the count algorithm described above, with one word devoted to the X coordinate of the leading edge of a picture element and another word containing a width count. With a longer word length it is possible to combine these two, X coordinate and width count, in one word. In addition, one bit may be used as a running Y coordinate status indicator. There is no Y register for each new picture point edge. The Y bit is set to one when the end of a line is reached, signifying that the Y coordinate buffer should be incremented. The efficiency of these "count" algorithms makes it unnecessary to consider representation of picture information by only the edges of the elements or differentiation of the picture.

An algorithm for this scan is shown in Figure 8 as it is programmed for a PDP-7. An exposition of the allotment of bits in the 18-bit PDP-7 word is basic to an understanding of this algorithm. The nine left bits of the 18-bit word specify the X coordinate. The next right bit is the running Y coordinate bit. It is set to one whenever the Y coordinate is to be incremented by one. If this bit is

---

[3] The basic algorithm for this was suggested by Dr. W. Simon.

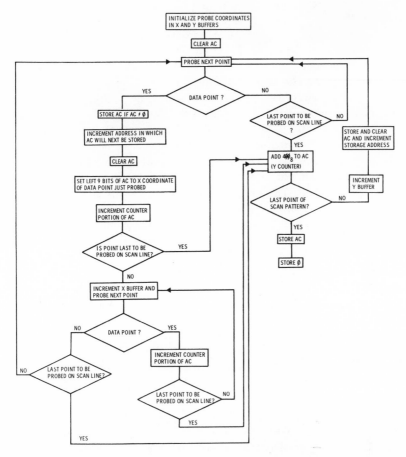

Figure 8. Algorithm for scan that does not explicitly store all X coordinates of picture elements, as the scan outlined in Figure 7. In addition, Y coordinates are never explicitly stored but are kept track of by means of a Y coordinate increment bit in each data word. X, Y and count information are all contained in one 18 bit word. (See text for discussion).

0, the Y coordinate in the scanning oscilloscope D-A buffer is not incremented. The next right eight bits are used to count the number of "connected" data points encountered at successive points along a line of the scan, in the same manner as was outlined for the "Counter" scan outlined in Figure 7. It is important to this program, as shown in Figure 8, that in the PDP-7, unlike the PDP-5, analog-to-digital conversion and manipulation of the scanning oscilloscope X and Y buffers are both accomplished without the accumulator. Thus, the scanning beam can be moved and analog data collected without disturbing the contents of the accumulator. In using computers without this feature, a register can be designated for the purposes that the AC serves in this algorithm. After setting the X, Y coordinates of the first point to be probed into the D-A buffers of the scanning oscilloscope, the accumulator is cleared and the point is probed. If the PMT output exceeds threshold, the point defined by the current X, Y coordinates is taken as a data point. The accumulator will already be zero when the first data point is encountered, and the left nine bits of the accumulator will then be loaded with the X coordinate of the point just probed. In addition, the accumulator will be incremented—*i.e.*, a count of one added to the right 8-bit count portion of the AC word.

Assuming the 9-bit X buffer of the D-A converter has not yet reached its limit of 777_8, the X buffer will be incremented and the next point on the line will be probed. If this too is a data point, the count portion of the AC word will again be incremented and, if the end of the line is not yet reached, the next point will be probed. The program will remain in this small loop, probing successive points on a line until (a) reaching the end of the line or (b) encountering a point that gave a PMT reading that failed to reach threshold. In this latter case, a trailing edge of a picture element has been defined. The contents of the accumulator now contain the X coordinate of the leading edge and the number of X increments to the trailing edge. The AC is not stored however until the leading edge of another object is encountered on the same scan line or until all of the points on the scan line have been probed. The delayed storage allows the "Y" bit to be set if the data word is the last object encountered on a scan line.

When the end of a line is reached, either on a data point or on a "no-data" point, 400_8 is added to the accumulator (*i.e.*, the running Y coordinate bit is set) and, assuming the last point of the scan pattern has not yet been reached, the first point on the next scan line is probed and the contents of the accumulator (as defined when the last point on the previous line was probed) with the Y bit set are stored. If the end of the line is reached on a "no-data" point, and data points have not been encountered, the accumulator is stored with contents equal to 000400_8. The contents of the accumulator are, then, stored whenever one of two conditions is met: (1) The leading edge of more than one object is encountered on a scan line, or (2) the scan reaches the end of a line. Each time the contents of the accumulator are stored, they are placed in the next location in a data storage area in core, thus building up a table, referred to as Table 1, that defines the picture scanned. The end of Table 1 is signified by depositing zero in the table when the last point of the scan pattern has been probed.

The display of picture information deposited in core in this manner is basically similar to the display of data derived from the counter scan whose algorithm is shown in Figure 7, with the display advancing through successive registers in Table I. The only difference is that the Y coordinate is started at 0 and incremented each time a word in Table I is encountered in which the running Y bit is set. When 0 is encountered in Table I, and X and Y buffers are reinitialized and the display restarted.

APPLICATIONS OF NON-ADAPTIVE SCANS

The computerized flying spot scanning device described above can easily be programmed using fixed scans to measure and count populations of structures on photographic plates and microscope slides. Some examples of possible applications include: counting and sizing synapses in electron micrographs of E-PTA (ethanolic phosphotungstic acid) stained nervous tissue, counting grains on autoradiographic preparations, counting degenerative terminals in Fink-Heimer material, counting and sizing cells and obtaining quantitative measurements of capillary networks in material injected with Microfil or similar material. The objects being quantified are required only to have sufficient contrast with the background to be detectable by the scanner on the basis of the amplitude of the PMT output.

The use of a fixed scan program in the development of quantitative data may be illustrated by our use of this system in determining the size and number of synapses in E-PTA (Aghajanian and Bloom, 1967) stained nervous tissue. The stained tissue is viewed in the electron microscope and electron micrographs are obtained by conventional means. We have found it advantageous to enhance the contrast of the electron micrographs by transferring them to a high-contrast graphic arts film. The high-contrast transparency is then positioned between the scanning beam and the photomultiplier tube by placing it against the face of the scanning scope.

We have used electron micrographs of E-PTA stained cortex taken at a magnification of 8000X. At this magnification, recognizable E-PTA stained profiles are about 1 to 3 mm across their longest axis. This dimension represents about 7 to 21 points in the scanning grid. At 8000X magnification, one seldom observes two synaptic contacts within 0.25 mm of another. Since the system is capable of resolving this distance, the vast majority of synaptic profiles in this preparation are easily resolved from one another at this low magnification. The data obtained from such a scan virtually fills its allocated 5K of core memory, and represents approximately 5% of the total number of points probed by the scanner.

The scanning is done according to the algorithm shown in Figure 8. On an electron micrograph, this scan covers approximately 50 square cm and is made up of a 512- by 512-point grid. Before one can store meaningful information about the picture, it is necessary to define what black and white are on the micrograph. This can be accomplished by running a small "threshold" program as described above, in which the computer displays immediately, without storage, picture points that exceed thresholds set in the switch register. By changing the switch settings, one effectively changes definition of black and white in the picture by changing the threshold of the data points. In this way,

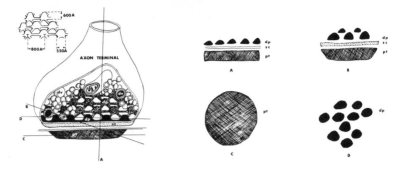

A. Three dimensional represention of a synaptic contact sectioned in four different planes.

cv = clear vesicles
dv = dense cone vesicles
dp = presynaptic dense projection
sc = synaptic cleft
pt = post synaptic thickening
(Adapted from Pfenninger et.al.1969)

B. Diagramatic representation of EPTA stained synaptic contacts as they appear in electronmicrographs when sectioned according to the above figure.

A. cross section
B. oblique section
C. tangential section through post synaptic thickening
D. tangential section through presynaptic dense projections

Figure 9. Diagrammatic reconstruction of a synaptic contact (left) with illustrations of the appearance of the synaptic region in electromicrographs of E-PTA stained material (right) when the synaptic contact is sectioned in the planes indicated on the reconstruction.

one is able to make a rapid visual evaluation of the picture information that will be stored when the same threshold is used during the data-storing scan (refer to Figure 4). The black or the white information from the full scan is stored according to the algorithm shown in Figure 8, in which part of the stored word contains the X coordinate of a data point, one bit is used in the running Y coordinate counter, and the remainder of the word is used as a counter that indicates the number of consecutive data points on the same line that start at the X value of the word.

The first phase of the analysis of the picture data consists of connecting data words on the same scan line that are less than a specified distance apart, *i.e.*, filling in small holes. In E-PTA stained material, this process effectively increases the contrast between objects and background even more, since before the connecting procedure many objects are made up of a number of separate but close data regions that are not always continuous with each other. For the analysis of E-PTA stained synaptic contacts, words within three scan points of another are connected. This distance is greater than the largest distance between data points within an object (*i.e.*, the distance between the edges of presynaptic dense projections or between pre- and post-synaptic elements of the same object), but less than the distance between the vast number of "synaptic contacts" in the preparation. The non-uniformity of the E-PTA synaptic contacts is dependent upon the plane of section of the tissue, as depicted in Figure 9a and b. After filling in the structures, the E-PTA profiles approximate a

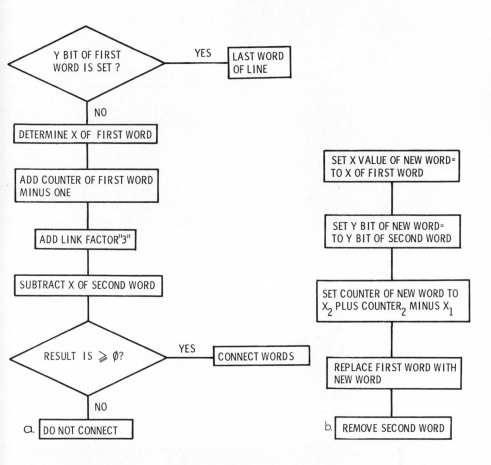

Figure 10. (a) Algorithm for determining if two "words" on the same line should be connected, (*i.e.*, represent parts of the same synaptic contact). The "link factor" is chosen so that it represents the maximum distance between components of the same synaptic contact (See Figure 9 and text). (b) Algorithm for connecting two data words on the same line that have been determined to be part of the same synaptic contact. This is accomplished by making one word from two. The X value of the new word is the same as that of the first word and the counter is equal to the sum of the count portions of the two words plus the count of blank points between the words.

disk shape cut at random angles, which as discussed further below, becomes important in the calculation of the number of structures per unit volume of tissue.

The logical steps in filling in the recorded picture of the E-PTA material are shown in the algorithm in Figures 10a and 10b, and the effect of this process is exemplified in Figure 11. If a positive number results when the X value of the second word is subtracted from the X value of the first word plus the counter of

MONITOR DISPLAY OF TABLE I
BEFORE FILLING IN

TABLE I BEFORE FILLING IN

Location	X	Y	Count	
1		1	000	blank
2	1	0	001	word 1
3	4	1	001	word 2
4	1	1	005	word 3
5		1	000	blank
6		1	000	blank
7		1	000	blank
8		1	000	blank
9		1	000	blank
10		1	000	blank
11		1	000	blank
12		0	000	end of scan

b. MONITOR DISPLAY OF TABLE I
AFTER FILLING IN

TABLE I AFTER FILLING IN

Location	X	Y	Count	
1		1	000	blank
2	1	1	004	word 1
3	1	1	005	word 2
4		1	000	blank
5		1	000	blank
6		1	000	blank
7		1	000	blank
8		1	000	blank
9		1	000	blank
10		1	000	blank
11		0	000	end of scan

c.

Figure 11. (a) Monitor display and Table I listing for a single object composed of three data words before the "filling in" process. Notice that words 1 and 2 are on the same line and closer than three blank "no data" points apart, which is the size of the "linkfactor" used in the algorithm in Figure 10a. (b) Monitor display and Table I listing after the object in 11a has been filled in according to the algorithm in Figure 10b. Notice that the object is now composed of only two words. Words 1 and 2 from Figure 11a have been replaced by one word, which represents the data points in the original words plus the gap between the components represented by the two words. (c) The effect of filling in spaces between components of the same synaptic contact. On the left is shown an electron micrograph of an E-PTA stained synaptic contact. In the center is shown a monitor display of the data gleaned from a scan of the micrograph before "filling in". On the right is a monitor display of data used to generate the center display but after words on the same line less than "Link factor" distance apart, have been "filled in".

402

a.

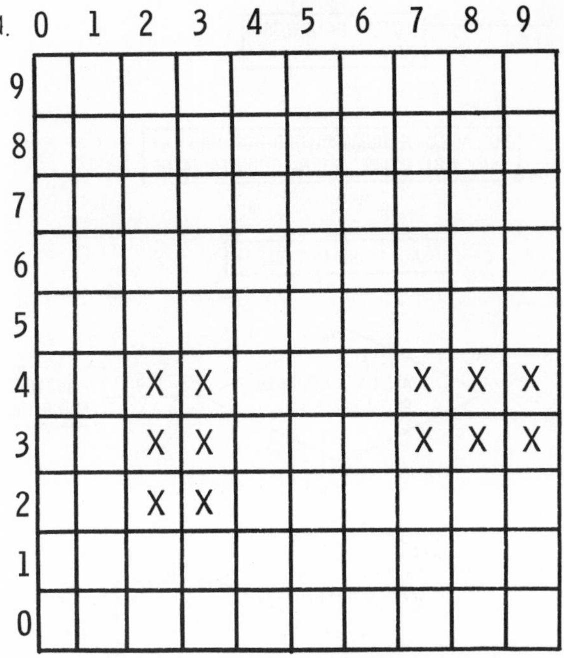

b.

Word	X	Y	Counter	
1		1	000	space
2		1	000	space
3	2	1	002	1st object
4	2	0	002	1st object
5	7	1	003	2nd object
6	2	0	002	1st object
7	7	1	003	2nd object
8		1	000	space
9		1	000	space
10		1	000	space
11		1	000	space
12		1	000	space
			0	end

Figure 12. (a) Graphic representation of the X, Y coordinates of two objects on a simplified scanning pattern of 100 points. Each of the 100 points is probed starting with the lower left point (0,0) and ending with the upper right point (9,9) (b) Contents of core memory after a scan of the simplified preparation depicted in 12a. Notice that Y coordinates are not explicitly stored but that this information is kept track of in a running "Y" counter. The leading X value for each "string" of data points is kept in the X column and the size of the "string" of data points in the counter column. With an 18-bit word machine, X, Y and counter information can be kept in one word (for further explanation, see text).

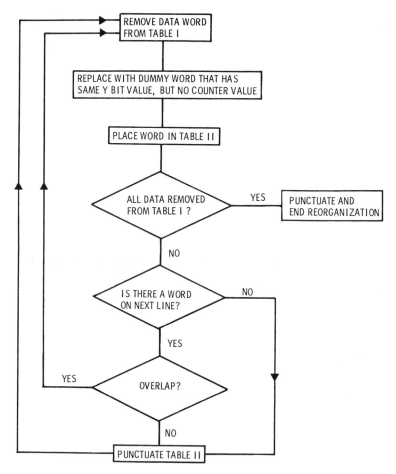

Figure 13. Algorithm for the reorganization of original scan data in such a way that the component words of an object will be sequentially listed in core memory and segregated from the words that make up other objects by punctuation points. Words that are part of the same structure are defined as those words on consecutive scan lines that have overlapping X values. For further explanation, see text.

the first word plus the number 3, (a variable number that represents the maximum X distance between words that are to be connected) the words should be connected. When the words are to be connected, they are replaced by one new word, which has an X value equal to that of the first word, a Y index equal to that of the second word, and a counter equal to the X value of the second word plus the counter of the second word minus the X value of the first word. The second word is then replaced by a dummy word that does not represent data points.

One may also think of this process in terms of the leading and trailing edges of the words on each line. If the trailing edge of the first word is within a certain specified distance of the leading edge of the second word (the "certain specified" distance in this case being distances between presynaptic densities or between pre- and post-synaptic densities), the two words can be considered part of the same structure and can be thought of as being connected. The two words then can be made into one word with a leading edge equal to that of the first word and a trailing edge equal to that of the second.

With all the closely spaced words on the same line now connected, we have considerably fewer words per line and the next part of the analysis can be accomplished with much greater ease and speed.

The next phase of the analysis requires a reorganization of the data now in a block of core locations that has already been referred to as Table I. Because of the raster pattern of the scan, the words that are components of the same object are not sequentially deposited in Table I. In Figure 12a, two objects, each made up of six data points, are shown as if on a monitor screen. Figure 12b shows the way the data are originally stored. One must determine what words represent parts of the same object. This can be accomplished by utilizing a modified neighbor-analysis technique.

One can logically determine the words in Table I (Figure 12b) that make up one object by determining if a word on one line has a range of X values that overlaps the X range of a word on a preceding line. The X range, it will be remembered, is from X_{min}, which equals the X value of the word, to X_{max}, which is equal to the X value of the word plus the counter value of the word minus one. This method of testing for overlapping words on consecutive scan lines is a simplified form of neighbor analysis in which one determines whether a word has a neighbor in one direction only. It is not necessary to test in all directions because the filling-in phase of the analysis alters the data so that there can only be one word per scan line for each object (refer to Figure 11). Also, since the reorganization of Table I is started with the first stored word, which is the lower left-most series of consecutive data points of the picture, it is not necessary to test for a neighbor below the word being considered. If one is dealing with types of object (*e.g.*, other than E-PTA stained synaptic profiles) that cannot be appropriately filled in to remove concavity, then testing for neighbors must be done in all directions. The algorithm in Figure 13 depicts the logical steps in the reorganization of that data in Table I.

For example, the neighbor analysis would start with word 3 in Figure 12b. This word is replaced by a dummy word in Table I and stored in Table II. The X range of this word is then determined. One then determines if there is a word on the next scan line that has an overlapping X range. If overlap does occur, as it does in Figure 12b for word 4, that word is also replaced in Table I and deposited in Table II. When this analysis has proceeded until no overlapping is found, as happens after word 6 has been considered, Table I and Table II will appear as in Figure 14. Words 3, 4, and 6 have been removed from Table I and

Table I

X	Y	Counter	
	1	000	
	1	000	
2	1	000	(dummy)
2	0	000	(dummy)
7	1	003	
2	0	000	(dummy)
7	1	003	
	1	000	
	1	000	
	1	000	
	1	000	
	1	000	
		0	

Table II

X	Y	Counter	
	1	000	space
	1	000	space
2	1	002	1st object
2	0	002	1st object
2	0	002	1st object

Figure 14. Partial reorganization of the original scan data shown in Figure 12b. Notice that the words that comprise the first object are now sequentially listed in a new core location (Table II) and are appropriately spaced. Table I now contains "dummy" words, which contain a 0 counter value and represent words that have already been defined as part of an object. These dummy words maintain appropriate Y counter information for Table I.

are deposited in Table II. Dummy words have replaced them in Table I with the "Y" bit set to the value of the original word, but the counter equal to zero. The dummy words keep the correct spatial order of the words by registering "Y" increments when necessary.

When no overlapping occurs on the next line, the next location in Table II is punctuated, designating the end of the sequential listing of the words that make up an object. The program then reexamines the remaining words in Table I for overlaps starting with what has newly become the first data word after the replacement of the words describing the first object. Analysis is continued as above until all of the data words have been removed from Table I. When this occurs in our example, Table II will appear as in Figure 15 and Table I will contain no data words.

For this type of neighbor analysis, which is actually a form of propagation (Rosenfeld, 1969), a large core memory is desirable. It is necessary to maintain

Original Word	X	Y	Counter	
		1	000	space
		1	000	space
3	2	1	002	1st object
4	2	0	002	1st object
6	2	0	002	1st object
	1	0	000	(punctuation & reset Y buffer to 0)
		1	000	space
		1	000	space
		1	000	space
5	7	1	003	2nd object
7	7	1	003	2nd object
	1	0	000	(punctuation)
			0	(end)

Figure 15. Core memory (Table II) after reorganization of the original scan data, Figure 12b. The informational content is the same, but the sequential listing of words that represent parts of the same object and the punctuations that delineate the components of different objects make quantification easier as explained in the text. By including appropriate spacing between words, the reorganized data can be easily displayed on the monitor scope.

Table I during the reorganization of data in Table II to keep track of the words that have been analyzed. Consequently, twice the storage area required for the mere storage of the picture data is necessary for this phase of the analysis. Since Table II is sequentially built up, it is possible to deposit the reorganized data in a peripheral storage device, such as magnetic tape. When Table I, which was originally deposited in core memory, has been depleted of data words, the reorganized data in Table II can be read into the core memory locations originally occupied by Table I and processed further. By appropriately spacing the reorganized data, a monitor display of the data can be easily generated.

The reorganized picture data makes quantification of the picture easy and rapid. A count of the number of punctuations in Table II is a count of the number of objects. This can be accomplished by a logical "and" of each Table II word with a mask word for the punctuation. All of the words that comprise an object can also readily be isolated and further analyzed by considering the data words between two punctuations in Table II.

For isolated objects it is possible to assign X, Y values to the leading and trailing edges of its constituent words. The X value is equal to the X_{min} or X_{max} of the word and the Y value is set to the relative position of the word in the sequential listing of the component words of the isolated object. In Figure 15, word 5 of Table II would be assigned a relative Y value of 1 and word 7 a

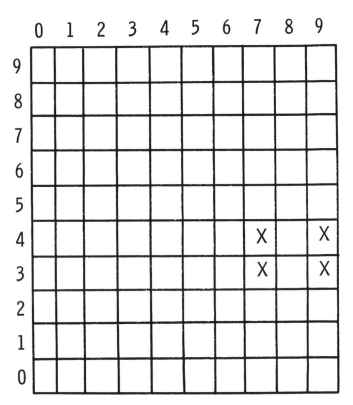

Figure 16. Graphic representation of the leading and trailing X values for words which comprise object two of Figure 12b. Knowing the X, Y coordinates of these points permits a calculation of the length of the long axis of the object. (See text.)

value of 2. The X, Y values of the leading and trailing edges of these two words are (7, 1; 9, 1) and (7, 2; 9, 2) respectively and are shown graphically in Figure 16. By Pythagorean Theorem one can determine which two points in the object are the most distant. Logically, the distance between two points is determined by finding the square root of: the square of the difference between the X values of the two points plus the square of the difference between the Y

Figure 17 (opposite). (a) Algorithm A for determining the leading X, Y value of a word by setting the X equal to the X value of the data word and assigning a Y value relative to its position in the object (or data list). (b) Algorithm B for determining the trailing X, Y coordinates of a data word by setting the X equal to the X value of word plus the counter of the word minus 1. Again, the Y is a relative value. (c) Algorithm C for determining the two most distant points in an object. Since one knows the X, Y coordinates of the leading and trailing values of the words that make up one object one can determine the most distant pair by Pythagorean Theorum. This determination is a measure of the long axis of the object.

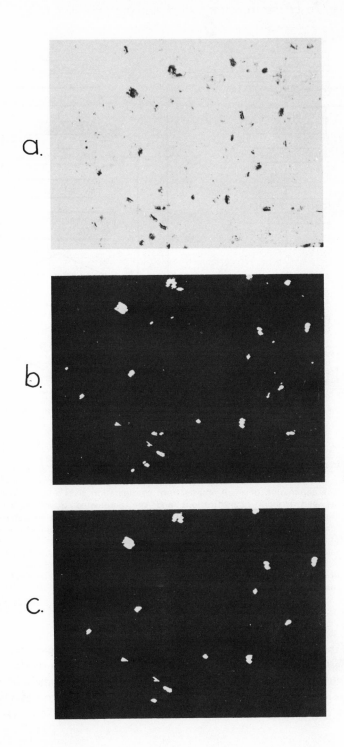

a.

b.

c.

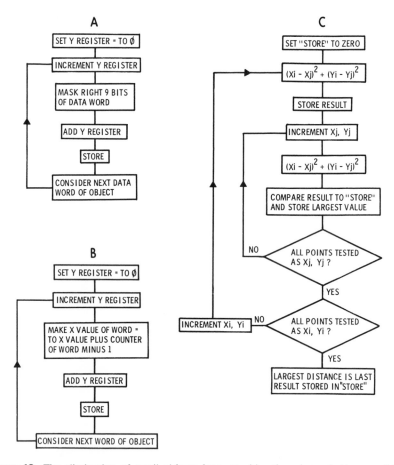

Figure 18. The elimination of small objects from consideration gives a better correlation between manual quantifications and the automated quantifications. The elimination can easily be accomplished by erasing objects that are composed of fewer than one operator defined number of data points. An electron micrograph of rat cerebral cortex stained with E-PTA is shown on the top. In the center is shown the monitor display of the data gleaned from a scan of the micrograph. Below is shown a monitor display of the reorganized data after the elimination of small objects. For illustrative purposes this picture is at a higher magnification than those used for obtaining quantitative data.

values of the two points, and selecting the combination that gives the largest result. The logical sequence of arguments for this determination are depicted in the algorithm in Figure 18, which includes determinations of the leading and trailing coordinates of words comprising an object and the determination of the two most distant data point coordinates. Objects composed of a specified number of data points or words can be selected from the reorganized data and either eliminated from the list, as in the case of noise reduction, or quantified to give histograms of the distribution of different size objects, or a count of a specified size object. Figure 17 is an illustration of the removal of small objects from an electron micrograph of an EPTA stained preparation.

A summation of the "count" portions of all the data that make up one object is a measure of the cross sectional area of that object in the picture. This measure may be useful in generating size distribution histograms or for eliminating or selecting a population of a particular size. The summation of counts in all the data words divided by the total number of possible data points in the picture is the ratio of the sectioned surface area of the objects to the surface area of the tissue section. This ratio is very helpful in determining the number of E-PTA stained synaptic contacts per unit volume of tissue according to the principle mathematically developed by Weibel and Gomez (1962). This principle is based on Delesse's Theorem, which states that the fraction, PV, of unit volume, V, occupied by a given population of randomly oriented and randomly distributed objects is equal to the fraction, PS, of unit area, S, of a cut surface of this volume covered by transectional area of the objects.

According to the principle of Weibel and Gomez, it is possible to compute the number of objects per unit volume of tissue from the data obtained during the scan, as long as the objects are of a standard shape randomly oriented and the tissue section is thin compared to the diameter of the object. The following formula (Weibel and Gomez, 1962) can be applied to populations of E-PTA synaptic contacts to determine the number of these contacts per unit volume of cerebral cortex.

$$N_V = \frac{N_A^{3/2}}{B \cdot P_P^{1/2}}$$

Where:

N_V = number of objects per unit volume of tissue

N_A = number of object transections per unit area of tissue

B = object shape index (for flat disc (cylinder) $B = 1.8$)

P_P = ratio of $\dfrac{\text{number of data points}}{\text{total number of points on grid}}$

Both N_A and P_P are computed from the picture data as described above. Because the E-PTA synaptic contact shapes are highly irregular on the electron micrographs, it is necessary to idealize the shapes to disks (as described above), so that the Weibel and Gomez principle can be applied to these populations. B is the shape coefficient for disks, which is the idealized shape of the filled-in synaptic contacts.

ADAPTIVE SCAN PROGRAMS[4]

Our use of adaptive scans has been directed at the analysis of neuronal dendrite trees. The topological and the metrical properties of dendrite trees may be characterized in terms of morphometric parameters, such as the number of primary order dendrites (immediate offshoots from the nerve cell body), their angular orientation, the number of branching points, the segment length between branching points, or the spatial distribution of branching points and terminal or intermediary segments. These parameters then may be used as a basis of an attempt to generalize dendritic branching patterns in terms of appropriate stochastic models. The comprehensive study of Ten Hoopen and Reuver (1970) outlined some of the features of theoretical concepts used for a probabilistic analysis of dendritic branching patterns.

Common to all analytical approaches is the prerequisite of a sizable amount of quantitative information and, therefore, the use of modern pattern recognition systems. We have implemented such a system with a circular scan. The dendritic image is scanned by a circle with center P (X, Y) and radius R, and the density samples (PMT output) displayed as a function of an angular scan parameter, T, which specifies position of the scanning point at one of 56 points around the scan circle (Figure 19).

Since Golgi-Cox staining provides high contrast, we have attempted to reduce density samples on the circular scan to a two-level black-and-white mode with the use of a threshold criterion that defines a black or white cut-off.

Figure 19, which shows a nerve cell body with a dendrite and some characteristic PMT output patterns as a function of position of the scan on the dendrite, may be used to illustrate the procedure. Sinks of PMT output indicate region of high density and thus the presence of portions of dendrites. It is then assumed that these portions constitute a modular pattern, which is represented by the pattern of sinks obtained around the circular scan. The spatial location of the circular scan is specified rather arbitrarily by the circle center P (X, Y). Contour analysis and modular pattern recognition is carried out on-line and the circular scan raster successively displaced along the dendrite in order to track the dendrite extensions. If an object tends to fade out of focus, the microscope is focused under program control and the scan procedure resumed. It must be emphasized that the circle radius, R, is determined according to the size and shape of the object.

This procedure has been implemented on the PDP-5 with 4K 12-bit words of core and two DEC tape transports as shown in Figure 1.

The circular scan and sampling of resultant PMT outputs are controlled by routine RSCAN. This routine creates a "circular" scan of 56 points around any

---

[4] The algorithms in this section were developed by Urs Wyss and implemented by him during a visit to the University of Rochester.

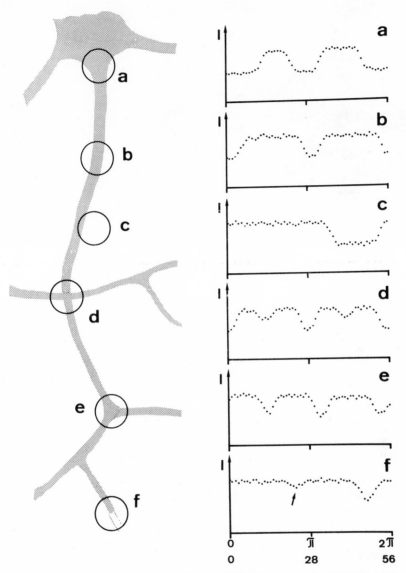

Figure 19. Reconstruction of a dendrite branch. Black circles indicate the sites where density samples have been taken. Corresponding PMT outputs (averaged) are shown on the right side. Objects are scanned in the clockwise direction at 56 points of a circle raster. Sinks of PMT output indicate stained regions. Vertical axis = PMT output, horizontal axis = position on circumference of scanning circle.

X, Y location on the oscilloscope screen specified as the center of the circle. The PMT output at each of these 56 points is sampled N times and averaged. Figure

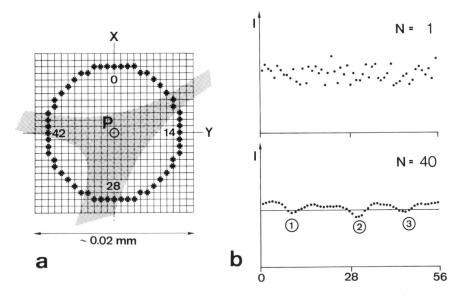

Figure 20. (a) The circular scan raster: density samples are taken at 56 points on a circle raster around P (X, Y). Due to the incremental circle approximation the radius R may vary within limits $9.85 < R < 10.44$. Depending on both microscope objective lens and CRT deflection gain, the circle diameter is usually 10 to 20 u at the object level. (b) Intensity samples displayed as a function of the circular scan index T (T = 0, 1, 2, ...55). Two records display the output of the signal averaging program after the first and the fortieth sample cycle. Processes of the bifurcation segment (Figure 20/a) are indicated by three sinks below the black-and-white cutoff level.

20 illustrates the circular scan and the results of the averaging process. These averages are stored in a 56-word table called COMPAS. The algorithm for accomplishing this is shown in Figure 21.

The sample index, T, which ranges from 0 to 55, indicates positions around the 56-point circle scan. The value of T is used to calculate X, Y coordinates around the scanning circle and to order resulting averaged PMT readings in COMPAS. The X, Y coordinates around the scanning circle are obtained from a table, SINTAB, according to:

$$X = X0 + SINTAB (T)$$
$$Y = Y0 + SINTAB (T + 14)$$

Where: SINTAB (T) $= R \cdot$ Sine $(\pi \cdot T/28)$ and R = circle radius.

Note that in the illustrations of the circular scan in Figure 20 a, angles are measured from the vertical axis.

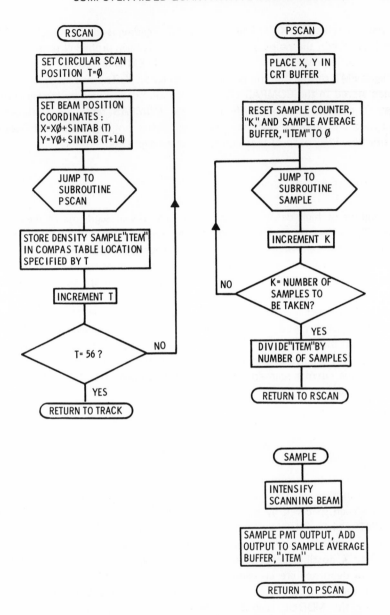

Figure 21. "RSCAN" algorithm for scanning in a 56-point circle and storing averaged PMT outputs in a 56-word table referred to as "COMPAS".

In other words, a set of X, Y coordinates representing a point on the circular scan pattern is placed in the X, Y buffers of the scanning oscilloscope, the oscilloscope beam is intensifed and the output of the PMT sampled N times at the point specified by X, Y. The resulting PMT reading is added to register ITEM each time. When the point on the scan circle has been probed N times, the sum of the resulting PMT values that are stored in ITEM is divided by N to give the averaged PMT output for the point specified by X, Y. The average ITEM output is then stored in the COMPAS table in a location determined by the value of T. When T reaches 55, the contents of the COMPAS table are analyzed to determine the presence, location, size, and pattern of regions of high staining density (low PMT output) that signify dendrite segments.

PATTERN RECOGNITION

Regions of high density are specified in terms of segments of the sample index, T, and are derived from sets of consecutive PMT output words in the COMPAS table that satisfy a threshold level criterion. The program locates these segments by means of a software Schmitt-trigger whose behavior is such that when the averaged PMT output in the COMPAS table drops below the cut-off level, the trigger is considered to be set and, conversely, if the COMPAS value exceeds the cut-off level the trigger is considered to be reset. Thus, if the trigger is set at T_{on} and reset at T_{off}, the dendrite segment intersected by an arc of the circular scan may be defined in terms of the circular scan index, T, by T_{on} and T_{off}. T_{on} and T_{off} are then used to specify the segment angle or argument, ARG, on the circular scan and the intersected segment extent (dendrite width) ARC according to:

$$ARG = (T_{on} + T_{off})/2$$
$$ARC = T_{off} - T_{on}$$

Arguments are thus computed modulo (56) and the segment extent, ARC, is expressed in units of 1/56 of the circumference of the scanning circle. ARC and ARG are each specified by six bits that are then concatenated to form a 12-bit SEGMNT word, which specifies the angular position and extent around the scanning circle of a dendrite segment. A set of four SEGMNT words, specifying from 0 to 4 possible dendrite segments (four segments would be encountered when two dendrites are crossing, illustrated in Figure 19d), together with the position vector, P(X, Y), a stage focus status word and the pattern code constitute the MODUL record, which is stored in a pushdown list for later analysis. Such a MODUL record is listed below, with data referring to the dendrite branching pattern and PMT output distribution illustrated in Figure 20. Thus, three segments (a branch point) have been located on a circle scan centered at X = 274, Y = 543 with angular positions (arguments) of 9, 30, and 43 and segment extents of 2, 5, and 3 respectively. The count of three segments is located in word 0000 in the MODUL record which is designated CODE. The

ONE MODUL RECORD (8 WORDS)

CODE (number of segments)	P (X)	P (Y)	P (Z) (stage focus)	SEGMENT WORDS Segment Argument & Extent concatenated in each word			
				Segment 1	Segment 2	Segment 3	Segment 4
WORD: 0000 CONTENT	0001	0002	0003	0004	0005	0006	0007
(octal): 0003	0422	1037	7771	1102	3605	5305	0000
DECIMAL: 3	274	543	−7	9/2	30/5	43/3	0/0

microscope stage was at focus level −7 with respect to the reference level. Since the PMT output distribution of Figure 20 contained only three sinks, word 0007 contains only zeros. A dendrite crossing (19d) would have produced four SEGMENT WORDS and 0007 would have contained data. The current provision in the MODUL record for four SEGMENT words only is implied by the logic of the rout-and-track processor described below.

Figure 22 shows the algorithm for the SCANCOMP routine that accomplishes the initial organization for pattern recognition of the data from one circular scan. SCANCOMP analyzes the density distributions in the COMPAS table. First, the 56 values in the COMPAS table are tested to see if they satisfy the specified threshold (THRESH) indicating a portion of a dendrite. If none of the 56 values falls below threshold, i.e., if a blank field has been scanned, SCANCOMP returns to the main program, with the first word of the MODUL record at zero. If a COMPAS value that satisfies THRESH is found, a loop (loop A) is entered in which the segment extent counter, ARC, is incremented for each successive COMPAS value satisfying threshold until a COMPAS value is encountered that does not satisfy threshold. At this time, the sequence of "dark" values is considered terminated and the segment defined from T and ARC. Segments are then coded in terms of their extent (ARC) and the argument of their mid-point (ARG) by a subroutine, EDIT, which determines ARG and combines ARC and ARG into one 12-bit word. After the newly defined segment has been coded, the first location of the modul record (called CODE), which keeps a count of the number of segments encountered around the circle, is incremented, and the ARC counter is reset to zero. The program then returns to examine the next COMPAS value until T = 55. If T > 55 while the program is in loop A, loop A terminates. If a previous segment has been completed (CODE = 1 or greater) when there is a termination in loop A and both COMPAS 55 and 0

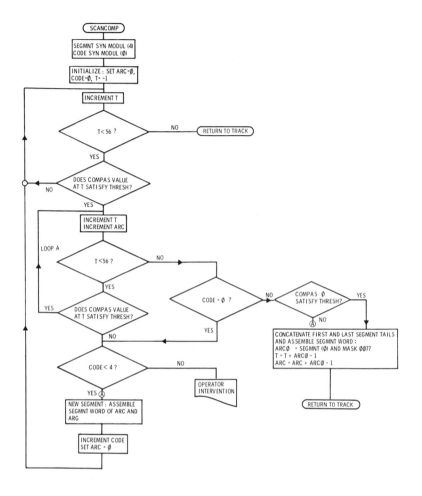

Figure 22. "SCANCOMP" algorithm for analyzing the 56 values in the COMPAS table to determine which values satisfy threshold criterion (signifying intersection of the scanning circle with a dendritic segment) and to describe these segments in terms of their extent, ARC, and angular location, ARG. The specification of both ARC and ARG are based on positions around the scanning circle. "T" counts the 56 points around the scanning circle. "CODE" counts the number of dendrite segments intersected by the scanning circle.

satisfy threshold, then the terminal segment is considered to be a portion of the first segment and the two segment tails are catenated. by:

$$ARC = ARC + ARC\,0 - 1)$$

and

$$ARG = \left| \frac{ARC\,0 - (ARC - 1)}{2} \right|$$

If COMPAS 0 did not satisfy THRESH, ARC and ARG are assembled in the usual fashion. If CODE becomes 4, indicating dendrite crossing with a foreign dendrite, operator intervention is requested.

Information generated by the SCANCOMP routine is utilized by the main ROUT and TRACK (RAT) processor, which evaluates the dendritic pattern indicated by a MODUL record. Depending on the pattern CODE of the MODUL record, the RAT processor operates in either the TRACK or the ROUT mode. If CODE = 2 or 3, in other words if SCANCOMP was entirely on a continuous portion of a dendrite or on a branching, the processor operates in the TRACK mode. If CODE = 0 or 1, signifying a blank area or an apparent ending, the processor operates in the ROUT mode. An understanding of the TRACK mode, which will be discussed first, may be aided by reference to Figure 23, which illustrates that in the TRACK program the dendrite is covered with a series of mutually overlapping circles with centers on the circumference of adjacent circles. The TRACK routine determines the vectors:

— TRAILER which leads from P_n to P_{n-1}

— LEADER which leads from P_n to P_{n+1}

Where: $(..., P_{n-1}, P_n, P_{n+1}, ...)$ is the sequence of scanning circle centers. These vectors are of length R (the radius of the scanning circle) with direction (argument, ARG) specified in terms of the circular scan index, T. The arguments of the trailing and leading vectors are called TRAIL and TLEAD respectively. In other words, the RAT processor determines which point on the circumference of a scanning circle should be taken as the center of the next scanning circle.

Given a set of arguments in a MODUL record obtained from a circular scan, the first task of the TRACK routine is to determine which are the trailing and which the leading vectors. It does this by first determining whether the scan circle was over a: (1) blank field, (2) ending, (3) unbranched dendrite segment, or (4) branch point, $i.e.$, CODE = 0, 1, 2, or 3. If CODE is either 0 (blank field) or 1 (ending), the ROUT routine is called. If CODE is 2 (unbranched segment), or 3 (branch point) TRACK next defines the current trailing vector as being represented by the argument closest to the argument, 180 degrees from the LEADER vector of the previous MODUL record ($i.e.$, previous circle scan), P_{n-1}. Thus, the N segment arguments (where N=3 for a branch point or 2 for a continuous dendritic segment) of the current MODUL record are analyzed in order to find the ARG that is closest to the value $(TLEAD_{n-1} - 28)$.[5] The

---

[5] It may be expected that $TRAIL_n$ equals $(TLEAD_{n-1} - 28)$ in a straight region of a dendrite, but since the description of dendrite fragments in terms of segment arguments does not take the segment extent ARC into full account, the forward and backward extensions of the same dendrite fragment may field slightly divergent arguments. In addition, $TRAIL_n$ may also diverse from $28 + TLEAD_{n-1}$ due to the curving of the dendrites.

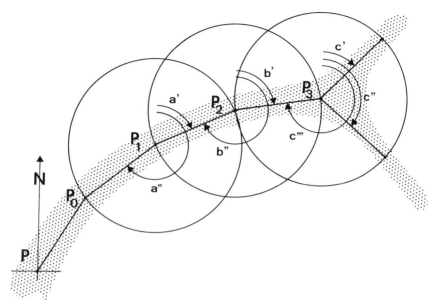

Figure 23. Chord approximation of a dendrite branch. The scan circle around P2 identifies a dendrite segment in terms of the segment arguments b' and b''. Next b'' is associated to the leading argument a' and thus identified as the trailing argument of P2. The choice of b' as the leading argument of P2 is unambiguous and hence leads to the next sample point, P3, where a bifurcation segment is identified by c', c'', and c'''. The procedure is now to analyze the most counterclockwise branch first and thus c'' is assigned as the leading argument of P3. The equidistant chord segments are equal to the scan circle radius R.

argument closest to this criterion is assigned to $TRAIL_n$, which specifies the trailing vector of the current MODUL record. By means of the trailing vector, the current $MODUL_n$ is linked to the previous $MODUL_{n-1}$.

Next, the current leading vector is specified by assignment of its argument $TLEAD_n$. If CODE = 2, as in the case of an unbranched dendrite segment, the choice is unambiguous with $TLEAD_n$ specified by the one remaining argument. If CODE = 3, signifying a branching, the most counterclockwise branch is followed first. The same branching point will be encountered again during the trace-back procedure and the other branch analyzed then. Figure 23 illustrates the succession of scan circles along a dendrite and relationships among arguments of successive circles.

After determination of the trailing and leading vectors, TRAILER and LEADER, the circle scan generator, RSCAN, is instructed to collect samples around the new center:

$$P_{n+1} = P_n + LEADER_n$$

Thus, the function of the RAT processor is to follow and measure the curvilinear dendrite pattern.

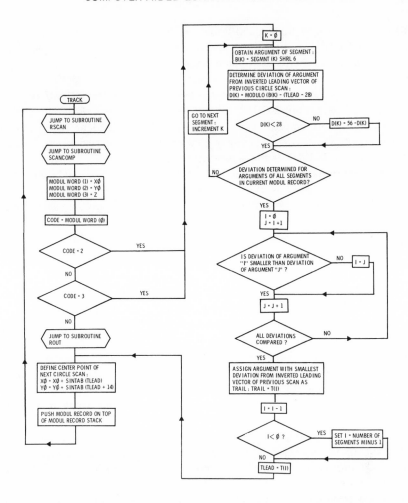

Figure 24. Algorithm of the main program "TRACK." The course followed by this routine depends on the number of dendrite segments (specified by CODE) intersected by the scanning circle. If CODE = 0 or 1 the focusing routine, "ROUT" is called. If CODE = 2 or 3, the TRACK routine first determines the trailing portion of the dendrite segment, then the leading portion that determines the center of the next circle scan.

The algorithm, shown in Figure 24 for the main program, TRACK, first calls RSCAN to take density samples around point P (X0, Y0), then calls SCANCOMP to analyze the samples by counting and specifying extent and position of segments around the periphery, and finally, completes the MODUL record by assignment of its coordinate labels in MODUL word 1, (X), MODUL word 2 (Y) and MODUL word 3 (focus). If CODE is 2 or 3 (uninterrupted dendrite segment or dendrite branching), the MODUL record is evaluated by TRACK. If CODE is 0 or 1, the ROUT subroutine is called. In the evaluation by

TRACK to determine trailing and leading vectors, the first segment argument of the current MODUL is dissected away from its associated ARC values by a right shift six places and then stored in a temporary buffer, B. Then the deviation, D, of B from the inverted leading vector of the previous MODUL record (TLEAD-28) is calculated and saved. This is repeated for all two or three arguments in the current MODUL record. Next, the smallest deviation, D (I) is determined and its corresponding argument T (I) assigned as specifying the trailing vector. The new leading vector is taken in the counterclockwise direction by determining TLEAD as the argument one removed (I = I – 1) from TRAIL. If the smallest deviation, DI, is found when I = 0, then I = I – 1 will be a negative number. In that case, I is set to the number of segments minus 1 to define TLEAD. The X0, Y0 coordinates of the center of the new circle are specified as:

$$X0_{n+1} \; = \; X0_n \; + \; R \, ^* \, SIN \, (\pi \, TLEAD/28)$$

$$Y0_{n+1} \; = \; Y0_n \; + \; R \, ^* \, COS \, (\pi \, TLEAD/28)$$

by use of the SINTAB table. The MODUL record is now saved (pushed) on top of the MODUL record stack for later analysis.

If the TRACK routine has not located either two or three segments, the ROUT routine is called for help. During all the ROUT procedures, the circle scan remains at its last position P (X0, Y0) and samples are taken at different focus levels, which are adjusted by means of a computer-driven stepping motor coupled to the microscope fine focus. The procedure is discussed for the sequence when a TAIL pattern is identified, *i.e.*, only one segment argument ARG has been identified.

A TAIL pattern might result from one of two events: (1) a dendrite branch fading out of focus (Figure 19f), or (2) a terminal branch being encountered. The ROUT processor attempts to rout out the cause of the TAIL pattern by use of a procedure in which focus is changed in a trial-and-error manner. First, the microscope stage focus is changed. If again a TAIL pattern is encountered, the focus is again changed. Alternatively, if a NULL pattern (CODE = 0) is located where there had previously been a tail pattern, the focus stepping motor is instructed to move the focus in the opposite direction. The total number of allowable focus steps is limited to prevent self-destruction of the equipment or the slide. If a BRANCH or SHUNT pattern is identified for the current $MODUL_n^k$, (at a location where there had been a TAIL at a different focus level) $MODUL_h^i$ on top of the push-down list is replaced by $MODUL_n^k$, and the procedure continued hereafter according to the TRACK strategy. If the procedure does not yield a solution (*i.e.*, a dendrite continuation is not found), it is assumed that a terminal branch segment has been located with $MODUL_n^k$. The leading vector then is specified by the assignment:

$$TLEAD_n = ARG_n^i$$

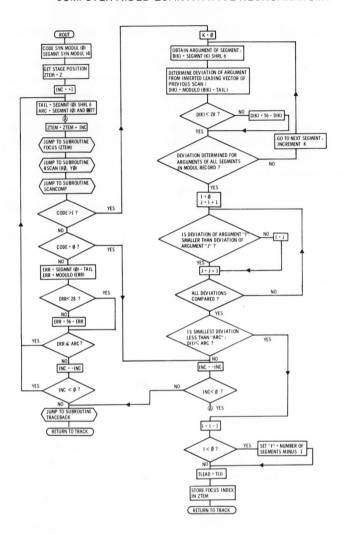

Figure 25. Algorithm of the ROUT focusing routine. When the TRACK routine fails to find a continuation of the dendrite being tracked, the ROUT routine is called to focus up and down until either: (1) finding what is judged to be the appropriate continuation or (2) deciding that the proper continuation will not be found. If the continuation is found by focusing, the trailing and leading segments are determined and the TRACK routine re-entered. If the continuation does not appear, the program assumes that a dendrite termination has been found and the TRACEBACK routine is called, which follows the dendrite back in order to pick up branches that had been by-passed earlier.

and the trace-back procedure initiated. Figure 25 illustrates the algorithm for the ROUT subroutine. The stage focus status word is saved in temporary storage at ZTEM. Next, the focus stepping motor increment, INC, is set to +1, indicating direction and magnitude of the focus adjustment. The next step in the flow chart describes the procedure when CODE = 1 in the MODUL record under consideration; *i.e.*, when an apparent terminal segment has been encountered. The segment word is dissected into its ARG and ARC components by a right shift six and a logical AND with a mask = 0077 respectively. The ARG is designated as TAIL and the extent as ARC. The temporary focus word ZTEM is incremented and the focus subroutine instructed to move focus to the new position. A new scan is made at this new focus level, analyzed by SCANCOMP, and the subsequent procedure scheduled according to the number of segments found by the scan at the new focus level.

If CODE = 0 (if a previously scanned TAIL segment has disappeared as the result of focus adjustment in one direction), the direction of focus adjustment is reversed (INC = −INC) and a new circle scan initiated by RSCAN (*i.e.*, jump to point A) without assignment of TAIL or CODE. After two reversals of focus direction in this loop with CODE remaining 0, INC will again be positive. This indicates failure to find a dendrite process in either direction of focus adjustment, the TRACEBACK is initiated.

If CODE = 1 again, the new argument of the segment (0) is compared with the argument of the old segment, TAIL. If the deviation, ERR, between SEGMENT 0 and TAIL is less than the segment extent (ARC) it is assumed that the same branch has been scanned again, and another circle scan in the same position is initiated at an altered focus, with the focus change continuing in the same direction. If ERR is greater than the segment extent, ARC, it is assumed that a new dendrite has been encountered at the new focus level and the direction of focus adjustment is reversed (INC = −INC). If the increment has reverted to positive by the change of focus direction at this step, *i.e.*, if neither direction of focus adjustment led to finding a continuation of the dendrite, the ROUT procedure is interrupted and the TRACEBACK procedure is initiated.

If CODE is neither 0 nor 1, but is 2 or 3, which is the case when focus adjustment unearths a continuation of the dendrite that was being tracked, the procedure is analogous to that already described for the TRACK routine. The sequence of arguments is analyzed in order to find which argument shows the smallest deviation, D (I) from the TAIL argument. If this deviation turns out to be smaller than the corresponding ARC, it is assumed that the newly located segment is a continuation of the old (TAIL) segment and the new leading vector TLEAD is assigned and the focus index updated. If none of the newly encountered segments satisfy the criterion for continuity with the old segment (*i.e.*, D (I) < ARC) it is assumed that the new segments belong to neighboring processes and either a new focus adjustment is tried or the TRACEBACK routine is called, depending on whether the new focus increment, INC, is positive or negative when the old focus increment is multiplied by −1.

In the TRACEBACK routine, the path of the dendrite just ended is followed back to the most terminal branching and the previously ignored branch is then followed. This is done by popping successive MODUL records off the MODUL push down list until the last branch pattern (CODE = 3) is located. As each MODUL record is popped off the list, its position information is saved. When a MODUL record is reached in which CODE = 3, the three segment arguments are compared with the vector pointing to the preceding MODUL record popped off the stack. When a matching argument is found for some K segment (K = 0, 1 or 2), the new leading vector is assigned by permutation of K (counterclockwise) and the MODUL record CODE word decremented from 3 to 2 (after saving branch location information). Branch location information is saved in the form of P_n in a BRANCH stack. Once this has been accomplished, the TRACK routine is entered with the new leading vector, and the new dendrite branch followed in the usual fashion by TRACK. Thus, on subsequent entries into the TRACEBACK routine, the branch patterns more proximal to the cell body will be found, and previously bypassed branches followed.

SYSTEM SET-UP AND CALIBRATION FOR ADAPTIVE SCANNING

The sequence of events in operating the computer and the flying-spot scanner is as follows:

The microscopic preparation is fixed on the stage, and the CRT hood is removed so that the CRT screen is visible. The substage illumination is intensified and the object to be scanned thrown on the CRT screen for inspection.

Via teletype keyboard, the program is requested to display a square graticule and the circle raster on the screen. The circle center $P(X, Y)$ may be adjusted by means of two potentiometers connected to the analog-to-digital input of the computer.

The circle diameter is adjusted by means of CRT deflection gain control knobs.

With the CRT hood replaced, the photo-multiplier tube is chained to the optical system by insertion of a gating mirror (Figure 1). A specified area of the object is scanned with a line raster and a black-and-white picture displayed on-line on a monitor CRT screen. The black-and-white cutoff level is adjusted by means of a potentiometer.

The specimen is now replaced by a 0.01-mm graticule slide and the program is requested to measure the graticule distances in terms of raster increments. The graticule constant $(10\,\mu)$ is divided by the mean number of raster increments and thus yields the calibration factor CAL, which is stored as a three-word floating point constant for later use in morphometric analysis. (*e.g.*, CAL = $+0.6896667E+00\,\mu$).

The CRT hood is removed again, the graticule slide replaced by the specimen, and a write-through cursor set to the center of a cell body. With the hood fixed and the photo-multiplier mirror gated on, the system is released. The RAT processor starts to move the scan raster out of the dark zone, proceeds along the cell body contour until the first offshoot is located, and continues with the chord approximation of the first primary order dendrite. If, during a trace-back procedure, the offshoot is identified again, the topological and metrical statistics are listed on the teletype. A plotter or oscilloscope drawing of the chord approximation is optional.

CONCLUSIONS

Our intention has been to encourage the morphologist and potential user of a small laboratory computer to improve the technique of quantitative image analysis by use of an automatic scanning system. Depending on the structure of the object, the design of the scan and pattern recognition strategy may be a pretentious attempt. But pattern recognition is largely a "software" problem and thus requires imagination. It is quite another problem if we consider the hardware components of an automatic image analysis system. Here, financial support and a cooperative engineering staff will save time and discouraging incidents. Most of the inconveniences we met with in the scanning system described are due to hardware. However, problems are no reason to abandon, but rather a challenge to continue the effort.

REFERENCES

Aghajanian, G. K. and F. E. Bloom. The formation of synaptic junctions in developing rat brain: A quantitative electron microscopic study, *Brain Research*, 1967, *6*, 716–727.

Pfenninger, K., C. Sandri, K. Akert, and C. H. Eugster. Contribution to the problem of structural organization of the presynaptic area. *Brain Research*, 1969, *12*, 10–18.

Rosenfeld, A., *Picture processing by computer*. New York, Academic Press, 1969.

Ten Hoopen, M. and H. A. Reuver. Probabilistic analysis of dendritic branching patterns of cortical neurons, *Kybernetik*, 1970, *6*, 176–188.

Vetter, H. G. Restoration of biological images using limited sampling, *Physiology and Medical Biology*, 1969, *14*, 417–430.

Weibel, E. R. and D. M. Gomez. A principle for counting tissue structures on random sections. *Journal of Applied Physiology*, 1962, *17*, 343–348.

CHAPTER ELEVEN

ADVANCED TECHNIQUES
FOR THE
SMALL COMPUTER

WILLIAM SIMON
University of Rochester School of Medicine and Dentistry

INTRODUCTION

The laboratory computer has come of age. A few years ago, the substitution of a computer for almost any manual operation was deemed worthy of an article or at least a publicity release. Now, the on-line computer is so thoroughly established as a laboratory instrument that nothing less than a foolproof prediction of the future of France is likely to be published in the better journals simply because a computer has been used. The ubiquity of computers is affirmed by the fact that some manufacturers can supply adequate field service even in locations as remote as five miles from Boston.

Yet, beyond the elementary principles of programming and endless articles about how to interface a computer to an automated corkscrew, there is very little information available for the reader, with some computer background, who wants to know how to implement his own application or how to choose a computer system. This article is a collection of principles and techniques that have been found useful over several years experience with on-line computing. It is doubtful that the reader will find it profitable to duplicate exactly any of these techniques, but it is hoped that he will find them stimulating to his own ideas and that, as a result of this article, he will not have to re-invent the wheel.

CHOICE OF A COMPUTER

The choice of a computer is at best an uncomfortable decision for a beginner in the computer art. Usually it is done by asking a colleague what he is using and assuming that he has made a good choice. Frequently, it is based upon the list of software the manufacturer claims he can supply. Too often it is done under subtle pressure from granting agencies anxious to prove that their last year's programs made sense.

The correct choice of a computer often depends more on the circumstances at the user's laboratory than on the technical specifications of the machine. In areas where computer specialists abound, technicians are available, and manufacturers maintain good field offices, one can afford to pick a computer configuration as exotic as one chooses. Here, indeed, the criterion is maximum computing power per dollar. Where this is not the case, which is most of the world, the choice must often be based on ability to obtain maintenance and support from the manufacturer. If it is difficult to reach the salesman, one may be sure it will be a hundred times more difficult to reach a repairman. One of the largest computer manufacturers in the United States has had orders repeatedly cancelled because it has been found impossible to get through the red tape of their organization with the simplest questions. Although this company advertised small computers, it was always clear that they regarded a potential sale of one such computer as not worthy of their attention.

A very good test of a company's ability to support its product is its ability to answer questions from its local office. If the local representative cannot answer technical questions without referring them to the main plant, one can bet that he cannot provide adequate service.

In evaluating technical specifications of an on-line computing system the following are relevant:

1. Is the computer to be used entirely for on-line operation, or must it also serve as a batch processor or small time-sharing system?
2. Is there a larger machine nearby that can be used for difficult numerical computations and, if so, how will the smaller computer communicate with it?
3. Is the computer to be used for one purpose, or for a variety of purposes requiring different programming?
4. Is it fast enough?
5. What is the maximum continuous length of data that must be recorded?
6. How much core memory is needed?
7. What peripheral equipment is available?

THE CONTINUOUS DATA PROBLEM

This problem is discussed first because it is the one most often overlooked in the choice of an on-line computer system. Typically, manufacturers specify a data rate at which data can be transferred to a bulk storage device, but they make no mention of the maximum length of data run that can be stored at that rate. Thus, one encountered situations such as the following. One prominent manufacturer (who, in the third generation of the same computer, has finally recognized the existence of the continuous data problem) claims that data can be written on his small, inexpensive, magnetic tape system at a rate of 7500 words per second. This would be quite adequate for most biological applications. However, one tape holds only 130,000 data words so that after 17 sec, one runs out of tape. A minimum of a couple of seconds is required to start up a second tape transport so that one is, at this rate, faced with a break in the data every 17 sec and with a gymnastic problem of changing tapes. One is tempted to ask if the tapes can be run more slowly, since 7500 words per second is faster than is usually needed. Yes, they can run more slowly, but much more slowly, since the tapes must now be started, stopped, and backed up between write operations. If the write operation is checked, as is recommended, the effective transfer rate is about 1000 data words per second. Thus, when specifying maximum bulk storage data rate one must think not only of basic transfer rate, but also the minimum acceptable unbroken data length. For reference, it should be noted that with the simplest interfacing, IBM-compatible transports can run at rates up to 15,000 data words per second with about 20 min unbroken length and with essentially instant start-up time on a second transport.

The difficulty mentioned above can in many cases be substantially relieved by preprocessing of data before transferring it to magnetic tape. For example, if one is monitoring action potentials, it may be necessary to record only their times of occurrence. Typically, action potentials occur at a rate of perhaps 100 per second. Even if two data words are required to record each event (as will often be the case), a 130,000-word tape will last for 10 min and a start up time of a couple of seconds for a second tape is quite harmless. Unfortunately, this improvement in performance is not free. The computer must now be able to recognize an action potential. In some cases this is trivial. In others, where some subtle discrimination is required, it may require going to a faster computer in order to ensure that the data reduction can be accomplished fast enough to avoid missing valid data. Thus, the question of continuous data storage interacts with the problem of basic computer speed, which will be considered next.

MAXIMUM SPEED

The specification of the speed of a computer is difficult. Memory cycle time is a rough guide. The next most often used measure is that of so called bench-mark programs, which are asserted to be typical and useful by the manufacturer and which in the author's experience are rarely either typical or useful. Nor can an elaborate instruction set always be trusted to need significantly fewer memory cycles than a simpler, more cohesive set of instructions. A computer marketed a few years ago had the peculiar characteristic of being able to be operated in either of two modes; Mode A was a very simple two's complement instruction set and Mode B was a very elaborate one's complement set that had been touted by its designers as being ideally suited to biological applications. Indeed, Mode B was clever and efficient for many short programs encountered in biology. However, when one took the next step beyond the short programs to a double precision averaging program, the program was found to be both shorter and faster in prosaic Mode A.

Another prime example is a computer that has, in addition to two accumulators, a truly magnificent instruction set. One of its great virtues is that accumulator B can be used as an indirect address pointer for accumulator A. It was apparently deemed unnecessary to provide memory content indexing because the great power of an accumulator as an index register should more than suffice. Try to do a push down list! The author proposes the following measures of computer speed:

1. The time required to add two 16-bit or longer length words.
2. The time required to do a push down (or up) of a 20-place table.
3. The time required per sample to record a data string.

The above have been chosen to reflect the most common requirements for real-time processing (they are not appropriate for other than real-time work).

Item 1 is bound to raise objections from the proponents of 12-bit machines as being an unfair criterion. In this author's extensive experience with 12-bit computer, it has been found that single precision (12 bit) computation is almost always inadequate and is resorted to only in cases of desperate speed requirements.

With the exception of the following types of problems, PDP-8 class computers programmed in machine language are fast enough for most biological applications.

1. Multiple-unit action potentials.
2. EKG monitoring requiring extensive real-time analysis.
3. Complex displays.

In these three cases more speed has often been desirable. More important, however, is the restriction to machine language programming to realize sufficient speed. If the computer is to be used in only one or two applications one can afford to suffer with the trials of machine language. If it is to be used for a variety of purposes, every attempt should be made to acquire a computer fast enough for the applications when programmed in higher-level languages.

From the considerations above, the advantages of 16- and 18-bit computers over 12-bit machines are obvious. They are, of course, somewhat more expensive, and one is tempted to ask whether the longer word length results in the possibility of economies being realized by reducing the number of words required in core memory. Once again, the question must be asked in terms of higher-level languages. A 4K memory is usually adequate for machine language operation. The higher-level languages almost invariably make less-efficient use of memory and one is frequently severely limited by this. In particular, manufacturers tend to specify a minimum memory size for their operation of their languages. However, they rarely specify how many data locations are left while the operating system is in core. Sometimes, it is as few as 100, which is often inadequate. For general use, 100 is a bare minimum. Two hundred is considerably better but specific problems may require many more. The reader should not confuse memory locations with data locations. A single data location may require three or even four memory locations.

A difficult question is the comparison between a 12-bit 8K computer and a 16- or an 18-bit 4K computer at about the same price. The current 16- and 18-bit computers are much faster, both in real time and in memory cycles required to do typical operations, and it is unlikely that the 12-bit machine will reach the same speed in the near future. However, it is generally possible to develop much more elaborate programs with the 12-bit, 8K machine. This is perhaps not obvious, since the shorter word length causes some memory to be wasted by the need to employ more indirect addresses. However, a study of some typical programs indicates that the wasted space amounts to about 5%, which is rather little. More to the point is the need of a three-location data word where two locations would suffice in a 16- or 18-bit computer. In applications requiring table storage of floating point data, some of the advantage of the 12-bit computer's larger memory is lost. On the other hand, where complex programming is needed, the larger memory is to be preferred.

Naturally, if one can afford it, he should choose a 16-or 18-bit computer with an 8K memory. With regard to computers with word lengths longer than 18 bits, there are a number of 24- and 32-bit machines available. They are expensive but many have instruction codes that make them very fast for numerical problems, as opposed to real-time computation. If the same computer must serve both for real-time work and number crunching or bookkeeping operations the greater than 18-bit machine should be considered. But, since this document is not primarily concerned with off-line operations, the topic will not be pursued further.

PERIPHERAL EQUIPMENT

The real-time user does not actually purchase a computer. He purchases a computer system that usually includes an analog-digital converter, display oscilloscope, real-time clock, and, perhaps, a bulk-storage device, such as magnetic tape or disc. In the 12-bit class, a number of standard configurations are spoken of highly. The author is not devoted to any of these but they do have the advantage of alleviating one's feelings of insecurity resulting from having a one-of-a-kind computer system. Also, hopefully, better software is available for standard systems due to the existence of users groups who, if a bit less reliable than the manufacturers, have at least the advantage of imagination. This factor is not to be weighted too heavily because using someone else's programming is often more like wearing his shoes than courting his wife, but it is a better-than-nothing asset.

The standard systems may very well be the correct choice for a number of applications. However, the reader may want to read the sections of this article on analog-digital conversion and displays and *must* read the previous section on the continuous data problem before deciding whether to follow the pack or courageously go it alone.

If the proposed applications involve high-speed continuous data, this problem must receive primary consideration in the design of the system. If overlooked at this point, it may be extremely expensive to solve later.

Before entering upon a discussion of displays and analog-digital conversion, it is convenient to enumerate quickly other commonly used peripheral equipment with some indication of importance to typical systems. In this way the reader can visualize most of his proposed system as he reads the detailed sections that follow.

| Floating Point Hardware | Very desirable |
| Extended arithmetic units | Very useful. Contribute greatly to speed in systems without floating point hardware |

Real-time clock	Essential
High-speed paper tape reader	Very useful
High-speed paper punch	Useful
Direct memory access	Not essential unless required by bulk storage device
Small magnetic tape units	Very useful but only if continuous data problem is solved
IBM compatible tape units	If communication with other computers is required or if required by continuous data
Analog plotter	Generally not recommended
Digital plotter	Not as useful as is usually expected
Disk storage	Becoming competitive with tapes
Light pen	Very special-purpose device
Display	Essential

CHOICE OF ANALOG EQUIPMENT

In many real-time applications, the analog inputs to the computer are its principal connection to the real world. Thus, the system is only as good as its analog equipment. In some cases, analog inputs are provided as a standard part of the system, while in others, the user must supply his own or at least order it separately from the rest of the computer. This author's experience has been that the minimum acceptable analog-to-digital converter provides 10-bit accuracy, including the sign bit. At first glance, this appears to be demanding one tenth of one per cent accuracy, which for most purposes, would indeed be overly cautious. However, one is rarely able conveniently to use the full input range of an analog-digital converter due to slow drifts in the dc level of the signal source. Thus, one often wishes to use one-fourth of the full range or less for the dynamic parts of the signal, allowing the remaining range to accommodate drift. In this case, the true accuracy of the system is only four-tenths of one per cent, which is consistent with reasonable expectations for other parts of the equipment. For reasonable frequency response, analog-digital converters must be equipped with sample and hold circuits. The sampling aperture or window (the time over which the sample is taken) should be about one microsecond. One often hears the comment that too narrow a window accentuates noise. This is a misinterpretation of what actually happens. A wide sampling window restricts the frequency response of the system. It does not, however, produce a simple rolloff but, rather a $(\sin f)^2/f^2$ response that limits the useful bandwidth much more than it limits the noise bandwidth. It is therefore far better to limit the frequency response, when this is needed, by a low-pass filter ahead of the input to the system.

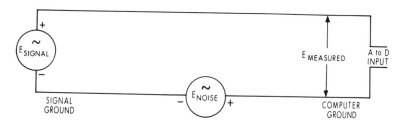

Figure 1. Equivalent circuit for how ground line noise is introduced into analog inputs to a computer system.

Most analog-digital converters are equipped with multiplexers to allow sampling of many channels. In some computers, some of the channels are connected to potentiometers, which can be used as parameter knobs on the front of the computer while others are used as signal inputs. This is not the best configuration. It is better to have all the analog multiplexer inputs available as signal inputs and to equip each input with a variable gain potentiometer and an offset potentiometer. In this way, corrections of signal level and amplitude are easily made and the knobs can be used as parameter inputs by leaving the signal input open. Signal inputs should be high impedance, between 10,000 and 100,000 ohms, and should present a pure resistive load to the signal source. The usual fault with many commercial multiplexer input circuits is that the input acts as a current source, which makes coupling to external circuits difficult. Inputs should be protected against damage due to overload and should recover from an overload in not more than a few microseconds. Check particularly that an overload on one channel does not cause cross talk on other channels. Most moderately priced analog-digital converters require about 10 to 20 μsec to complete the conversion. It is highly desirable that provision be made to overlap the conversion operation with operation of the computer, so that the computer need not wait for conversion to be completed.

It is often necessary to monitor analog signals from remote sources. The only difficulty encountered here is the noise pickup on the connecting lines. Over very long distances, telephone lines are usually used. The telephone company can supply noise-free interfacing, but unfortunately at relatively high cost. For distances of up to about 1000 ft, a simple shielded cable can be used if appropriate precautions are taken.

Most noise pickup is due to voltage differences at the ends of a nominally common ground line between the site of the signal source and the input to the analog-digital converter of the computer. This noise may have many sources of which the most common is 60-cycle ground current (Figure 1).

The cure is relatively easy. Consider Figure 2.

An operational amplifier has been inserted at the signal source, with its positive gain input connected to the computer ground. One finds by elementary analysis that:

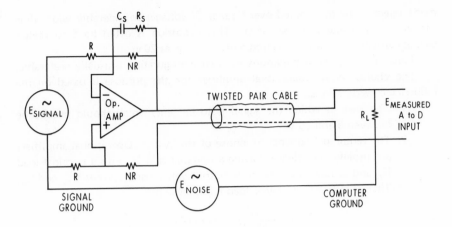

Figure 2. Operational amplifier placed at signal source. Note that the positive input is returned to computer ground.

$$E \text{ measured} = -\frac{N+1}{G+N+1} E \text{ noise} - \frac{NG}{N+G+1} E \text{ signal}$$

Which, for G much longer than N becomes:

$$E \text{ measured} = -\frac{N+1}{G} E \text{ noise} - NE \text{ signal}$$

Thus, the signal-to-noise ratio is improved by approximately a factor of G.

In principle, one can do even better by putting the operational amplifier at the computer end. This configuration has the advantage in the case of multiple signal sources of putting all the operational amplifiers in one place (Figure 3). It suffers, however, from two disadvantages. It requires better balance and shielding of the interconnecting lines, and it requires that the amplifier common

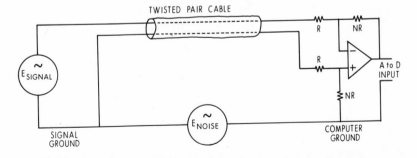

Figure 3. Alternative configuration with amplifier at the computer end of the line.

mode rejection be maintained over a range of voltages considerably wider than the largest anticipated noise signal. This condition is often hard to realize because ground-current noise is frequently as large as 20 v.

Thus, for long line installations the first configuration is usually preferable.

The choice of an operational amplifier for the purpose is based on the following considerations:

1. The level at which the signal is to be sent, which should usually be between 5 and 20 v.

2. The required frequency response of the system. Operational amplifiers are usually specified as having a nominal gain G_n into a nominal load R_n and as having a maximum output voltage and current V_m and I_m. Their gain G into a smaller load R_L is given by:

$$G = \frac{NG'}{1+N+G'} \quad \text{where } G' = G_n \frac{R_L}{R_n}$$

The maximum frequency response is given by the smaller of the following two frequencies:

$$f_i = \frac{1}{2\pi C_c} \frac{1}{R_L} + \left(\frac{G_n}{(1+N) R_n}\right) = \frac{1}{2\pi R_L C_c}\left(1 + \frac{G'}{(1 + N)}\right)$$

$$f_2 \quad \frac{I_m}{20 V_m C_c}$$

Where C_c is the capacity of the interconnecting cable, which is usually between 20 and 50 $\mu\mu$farads per foot. Thus, for 1000 feet of cable at 50 $\mu\mu$farads/ft and a typical amplifier:

$$
\begin{aligned}
N &= 10 \\
R_L &= 10^3 \text{ ohms} \\
R_n &= 10^4 \text{ ohms} \\
V_m &= 10 \text{ volts} \\
I_m &= 2 \; 10^{-2} \text{ amps} \\
G_n &= 10^4 \\
G' &= 1000 \\
f_1 &= 3 \; 10^5 \text{ H}_2 \\
f_2 &= 2 \times 10^3 \text{ H}_2
\end{aligned}
$$

With the given parameters, the system would be limited to a high-frequency response of about 2000 cycles per second.

C_s and R_s are usually required to stabilize operational amplifiers that are driving long cables. Their values are found empirically.

For quick temporary connections requiring only very moderate frequency response (less than 60 Hz), existing private exchange telephone lines can sometimes be used if the operators can be trusted to leave them alone. However, these must be directly connected private exchange wires, *i.e.*, a common telephone number for all extensions. Different numbers imply going through the central exchange, which may involve miles of wire between adjacent buildings and amplifiers that will not carry a dc signal.

DISPLAYS

Oscilloscopes are now commonly used as output devices from computers. Their speed and flexibility are of enormous value in real-time applications.

Some computers come equipped with displays and others require them to be purchased separately. The user often has a choice of screen size and a choice of a regular oscilloscope or a unit with storage.

The *sine qua non* of a display oscilloscope is the ratio of usable screen size to spot diameter. Spot diameter should be specified at the edge of the useful area of the tube and if possible, under dynamic conditions, *i.e.*, the spot should be deflected from the center to one side of the tube at the maximum rate at which the computer can do this operation. A 5-in. CRT can be expected to produce a spot of 0.025-in. diameter. Storage tubes should meet this standard in non-store mode but will usually not meet it in storage mode. Nevertheless, storage with remote erase is a highly desirable feature.

Some manufacturers have, unfortunately, adopted the practice of specifying the time to display a point as the time required to execute the display instruction. Usually, there is a much longer time following a display instruction during which another display instruction cannot be executed. Thus, in one case, the display is specified as 3 μsec but the next display instruction cannot be executed for 16 μsec. This is a serious limitation on the number of points that can be displayed without flicker. It is fairly easy to produce a display unit that can display a point in about 10 μsec. To go faster than this requires going to a high-voltage (20 kilovolts) display tube. While not technically difficult, such systems are expensive.

Most manufacturers offer display oscilloscopes as an option. Many of these are built around standard commercial units to which the manufacturer has usually added a considerable price markup. This is one of the few places where significant cost savings can be made by doing it yourself. Frequently, a more versatile display can be built rather than purchased. One basic method is shown in Figure 4.

This is not the usual technique, which uses separate D to A converters for vertical and horizontal signals and often digital buffers ahead of them. Sample

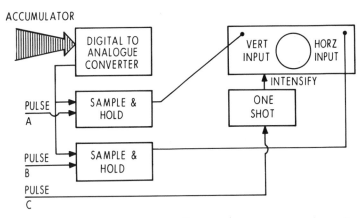

Figure 4. One method of connecting an oscilloscope to a computer as an analog display device.

and hold units are now so inexpensive that it pays to buffer the analog signal rather than the digital signals. The sequence of operation is: load the accumulator with value of horizontal coordinate. Send pulse B to sample the analog value. Load the accumulator with the value of vertical coordinate. Send pulse A to sample the analog value. Send pulse C to trigger the one-shot, which causes the oscilloscope to intensify.

Oscilloscopes may be paralleled with independent displays by the addition of other one-shots with separate control pulses. The sample and hold circuits required here are simple, inexpensive units, since the required hold time is only the few microseconds required to display a point.

Another, more elaborate, but useful method, makes use of direct memory access to run the display from a table in core memory without interrupting the running program. Horizontal and vertical coordinates are stacked sequentially in memory and direct memory access used to feed them to the D to A converter. Details depend upon the exact type of computer employed but the logic is quite simple.

It is extremely convenient to have display magnification by changing the gain of the display amplifiers. Two gain settings are used and a variable offset is provided at the high gain level, which allows the display to be positioned so that one can examine any part of the pattern. The following circuit has been used (Figure 5).

The smallest deflection that can be seen is about one-half of the spot diameter. Thus, a 5-in. tube with 0.025-in. spot can display 512 distinct spot locations on each axis. However, when the expanded display method is used it pays to allow 10 bits of display resolution so that full advantage can be taken of the expansion capability.

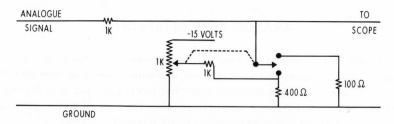

Figure 5. Expanded scale display system.

Some commercial computers and displays offer automatic character generation. The author has found these remarkably useless except in a very limited number of special applications. (Once again controversy is sure to fall upon us.) The usual advantage claimed for these in real-time applications is that of being able to display program text. Even with the best of inexpensive units, this is like reading a fourth carbon copy.

Remote displays are most easily done by use of a closed-circuit television system. While some manufacturers are advertising remote displays directly connected to the computer, their range is relatively limited and the cost of a remote display unit is comparable to a fairly good closed-circuit television system. The latter has a number of significant advantages; multiple displays are obtained at a small additional cost. Flicker can be reduced by using "sticky" vidicons. Large screen displays are relatively inexpensive. They have the disadvantages that some resolution is lost and that the raster lines of the display can be annoying. Most closed circuit television cameras have automatic dark level correction, which adjusts to keep the average picture level gray. This should be disabled for computer display use. Some cameras have a built in disable feature, but most do not, and the buyer should be careful to obtain one in which the dark level correction can be disabled (see note below).

Commercial closed-circuit monitors are available at reasonable cost but one does almost as well with a standard television set if the IF tuning is broadened slightly or is bypassed. Commercial television sets have a problem that is related to the dark-level problem mentioned above. The video amplifiers are ac coupled so that in many sets, a dark background tends to appear gray. Older sets avoided this by a dc clamping technique, but such sets are difficult to find now. One can overcome both the automatic light level control and the tendency of the receiver to "go gray" by putting a bright line at one edge of the picture area and then adjusting the receiver to overscan the screen so that the bright line is off screen.

Closed-circuit cameras will not usually focus close enough for viewing a 5-in. cathode ray tube screen. This is easily cured by moving the vidicon back about 0.50 in. or attaching a lens barrel extender, which can be obtained at most camera shops.

ANALOG TAPE RECORDERS

Analog tape recorders are used for two purposes; to record data without tying up the computer, and to slow down fast data or speed up slow data. The first of these used to be a common usage, but has become less so as the cost of small computers has become competitive with the cost of high-quality tape recorders. The speed change requirement is still frequently encountered.

There are many manufacturers of good analog tape recorders and many models to choose from. The following guide lines should be useful.

1. Home tape recorders are usually not good enough for scientific work.
2. Use standard 0.5-in. tape unless there is a compelling reason to do otherwise. Quarter-inch tape can be used where tape cost is a prime consideration but it is much less commonly used, which causes compatibility problems and it stretches badly, which is often troublesome. One-inch tape is required only if more than seven channels are needed.
3. Be sure that an adequate range of speeds is available. Some manufacturers emphasize their wide range of high speeds but the more common problem is at the low-speed end of the range. If, as is often the case in biological research, 24-hr data collection is required, the low-speed record must be slow enough to allow a single role of tape to last at least from 5 pm to 9 am. This usually requires a special-order tape recorder, but the added cost is only about $1000.
4. Speed change *including switching of the electronics* should be a single-button, front-panel operation over the full range of speeds. It is convenient to have full control accessible remotely so that the computer can maneuver analog tapes.
5. Be sure you understand the differences between direct and FM recording. Most scientific work uses FM recording and it is essential if low frequencies or dc levels are to be recorded.
6. Unit should be IRIG* standard or IRIG extended standard or both.
7. Super-speed control is not necessary. Synchronous motor control is good enough.
8. It is not usually necessary to buy full electronics on a seven-track machine. Four tracks are usually adequate, but by all means buy a seven-track head so that your unit will be compatible with most other users and so that you can add channels if necessary.
9. Insist on a trial period with an absolute money back guarantee. Tape recorder manufacturers are notoriously bad at service.
10. As a guide, a good tape recorder costs about $7000 to $15,000.

*Intermediate Range Instrumentation Group

STAFFING A COMPUTER

The most frequent mistake made by professional scientists buying computers is to fail to plan for an adequate staff. If the computer is to be used in a single application the following may not apply. But, if it is to be used as a general laboratory tool, which it should be and most often is expected to be, a full-time technician-programmer is absolutely essential. It is very difficult for someone who has not lived with a computer to visualize how much tedious work and detailed knowledge is required to make efficient use of it. Do not depend on part-time student help. In the current market, budget $10,000 a year plus the cost of a service contract.

PROGRAMMING TECHNIQUES

Almost anyone can learn to program a small computer but relatively few people learn to program well. No one collection of programming examples can hope to cover the variety of situations actually encountered in computer usage. Nevertheless, a few illustrative examples can go a long way toward training programmers and suggesting methods of handling common problems. All of the following are chosen from real-time biological problems that have been done in small computers. The speed requirement of real-time operation generally forces one to choose techniques involving relatively simple processing and a small machine forces a choice of techniques that can be done in limited memory. All of these examples have been used and operated in 4K computers.

It is difficult to describe programming techniques without referring to a specific type of computer. The PDP-8 has been chosen for illustration because it is the computer in widest use at the moment for this type of work. It is a 12-bit computer with a one-bit left accumulator extension called a link bit. Although the author now leans toward computers with longer word lengths, the choice of a 12-bit machine as an example is appropriate if only to show the nature of the difficulties encounterd with short word lengths.

RESPONSE AVERAGING

Averaging is probably the most commonly used technique of neuro-electric data processing. The principle is simple and well known. The techniques, however, are not so well understood and the difficulties are not apparent.

Let me first distinguish between averaging and summing. If R_n (t) is the response to the nth stimulus, the summing process consists of adding N such responses; $S = R_1 + R_2 + R_3 \ldots \ldots R_N$. The average response is obtained as $A = (R_1 + R_2 \ldots \ldots R_N)/N$. While the difference between them appears insignificant, the latter process is considerably more difficult if one wishes to watch the average build up, because each time a response is added, N changes and a new division must be done to see the average. Most small computers are quite slow at division, so that the process usually used is not really averaging but rather summing.

The most common difficulty in summing is overflow. If a 10-bit A to D conversion is done in a 12-bit computer, overflow can occur on the addition of the fourth response. It is sometimes argued that one ought to reduce the signal level to limit the range of the A to D conversion to fewer bits or to scale the values before adding, but this is not usually a winning game. The proper approach is double-precision summing. A double-precision addition takes considerably longer to do than a single-precision addition, but modern computers have enough core memory to store an intermediate table of the single-precision values and the double-precision addition can be done between stimuli. In doing a double-precision addition from a single-precision number, one must remember that the double-precision representation of a single-precision number is not simply zeros in the left half of the number. In two's complement arithmetic, the left half is filled with ones when the right half is negative. (Because of the possible occurrence of a long end around carry in one's complement arithmetic, double-precision operations are best done in two's complement.) A double-precision addition from a single-precision data word is done as follows:

CLA CLL	Clear Accumulator and link bit
TAD DATAWORD	Bring data word into accumulator
TAD LSSUM	Two's complement add of least-significant half of sum. If overflow occurs, the link bit is set to one.
DCA LSSUM	Store in least-significant half of sum, clear accumulator, do not change link bit.
TAD DATAWORD	Bring dataword into accumulator to check if + or −.
SPA CLA	If + skip next instruction. Clear accumulator whether + or −.
CMA	One's complement accumulator. If Dataword was negative, accumulator becomes all 1_s.
SZL	If link is zero skip next instruction.
IAC	Add one to accumulator. At this point most-significant half of dataword has been synthesized.
TAD MSSUM	Two's complement add most-significant half of sum.
DCA MSSUM	Deposit accumulator into most significant half of sum.

Total time = 17 cycles or 25.5 μsec.

If, as is usually the case, a table of response sums is being built up, indirect addressing is used, and the least-significant half of the sums and most-significant halves of sums are arranged in alternate locations in the table. The A to D converter is read at the beginning of the averaging loop and restarted so that conversion proceeds while the double-precision addition is being done. Done in this way, successive points are taken at intervals of about 50 μsec.

```
        CLA
        TAD     NEGATIVE OF NUMBER OF RESPONSES
        DCA     RESPONSE COUNTER
        TAD     TABLE BASE LOCATION
        DCA     POINTER
        TAD     NEGATIVE OF POINTS PER RESPONSE N
        DCA     POINT COUNT
AA, DCA i   POINTER
        ISZ     POINTER
        DCA i   POINTER     CLEAR TABLE 2N LOCATIONS
        ISZ     POINTER
        ISZ     POINT COUNT
        JMP     AA
BB, TAD     TABLE BASE LOCATION
        DCA     POINTER
        TAD     NEGATIVE OF POINTS PER RESPONSE
        DCA     POINT COUNT
        IOT     STIMULATE
CC, IOT     READ A to D CONVERTER INTO ACCUMULATOR
        DCA     DATAWORD
        IOT     RESTART A to D CONVERTER
        CLA     CLL
        TAD     DATAWORD
        TAD i   POINTER
        DCA i   POINTER
        ISZ     POINTER
        TAD     DATAWORD
        SPA     CLA
        CMA
        SZL
        IAC
        TAD i   POINTER
        DCA i   POINTER
        ISZ     POINTER
        ISZ     POINT COUNT
        JMP     CC
        ISZ     RESPONSE COUNTER
        JMP     BB
        DONE
```

Since the A to D converter is read once before it is started, the first sum in the table is ignored as invalid.

As previously mentioned, if one must go faster than a point every 50 μsec, an intermediate table of single-precision data words is stored and the double-precision operation done between responses. If the delay between responses cannot be allowed, one must go to a computer with a longer word length to avoid double precision.

Even with double-precision operations, it is sometimes hard to avoid excessive build-up of the dc level of the signal. A number of programming tricks can be used to remove dc build-up automatically, such as minotoring the pre-stimulus signal level and correcting the average of any systematic bias; a far simpler way is to have a variable offset built into the A to D converter, as discussed under the section on A to D conversion. The running sum can be watched and the correction easily entered on the offset. Another easy way is to let the dc build-up occur and remove it in the display process by the expanded display method discussed under the section on displays.

The other problem encountered in summing or averaging is pick-up of periodic noise from the 60-cycle power lines. If the stimulus is periodic, it is difficult to avoid some build-up of 60 cycles or its harmonics in the summing process. One trick that is sometimes tried is to set the stimulus rate slightly different from a sub-harmonic of 60 cycles on the theory that one steps through the phase of the interfering signal, thus cancelling build-up in the sum. Over a long time-summing process, this works fairly well but it causes considerable 60-cycle build-up in the intermediate sums. A somewhat better method is partially randomized triggering. This is most easily done by providing the stimulus trigger from the computer, which produces it from a count down of the sum of a base number and a random number. The random number can be produced from a pseudo random number generator but it is essentially as good to sample a high-frequency sine wave and use the digitally converted value as a "sufficiently random number".

Display of a double-precision sum requires a double-precision arithmetic shift operation. This process is very slow unless the computer has a double-length accumulator or extended arithmetic unit. When the DP arithmetic shift is available there is rarely any need to do true averaging, rather than summing. Without it, it is difficult to see the initial stages of signal build-up. Trying to display just one half of the DP word is not very satisfactory.

WAVEFORM ANALYSIS

The second most common problem in biology is waveform analysis. This may range from a simple process, such as finding the peak height of a pulse, to a complicated process, such as sorting pulses by shape, or characterizing the parts of an EKG. There are many techniques used for waveform analysis, depending upon what is to be recognized. The one technique invariably tried by beginners and almost invariably unsuccessful is Fourier analysis. The successful approaches to waveform analysis are usually based on some small number of simple characteristics of the signal. For example, one can sort pulses by shape by measuring height at two or three points on the pulse. One can, with reasonable success, distinguish the QRS complex of an EKG from muscle artifact by measuring the rates of the rising and falling phase separated by the appropriate time interval. Each of these applications requires a technique appropriate to it and some of these techniques are discussed in the following sections.

THE PUSH LIST

One of the simplest but most powerful methods of real-time data analysis is the push list. It consists of a list of N numbers stored in successive memory locations. Each time a new data point is acquired it is entered at one end of the list after each of the previous points has been shifted up or down one place in the list. The point at the other end of the list is discarded.

THE PUSH UP LIST

Memory location	Contents before push	Contents after push
L + N − 1	Data Point 36−N+1	Data Point 37−N+1
L + 5	31	32
L + 4	32	33
L + 3	33	34
L + 2	34	35
L + 1	35	36
L	Data Point 36	Data Point 37

THE PUSH DOWN LIST

Memory location	Contents before push	Contents after push
L + N − 1	Data Point 36	Data Point 37
L + 5	35	36
L + 4	34	35
L + 3	33	34
L + 2	32	33
L + 1	31	32
L	Data Point 36−N+1	Data Point 37−N+1

In our illustrative computer, the PDP-8, the push is usually down to make use of the convenience of the auto index locations. These are locations that, when used as indirect address pointers, automatically increment before being used as an address.

A push down is done as follows:

```
         CLA
         TAD     Neg. of number of points in list
         DCA     Counter
         TAD     Table base address
         DCA     A (an auto index location)
         TAD     Table base address −1
         DCA     B (an auto index location)
BB,      TAD i   A
         DCA i   B
         ISZ     Counter
         JMP     BB
         TAD     New data word
         DCA i   B
         DONE
```

The power of the push list lies in the fact that the analysis of data is simplified because the analysis program can refer to fixed addresses in memory. Suppose for example one wishes to find a running average of five data points.

```
         Clear 6 locations of list
         Clear Sum
AA,      Push List Down
         Enter Data Point at Top of List (Location L+5)
         Add Contents of L+5 to Sum
         Subtract Contents of L From Sum
         Let Average Equal Sum/5
         Repeat from AA
```

Note that the memory references in the averaging program refer to fixed memory locations and the resultant simplicity of programming. Suppose we wanted, instead, a weighted average in which the most recent point is multiplied by five, the next most recent by four, the next by three, *etc.*

```
         Clear 6 locations of list
         Clear Sum
AA,      Push List Down
         Enter Data Point At Top of List (Location L+5)
         Add 5 times Contents of L+5 to Sum
         Subtract Contents of L+4 From Sum
         Subtract Contents of L+3 From Sum
         Subtract Contents of L+2 From Sum
         Subtract Contents of L+1 From Sum
         Subtract Contents of L From Sum
         Let Average Equal Sum/15
         Repeat from AA
```

Once again we see that the programming is very simple and relatively fast in operation because no address computations need to be done except in the push process and that these are fairly simple and fast because they are sequential addresses.

Unfortunately, the speed of a push list process goes down as the length of the list gets longer. Therefore, if in the first example of the running average, the number of entries in the list gets much above 10, the process can be performed much faster by keeping the list stationary and instead moving the pointers that refer to the list. This rotating pointer technique is not nearly so neat as the push list because one must continually check for the time at which the pointer will go past the top of the list and reset it at that time.

THE RUNNING AVERAGE DONE WITH ROTATING POINTERS

Clear N Locations of List
Clear Sum
Set Pointer A to Point to L
Set Pointer B to Point to L+1
AA, Take Data Point
Add Data Point to Sum
Store Data Point Indirectly Through a Pointer
Get Data Point N−1 Entries Back Indirectly Through B Pointer
Subtract From Sum
Let Average Equal Sum/N
Index A
Index B
Check that A has not gone over top of table. If it has, reset it to L
Check that B has not gone over top of table. If it has, reset it to L
Return to AA

The use of rotating pointers leads to a more complicated program but one in which the time between sample points is independent of the length of the list.

WAVEFORM COMPARISON BY MEANS OF A PUSH LIST

A typical problem is that of detecting the occurrence of a particular waveform in a time sequence of signals. When the expected waveform is accurately known, by far the easiest way to detect its occurrence is by comparison to a stored copy of the expected waveform. The push list provides an easy way of doing the comparison. In effect, the push list allows the incoming signal to be slid past the stored reference until a match is found.

1. Push list
2. Enter new data point

3. Compare point by point each entry in the push list against the corresponding entry in the reference copy.
4. Decide if a sufficiently good fit has been found
5. Return

Item 4 deserves some comment. For some purposes, the criterion of fit is the sum of the squares of the difference between each point in the list and the corresponding point in the reference. However, this measure, while having some statistical justification, is slow because it involves computing the squares of N differences on each pass. It is usually not much superior to the sum of the absolute values of the difference, which is always much faster.

In fact, in some cases, the latter proves more satisfactory. A difficult question in both cases is to decide at which value of the sums of differences squared, or the sums of absolute values of differences, one will accept the fit. Unfortunately, no general rule can be given, as the criterion must depend upon the consequences of an erroneous detection and the consequences of missing the signal.

The above technique can be extended to the case where the incoming signal must be compared to a variety of stored references. In this case, to economize on running time, the push list should probably not be fully checked against each reference but, rather, a number of intermediate checks done and the particular reference entry rejected as soon as it becomes apparent that it cannot adequately match the signal.

A particularly difficult case is that in which the shape of the expected signal, but not its amplitude, is known. One obvious approach to this problem is to try to pick up the maximum value in the list and to normalize before comparison. This process, while workable, is extremely slow because of the need to find the maximum value and the multiplication necessary to change to a normalized value.

A much faster approach is to enter into memory a set of comparison waveforms, each of the same shape but differing in amplitude. The matching criterion is that the incoming signal in the push list must match one of the stored templates. One can use the sum of absolute values of the difference, or require that the stored template not differ from the push list at any point by more than a fixed value.

Another useful application of the push list or rotating buffer is the separation of a periodic component of a signal from aperiodic components. Let the input signal to the computer at time T be $V(T)$. At any time, the push list contains the current input and a list of inputs that occurred at previous times. Construct the moving sum (see Running Average) $S(T)=V(T)+V(T-t)+V(T-2t)+\ldots\ldots V(T-Nt)$ where t is the repetition interval of the periodic signal. Thus, if one wishes to remove 60-Hz interference, $t=16.6$ msec. The sum $S(T)$ divided by $N+1$ is approximately the periodic component of the signal with aperiodic components suppressed by the factor $N+1$. The aperiodic component can be recovered by subtracting the periodic component from the signal.

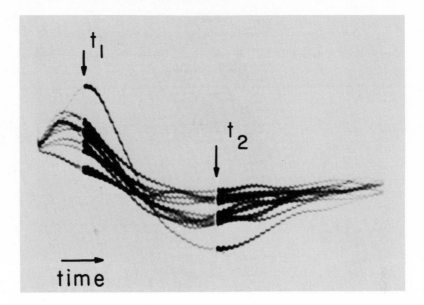

Figure 6. Classification of pulse shapes by measurement of voltages at two time intervals following a threshold crossing.

WAVE SHAPE CLASSIFICATION

Another simple but fast method of pulse-shape classification is based on a two-dimensional histogram of the values of voltages at two different times after a threshold crossing. Voltages V_1 and V_2 are measured at times t_1 and t_2 after the presence of a pulse is detected by a threshold crossing, as in Figure 6. A two-dimensional histogram is generated from a sequence of such measurements. The histogram of frequencies of occurrence of V_1, V_2 pairs can be displayed either as a bar chart in perspective (Figure 7) or as an intensity modulation by repeated display of the same point (Figure 8.) Clusters are then identifed with a light pen and subsequent pulses can be identified by the cluster to which they belong.

The following example shows how this is done in a 12-bit computer.

          Clear histogram table
AA,   Detect threshold crossing
          Delay until t_1
          Measure V_1
          Scale digital value of V_1 to produce a five bit positive number.
              $0 \leqslant N_1 \leqslant 31$
          Delay until t_2
          Measure V_2
          Scale digital value of V_2 to produce a five bit positive number.
              $0 \leqslant N_2 \leqslant 31$

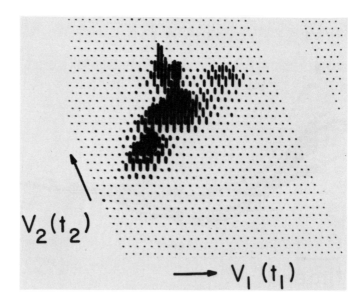

Figure 7. Bar graph display of voltages measured at times t_1 and t_2.

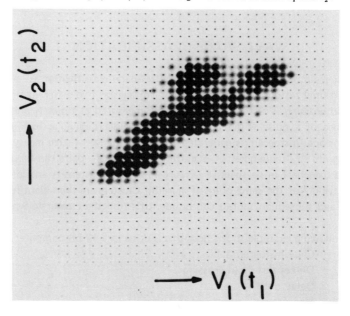

Figure 8. Intensity modulated display of voltages measured at t_1 and t_2.

Shift N_2 five places left and add N_1 to produce $N_3 \cdot 0 \leqq N_3 \leqq 1023$
Add table base address to N_3 to produce pointer P

Increment value in table at location P
Display table in a 32 x 32 array until next threshold crossing. Go
   to AA

The unused two left bits of P can be used to classify that position in the table. Subsequent pulses then generate addresses that are used to access the classification bits.

This method of classification is one of the few that can be done rapidly in a small computer. Pulses can be classified in less than 50 μsec.

EXTRACTING SIGNAL FROM NOISE

One of the most effective means of detecting the presence of a signal in a noise background is the digital analog of an electronic matched filter. The shape of the signal to be detected is divided into M divisions. The amplitude of the signal at each of these is entered in reverse order into a memory table called A (Figure 9). The incoming signal plus noise is compared to the signal stored in table A in the following way.

Each time a data point is entered into the push down list, Sum S is computed, which is made up of the total of the products of each entry in A multiplied by the corresponding entry in B (Figure 10). The value of this sum is checked against a threshold. If it exceeds the threshold, the signal specified by table A has been detected.

This method is occasionally extended by modifying table A each time a signal is successfully detected so that slow changes in the shape of the signal can be accommodated. This is known as an adaptive filter.

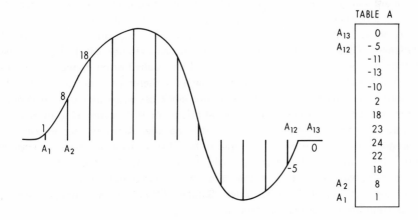

Figure 9. Method of storing a reference waveform.

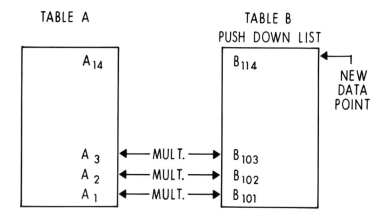

Figure 10. Digital matched filtering.

LANGUAGES

Most computer manufacturers now provide one or more languages designed to avoid machine language programming. However, those supplied for small computers are usually poorly suited for real-time operation. Although they provide the ability to patch in machine language routines, the amount of patching required is often extensive and the space in which to place the patch inadequate. There is, in addition, a fundamental difficulty in the use of a language not basically designed for real-time work. It is difficult to predetermine the times at which the real-time operations will occur. For example, one can insert into a FORTRAN program a machine language patch or link that will cause an analog input to be taken and stored as a parameter in the program each time it is reached in the program operation. In setting up a FORTRAN program, however, it is difficult to ascertain the time of execution of a FORTRAN statement. Thus, even though synchronized by an external real-time clock, one cannot be sure that the patch routine will be reached often enough to ensure that the sample is taken at the correct time. It is, therefore, necessary to include a routine that checks whether the real-time clock has passed the appointed time when the patch is reached and to signal this event if it occurs. One must then test the program and modify it if indeed it is too slow. Alternatively, one can use a program interrupt to cause a sample to be taken at fixed intervals and stored into tables, but one then runs the risk of overflowing the table if the running program cannot keep up with the data rate or, alternately, runs too fast and processes data in the wrong order. Similar difficulties are encountered in outputting from a FORTRAN program.

A satisfactory real-time language should have the following characteristics:
1. Built-in provisions for taking and outputting data.
2. Foolproof clocking of input-output operations.

3. Provisions to record on bulk storage and to read back in an unbroken data stream.
4. On-line program editing without paper tape operations.
5. Single instructions for frequently encountered input-output operations.
6. Adequate arithmetic operations.

The above may seem to be a combination beyond the capability of a small computer. It is not. The key is to recognize that, in general, real-time computations require much less arithmetic capability than is built into FORTRAN or most other higher-level languages. In 1965, the author published a language called SNAP, which met all of the above criterion except (3) in a 12-bit 4096-word computer (Simon, 1967). Although it took a number of months to write SNAP, the time saved subsequently by virtue of having such a language paid off manyfold. With the advent of reasonably priced 8192-word memories, all of the above criteria can easily be met and manufacturers should be expected to provide languages well suited for real-time operation. In the interim, users should not hesitate to develop their own languages if they have enough problems of a common type to justify the investment. It is not nearly so hard as it seems. The one great simplification that can be recommended for developing a special purpose language is to structure it in such a way that subsections of it are useful. In this way, small parts of the language can be tried out and one need not have the whole language working to debug it. This has the further advantage that in teaching the use of a language it is not necessary to understand all of it to do useful operations. This latter advantage is notably absent in most commercial computer languages.

Languages are most easily built on an interpretive principle. This means that the source language remains in core memory during execution of the program, rather than being replaced by a different machine language program. The source program is then executed one line at a time by interpreting that line by means of characters in the line, which identify the subroutines to be used and the parameters on which they are to operate. Leaving the source language in core memory allows program modification without an intervening paper or magnetic tape operation.

SNAP is a fairly sophisticated language and in its final form took almost a year to complete. In general, we do not recommend efforts of this magnitude except in special cases. Nevertheless, SNAP can be used to illustrate what can be done in a small machine and the ambitious programmer or laboratory that wishes to develop its own language for its own purposes will probably profit considerably by a study of SNAP and a description of its operation.

All SNAP operations start from the CONTROL phase, which is reached either from the program start point at the computer or can be reached at any time by depressing a single teletype key during program execution. From the CONTROL phase any of the following commands can be executed:

*PRO*gram   load program
*CON*stants   enter numerical constants

TBLE	load 100 numbers in A and B tables
AXIS	origin for plotter output
*STA*rt at	change starting point of program
*CAL*culate	run the program
*INS*ert	insert an instruction
*DEL*ete	delete an instruction
*CHA*nge	change an instruction
LIST	type-punch program and constants
TYPE	type a list of constants which have been set by the program
*EXT*end	extend the number of entries in the table

The interpretive program can be made up of up to 89 of the following instructions:

Arithmetic
Manipulations:

	A=B+C	add
	A=B-C	subtract
	A=B*C	multiply
	A=B/C	divide
	A=LGB	$\log_e B$
	A=EXR	exponentiation (e^R)
	A=SRB	square root of B
	A=SIB	sin of B
	A=CSB	Cos of B
	A=ATB	Arctan of B
	A=NEB	A=-B
Input-Ouput:	TYPE B	type value of B, do line feed, and carriage return
	T>PEB	type value of B, no carriage return
	PLOTB	plot B against X
	DISTB	display table values on scope
	L=AN4	L = channel 4 voltage input x1000, also sets T=real time.
Conditional:	BP13U	go to 13 if U is positive (incl. zero)
	BM12K	go to 12 if K is negative
	BZ13U	go to 13 if U=0
	BRSUL	branch setup L
	BR12L	go to 12, L-1 number of times
	BS12X	branch to subroutine beginning at line 12
	RETUR	return from subroutine to line following last executed BS instruction
Table lookup:	C=TBA	table A lookup
	M=TBB	table B lookup
	N=TBD	N as a function of D
	RESET	reset table A and B lookups
	GITBD	get D indirectly from the table (I pointer)

PITBC	put C indirectly into the table (I pointer)
RUBTB	inserts the value zero into one hundred table locations

Special
Instructions: GOPL2   perform machine language subroutine, Numbe 1-5 indicates which of 5 possible routines is to be executed.

In addition, SNAP provides table space for up to 210 floating point entries. All arithmetic operations are in floating point. While somewhat costly in speed, it was felt that this was essential from a pedagogical standpoint.

When SNAP was first developed, there was considerable skepticism about the usefulness of so simple a language, particularly by those who were used to higher-level languages or larger computers. Experience has shown that it has been invaluable. Thus, the reader who is considering writing his own language need have no fears inspired by the skeptics.

One may get some idea of the usefulness and power of SNAP from a few examples. A pulse interval histogram can be programmed in 11 instructions:

10	RUBTB	Clear Table
11	U=T+Z	Set U equal to time of last pulse
12	Y-AN1	Look for positive pulse
13	BM12Y	If no pulse go back to 12
14	I=T−U	Interval equals time of new pulse minus time of last pulse
15	I=I*K	Scale I to between 1 and 100
16	GITBC	Get value of C from table place I
17	C=C+D	Increase C
18	PITBC	Put new C into table place I
19	DISTB	Display the table
20	BZ11Z	Branch back to 11

At the other end of the scale of difficulty, programs have been written to solve, within the 89 instructions of the standard SNAP, systems of up to 14 simultaneous equations. Using a special version of SNAP, which allowed a double set of instructions and variables, programs have been written to separate multicompartmental exponentials (Simon, 1970). In fact, it can truly be said that a multipurpose biological computing laboratory operated almost entirely in SNAP for about three years.

The technique of structuring an interpretive language is well illustrated by examples from SNAP. In SNAP, each line of the program has five characters. Arithmetic variables are designated by single letters. The instruction mnemonics have been chosen so that selection of the appropriate machine language routine can be based on the second character of each line:

A=B+C	= identifies this as an arithmetic operation
TYPEA	Y identifies this as a type operation of the value of A
PLOTY	L identifies this as a point display of the value of Y

When a SNAP instruction is executed in program operation, the second character of the line is checked against a table of allowed second characters. If it is found, a JUMP instruction is set up that causes the program to go to the correct subroutine. If the character is not found in the table, an error message is printed. This process, called vectoring, can be done in many ways depending upon the available instruction set of the computer.

Interpretive languages are particularly well-suited for multiple animal training experiments. In such experiments, it is frequently necessary to change the training sequence for one animal. This is difficult to do in machine language programs because a mistake in coding can cause the program to "hang up" in one animal's sequence, thereby breaking the timing for the others. Even worse, erroneous coding can cause the program to wipe itself out, so that it is quite risky to try to change sequence in mid-stream. Interpretive languages are easily protected against such disasters. Each animal's program can be arranged so that it cannot interact with any others.

The easiest, but not the fastest way, to do this is to break the program into a set of sub-programs, which are executed in round-robin fashion, one interpretive instruction of each sequence then on to the next sequence. A coding error can cause one sequence to get stuck in a loop but it does not interrupt execution of the other sequences and interpretive address coding ensures that one sequence cannot wipe out the others. The only real difficulty of such a language is teletype congestion. If the teletype is to be used to print data or information generated by the program sequence it is necessary to provide each sequence with a data buffer list. Between interpretive instructions, these buffers are checked to see if there is a data message waiting. When a buffer is found with a message to be typed, it is typed one character at a time between interpretive instructions. In this way, the sequence timing is not seriously disturbed. It is necessary to finish with the contents of one sequence buffer before starting with the next.

REFERENCES

Simon, W. SNAP—an interpretive real-time language for biology. *Medical and Biological Engineering*, 1967, *5*, 83—85.

Simon, W. A method of experimental separation applicable to small computers. *Physics in Medicine and Biology*, 1970, *15*, 355—360.

AUTHOR INDEX

457

SUBJECT INDEX